INTRODUCTI

Consulting Editor

Professor D. Ince
The Open University

Titles in this series

Portable Modula-2 Programming	Woodman, Griffiths, Souter and Davies
SSADM: a practical Approach	Ashworth and Goodland
Software Engineering: Analysis and Design	Easteal and Davies
Introduction to Compiling Techniques: A First Course Using ANSI C, LEX and YACC	Bennett
An Introduction to Program Design	Sargent
Object Oriented Databases: Applications in Software Engineering	Brown
Object Oriented Software Engineering with C++	Ince
Expert Database Systems: A Gentle Introduction	Beynon-Davies
Practical Formal Methods with VDM	Andrews and Ince
SSADM Version 4: A User's Guide	Eva
A Structured Approach to Systems Development	Heap, Stanway and Windsor
Rapid Information Systems Development	Bell and Wood-Harper
Software Engineering Environments	Brown, Earl and McDermid
Introduction to Software Project Management and Quality Assurance	Ince, Sharp and Woodman
Systems Construction and Analysis: A Mathematical and Logical Framework	Fenton and Hill

INTRODUCTION TO VDM

Mark Woodman
and
Benedict Heal

Computing Department
The Open University

McGRAW-HILL BOOK COMPANY

London • New York • St Louis • San Francisco • Auckland • Bogotá • Caracas
Lisbon • Madrid • Mexico • Milan • Montreal • New Delhi • Panama
Paris • San Juan • São Paulo • Singapore • Sydney • Tokyo • Toronto

Published by

McGRAW-HILL BOOK COMPANY EUROPE

Shoppenhangers Road, Maidenhead, Berkshire, SL6 2QL, England

Tel 01628 23432; Fax 01628 770224

British Library Cataloguing in Publication Data

Woodman, Mark
Introduction to VDM – (McGraw-Hill
International Series in Software
Engineering)
I. Title II. Heal, Benedict III. Series
005.1

ISBN 0-07-707434-3

Library of Congress-in-Publication Data

Woodman, Mark.
Introduction to VDM / Mark Woodman
p. cm -- (McGraw-Hill International Series in Software Engineering)
Includes bibliographical references and index..
ISBN 0-07-707434-3
1. Computer software--Development. I. Heal, Benedict.
II. Title. III. Series.
QA76.76.D47w66 1993 92-35028
005.1'2--dc20 CIP

2345CL 965

Typeset by Mark Woodman with contributions from Benedict Heal, Jenny Chalmers and Ros Wood.

Printed and bound in Great Britain by Clays Ltd, St. Ives plc.

Printed on permanent paper in compliance with ISO Standard 9706.

CONTENTS

PREFACE

This book is an attempt to present the main elements of the Vienna Development Method (VDM) in an elementary and readable way. While there are beginning to be a number of books aimed at the professional practitioner, the newcomer often finds them unapproachable. We have tried to explain to the absolute novice what formal methods like VDM are aiming to do, and to give enough elementary practice so that the reader will feel happy to tackle more advanced, but more austere, books such as C.B Jones' *Systematic Software Development using VDM*. The recent book by Derek Andrews and Darrel Ince, *Practical Formal Methods with VDM*, is to be recommended.

VDM has developed very rapidly over the last decade and as a consequence its notation exists in various dialects. It is currently in the process of being standardized and the new notation is known as VDM-SL. We have adopted this notation but have restricted our use of it for the sake of simplicity. (Andrews and Ince describe current developments in VDM.)

This book owes its origins to an Open University course, M355 *Topics in Software Engineering*, which contains a similar treatment of VDM; this second edition replaces the original course material from 1995. The book maintains the distinction employed on that course of using 'exercises' to lead to new points for discussion (the reader is invited to work through exercises, but may simply study them) and 'review questions' which allow the reader to pause and check comprehension. The book also contains many additional exercises to encourage further practice.

We would like to acknowledge the contributions of members of the M355 Course Team. In particular we acknowledge the contribution of Mike Martin, University of Denver, and Peter Gibbins, Sharp Research Laboratories, who drafted much early VDM material for the course. We are also very much indebted to Gerry McGrogan, Haberdashers' Aske's School, and Derek Andrews, University of Leicester for their comments and suggestions.

VDM continues to be developed and used in different ways. We have mostly adhered to the new style of the VDM specification language, VDM-SL, which is currently being standardized (see Dawes, 1991). However, we have followed the approach of Jones (1989) rather than the more recent approach of Andrews and Ince (1991) and occasionally stray from the notation where we find it unhelpful for the novice.

The bibliography below lists recent texts on the subject.

Bibliography

D. Andrews and D. Ince, *Practical Formal Methods with VDM*. McGraw-Hill, 1991.

J. Dawes, *The VDM-SL Reference Guide*. Pitman, 1991.

I. Hayes (ed.), *Specification Case Studies*. Prentice Hall International, 1987.

C.B. Jones, *Systematic Software Development using VDM* (2nd edition). Prentice Hall International, 1989.

J.T. Latham, V.J. Bush and I.D. Cottam, *The Programming Process, an introduction based on VDM and Pascal*. Addison-Wesley, 1990.

INTRODUCTION

Software engineering addresses the problem of maintaining intellectual control over highly complicated structures of software. Indeed, computer software systems are arguably some of the most complicated systems ever created by mankind. Some have millions of lines of code and have been developed by large teams over many years. Even small systems contain myriads of detail concerning data description and algorithm expression. How can something so complex be specified, designed, and built? The only answer which is generally agreed upon among the software engineering community is to partition the system: to break it up and work on the pieces. The same partitioning strategy can be applied to the software development process. This process may be regarded as occurring in phases, even though the phases are highly interrelated.

In this book we use a well-accepted model of how large software systems are created. We assume that development proceeds through requirements analysis, (resulting in a functional and non-functional specification), and system and detailed design before implementation and final validation take place. First, the customer's requirements are obtained and documented in some fashion. Then the developer of a system specifies, designs, and codes the system. During this process the developer verifies that each phase has been properly carried out by checking that the 'output' of a phase corresponds to its 'input'. Finally, the system is validated (tested) against the original requirements. These phases of development are not explicitly covered here but will be referred to from time to time. We begin with specification of what functions a system is to provide; since VDM does not help with specifying non-functional requirements (e.g. performance) we shall not consider these.

A useful functional specification should be precise, concise, and understandable. Furthermore, it should make it easier for reasoning about its logical consistency and its relation to the customer's requirements.

Since a system design should be produced from considering a specification, developers should have some method of verifying that the design meets the specification. If there is also a way to verify that program code matches the design, then verification becomes a reasoning process rather than a testing process.

This is the primary motivation for introducing formality into the software development process.

Ultimately, program code must be written to implement a software system. Program code is itself a formal notation; source code is expressed in a formal language, the programming language, which is unambiguous and is amenable to analysis. In fact, program source code can be thought of as a mathematical notation. If the specification and design are also written mathematically, it is possible to construct formal mathematical proofs that code matches design, and that design matches specification. This use of mathematics for verification leads to a greater degree of confidence in the development process than can be achieved by testing alone.

However, a functional specification cannot be proved to match requirements for two reasons. Firstly, requirements are expressed in a terminology that is not formal; a statement of requirements is usually expressed using a mixture of everyday language and jargon from the customer's business, and cannot be regarded as a piece of mathematics. Secondly, it is only the functional requirements that are addressed in a formal specification. Issues such as cost and efficiency are not introduced.

Software engineering is a new discipline still in the making. There are alternative approaches to every type of software development method and formal development methods are no exception. All formal methods employ a mathematical notation for functional specification and design. They all include methods of proof to verify that the implementation meets the specification. They differ in notation, in emphasis, and in the specific proofs they require. However, all demand a disciplined approach very early in the development process. This book introduces VDM, the Vienna Development Method, as an example of a formal method of system development. VDM originated at the Vienna Laboratory of IBM, originally for specifying programming languages. It is used widely in industry but is by no means the only formal method in use.

Note that the term 'VDM' is used colloquially to refer to both the notation and to the technique of formal software development—the method.

The method starts with the process of writing a formal specification of the software functions a system is to provide. This involves the development of abstract models of data and operations, which are written down precisely using a notation that blends mathematics with computing. Chapter 1 outlines the formal development process, and Chapter 2 briefly reviews some of the discrete mathematics needed later.

As part of the formal specification, specific proof obligations which guarantee that the specification contains no internal contradictions must be discharged. This is described in the discussion of the VDM notation for formal specification in Chapters 3–8.

After specification comes design. During design the abstract models of data in a VDM specification are remodelled by more concrete data types; these themselves are modelled by data types available in the language of implementation. This process, called 'data reification' in VDM may require a number of iterations and is the topic of Chapters 9 and 10. These chapters also deal with 'operation modelling', which is the process of remodelling operations for a data model changed by reification.

A specification contains operations which are usually implicit: what they are to do is specified, but how they are to do it is not. During design the operations must be made explicit by way of algorithms which are expressed in an implementation language, in this case Pascal. This too may require several steps and is called 'operation decomposition' in VDM (this is discussed in Chapter 11). Both data reification and operation decomposition generate specific proof obligations which, when discharged by the software developer, guarantee the conformity of the design to the specification, and the program code to the design.

As you will observe, the proofs used in the book, particularly in Chapters 9–12, are somewhat informal. That is, we do not cite proof rules to justify the proofs; rather, we present rigorous argument. This rigorous, rather than strictly formal, application of formal methods is a common practical approach to the subject, and one which is more suited to a short primer such as this text.

This new discipline of software engineering benefits greatly from the much older discipline mathematics which is not a spectator sport: fluency can be gained only by practice. To learn the VDM notation, use it correctly, and be able to reason with it, you should expect to go slowly and to backtrack frequently.

1 FORMAL SOFTWARE DEVELOPMENT

In this chapter we define the term 'formal method' and explain the role of a formal method in the software development process.

1.1 The software development process

There are many paradigms of the software development process. Many are variations of a phase-oriented process in which the developer moves from a customer's expression of a business need—the statement of requirements—through a number of phases to an executing software system. Each phase includes a major technical activity which takes a set of documents as input and produces a set of documents as output. For example, ***requirements analysis*** is the activity in which the customer's vaguely expressed needs are investigated and translated to a precise set of functional requirements which the software must meet; it is carried out using the statement of requirements as input and evaluates to a system specification.

Requirements analysis is followed by ***system design*** and ***detailed design*** in which the software is considered at a structural level and at a detailed level respectively. The design phases are followed by ***implementation***—the production of code—and ***maintenance***—the correction, improvement and change of a system.

Changes which have to be made early in the process cost much less than changes which occur late; indeed the cost of change increases by an order of magnitude as each phase passes. It is therefore important to ensure correctness throughout the development process. Consequently, the developer should check that the output from a phase has been properly developed from the input, which is called ***verification***, and should check all outputs with the original statement of requirements, which is called ***validation***. Verification and validation are often carried out by testing software which is produced late in the development process. Hence errors may be discovered late, resulting in a high cost for correction.

The classical phase-oriented model of the software development process begins (after the tendering and project planning activities) with requirements analysis of the customer's statement of requirements. This phase results in the ***system specification*** which contains both the ***functional*** and ***non-functional specifications*** (the former being a description of what the system must do, the latter being constraints/goals on the provision of functions).

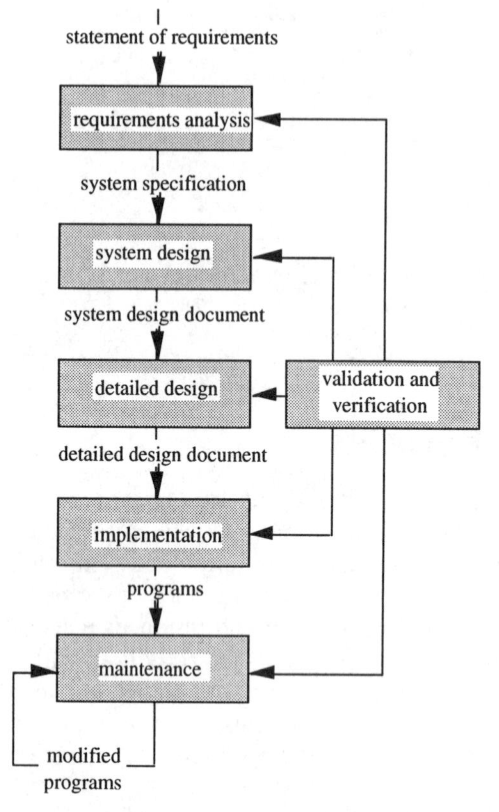

Figure 1.1

The design activities may be divided into system design and detailed design. System design considers the architecture of the system and takes into consideration practical matters such as hardware architecture, operating system facilities, etc. Detailed design concentrates on the specification of individual program units: algorithm selection, complexity avoidance, etc.

While many practitioners consider implementation (coding, testing and installation) to be the last phase of software development, ***maintenance*** can now take as much as 70 per cent of project resources and involves considerable repetition of the 'earlier' phases.

Figure 1.1 depicts the process. However, it does not show the inevitable iteration which results from requirements changing late in the process and from the discovery of errors.

Formal methods are the application of mathematics to the software development process. They have not yet evolved sufficiently to allow their application to all the phases outlined above. Nevertheless, they are proving extremely useful in producing the functional specification, in the process of design and in the implementation of software. They also allow validation and verification activities to be introduced early in the development process.

A formal method may include the following: a notation for the expression of specifications and design; and a system of mathematical proofs for verification that an implementation matches a design and that a design meets a specification. So a formal method need not be just a notation but also a process of development. The Vienna Development Method, VDM, is just such a method. In this book you will be introduced to formal specification in VDM, i.e. how to produce a system specification using VDM notation and to formal development, i.e. how to develop program code from a specification.

1.2 Formality in software development

A ***formal method*** is a systematic application of mathematical notations and mathematical reasoning (proof) in software engineering. Mathematical notations may be used for the formal specification of the functional requirements of a system; they may also be used to express the design of portions of programs, and mathematical proof may be used to develop code and to verify that the code matches the design.

The benefits of the mathematical approach are twofold:

- The use of a formal notation for design allows errors to be caught before implementation by precisely and unambiguously specifying what a system must do.
- Verification is done by proof instead of by testing and reviews. Confidence in the verification, and thus in the verified design or program code, is thereby increased.

By ***formal notation***, we mean a notation with a mathematically defined (and hence precisely defined) syntax and semantics.

Mathematical reasoning in software development may be applied only to mathematical descriptions (and not to descriptions in natural language); a document written in a formal notation can be regarded as a mathematical description.

The statement of requirements is a document written in the language of the customer: it expresses the customer's needs and wishes in terms of the customer's application. That is to say, the requirements are written using the vocabulary of satellites, telephones, chemical plants, banks, games or whatever the customer's business happens to be. The computer programs used to solve the problem are expressed in terms of the vocabulary of programming languages—arrays, pointers, loops, procedures, or whatever facilities are available in the language of implementation. Hence, computer programs themselves model the real world of the problem, and so well-engineered software should provide a match between the problem and its solution.

A statement of requirements is not a mathematical description because it is a document which is not written in a formal language. A computer program *is* a mathematical description: it is a document written in a formal language, a programming language, which has precise syntax and meaning. During the software engineering process documents which are not mathematical must be converted to documents which are mathematical. Proponents of formal methods argue that the sooner in the development cycle the conversion is made, the better the final product.

Despite the fact that a program source is a document in a formal language, it is difficult to reason about software; it is far too detailed, for example. If our aim is to improve software quality, we need to reason about documents which are used earlier in the development process—documents which record the functional specification or design of a system. The use of formal language in a system specification or design document allows us to reason mathematically early in the development process.

Most formal development methods introduce formality at the requirements analysis phase of the development process which produces a functional specification. In fact the term 'formal method' often refers to the use of a formal language in requirements analysis and the use of mathematical proof for verifying that a design meets its specification and that an implementation matches its design.

It is usual to regard a system specification as having two parts: there is a functional part which describes what the system does, and there is a non-functional part which gives cost, efficiency, and other constraints on the developers. Although research is in progress on using formal methods to express non-functional constraints, we will only use formal methods in requirements analysis to produce a functional specification. When using VDM in this way, non-functional constraints will be ignored.

The likelihood that the system will satisfy its statement of requirements is also increased by the use of formal methods, because in going from the statement of requirements to implementation there are only two places where mathematical proof is not used for verification. Firstly, non-functional parts of the specification such as considerations of cost and efficiency may guide design decisions but it is usually not possible to conclude that a design meets such specifications without testing the code. Secondly, it is not possible to prove mathematically that a system specification meets a statement of requirements because the latter is not expressed in a formal language.

There is much research being done on the use of formal methods which may be able to show that these are helpful in other aspects of the development process. In this text we shall concentrate on how formal methods are used in producing specifications, designs and code, and how they may be used to verify phases in the development process where mathematical methods have already shown their value.

1.3 Software development with VDM

The introduction contains a list of desirable properties for a functional specification which we expand here:

- A specification should be precise and unambiguous.
- A specification should be concise; it should omit all unnecessary detail and be free of bias toward any particular implementation.
- A specification should be understandable by being written in a language that can be understood by its readers.

- A specification should be usable; ideally it should assist the design process by being expressed in a way which assists reasoning, and it should allow verification that it is satisfied by a design.

Subject to the proviso that all readers have relevant mathematical training, which is a common assumption in other engineering disciplines, the VDM language largely meets the above criteria.

One thing about VDM should be spelled out right away: VDM is *not* a programming language—it is not intended to be executed on a computer, although executable subsets have been developed. It allows the developer all the freedom of predicate logic for producing specifications and designs. VDM also encourages the use of mathematical set theory to extend the domain of what can be specified. As we shall see, this mathematical structure enables the developer to start out thinking in terms of the customer's problem without being forced to worry about the constraints of a particular programming language. On the other hand, VDM has been constructed to specify systems that will eventually be implemented on a computer. The VDM language takes this into account in some of its constructs. Many VDM constructs are similar to those that appear in a programming language like Pascal. You will first see some of these constructs when operations are introduced in section 3.4.

In the chapters which follow you will be introduced to the VDM notation and method. It is easy to get lost in the detail of a new notation and a new technique. You can keep your bearings by remembering how formal methods work. Many formal methods, including VDM, proceed in the following fashion. First, an abstract mathematical notation is used to build a model which specifies what a computer software system is to do. The model has two components: data and the operations on the data. This process is depicted in Figure 1.2.

Of course, in reality, there are few software developers who can devise a suitable model first time as the result of initial analysis. Hence, iteration is common; building a formal model exposes weaknesses and errors in analysis which, when corrected, leads to a new model. Subsequent work may lead to further analysis and to revision of the model.

Chapters 3–8 introduce the basic notational tools for developing data models and associated operations.

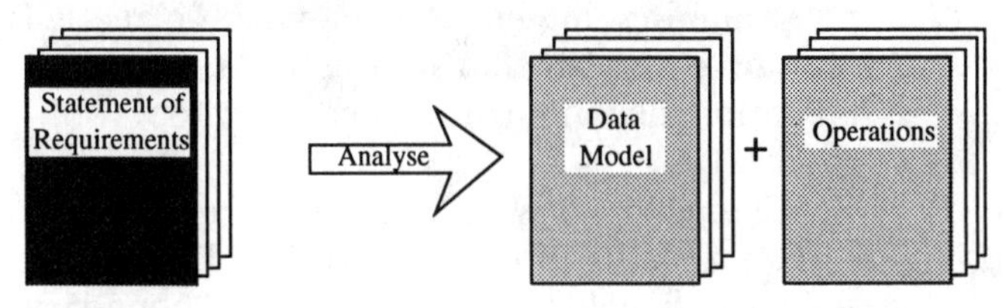

Figure 1.2

After satisfactorily completing an abstract model it is refined—making it less abstract. For example, data which is modelled as a mathematical set (see Chapter 3) may be 'reified' to another type, such as a sequence (see Chapter 4). This is depicted in Figure 1.3. As with the initial modelling, this activity may be repeated in order to specify a more concrete data model and operations.

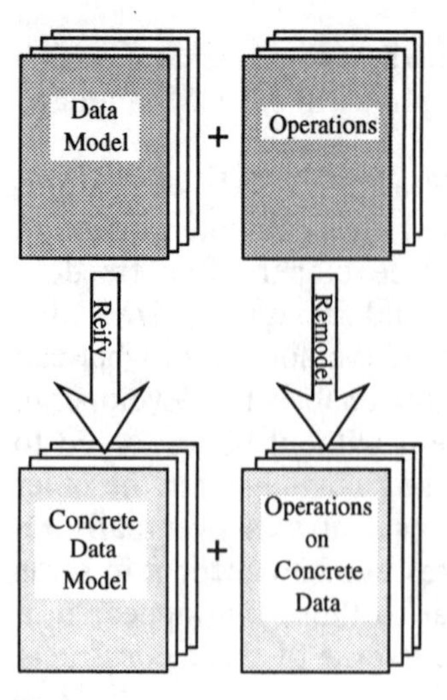

Figure 1.3

Early steps of the transformation from the abstract model to more concrete forms can be considered to correspond to design activities. This is because choices must be made as to which concrete data models should be used in a given situation. However, although these early steps should produce more concrete data types and more detailed operation specifications, these are unlikely to be directly implementable in a programming language. Later steps produce even more concrete types and more detailed operation specifications, and correspond to the implementation phase. It can be difficult to draw a line between design and implementation in a formal method, and it is common to refer to just design when what is meant is design and implementation. Eventually, the specification is transformed into program data and statements, as depicted in Figure 1.4.

Computer programs consist of data structures and algorithms. A formal specification in VDM is similar: it consists of an abstract mathematical model of data and of operations on that data. The design and implementation steps, which gradually transform the specification into code, incur specific proof obligations in VDM which verify that the results of a step match what came before.

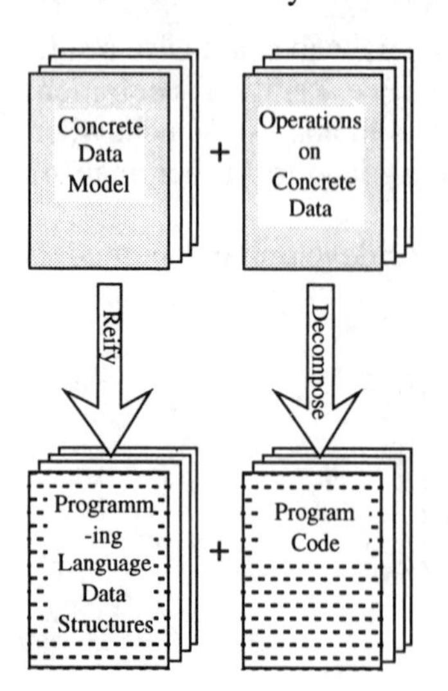

Figure 1.4

The transition from abstract mathematical models of data to data structures which are representable in the implementation language is called data reification. (Data reification and its attendant proof obligations are the subject of Chapters 9 and 10.)

The process by which mathematical specifications of operations are transformed into programming language statements is called operation decomposition. (Chapter 11 deals with operation decomposition and its proof obligations.)

Computer software systems are produced to solve problems in the real world. During the software development process the boundary between the informality of a statement of requirements and the formality of program code must be crossed. Formal methods enable the developer to cross this boundary as early as possible, in the functional specification of a system. Consequently, precision and the use of mathematical proof are introduced early in the software engineering process. In this way, potential errors are exposed early enough to be corrected cheaply, and confidence that the implemented code meets the statement of requirements is enhanced.

1.4 Summary of concepts

- The software development process can be considered as a phase-oriented process consisting of:
  - requirements analysis (resulting in functional specification);
  - system design;
  - implementation;
  - maintenance;
  - validation and verification.
- Formal methods can be used to develop precise and unambiguous functional specification and design.
- Formal methods can be used in verification, particularly in early phases.
- Formal methods assist in the development of a formal program from an informal statement of requirements.
- VDM consists of a notation and a method:
  - VDM is the Vienna Development *Method* but we the term is often used colloquially for the specification language as well;
  - VDM-SL is the specification language;
  - although subsets of VDM-SL can be used to generate executable programs; the language itself is not a programming language.
- Software development in VDM consists of:
  - analysing the statement of requirements to produce a data model and operations;
  - refining the data model to a more concrete specification;
  - respecifying the operations to match the concrete data model;
  - transforming the concrete data model to program types;
  - decomposing the concrete operations to program code.

2 MATHEMATICS FOR VDM

In this chapter we briefly review the predicate calculus and set theory. It is assumed that you either have experience of these concepts or have access to material which will provide a more detailed discussion if you require one.

2.1 Set theory

A ***set*** is an unordered collection of elements containing no duplicates. The concept of membership in a set is fundamental to sets.

Denoting set values

Sets may be written *explicitly* by listing their elements separated by commas within braces. The order in which elements are listed is unimportant. For example:

$$\{1, 3, 5\} \quad \{1, 5, 3\} \quad \{3, 5, 1\} \quad \{3, 1, 5\} \quad \{5, 3, 1\} \quad \{5, 1, 3\}$$

all denote *one* set value: the set containing the integers 1, 3 and 5.

In addition, an ellipsis symbol … can be used to indicate a range of contiguous values; for example $\{6, \ldots, 10\}$ is equivalent to $\{6, 7, 8, 9, 10\}$. (An ellipsis is also used informally in some explanations to mean 'etc.'.)

Set membership is indicated by using the symbol $\in$; its negation is denoted by the symbol $\notin$. For example:

$3 \in \{1, 3, 5\}$ evaluates to true

$2 \notin \{1, 3, 5\}$ evaluates to true

There is a special set, the ***empty set,*** denoted $\{ \}$, which contains no elements.

The operators and functions for sets most used in VDM are listed below.

Set operators and functions

Format	*Name, purpose*	*Example*
$t \in S$	*membership*: evaluates to true if t is in S, false if not	$13 \in \{0, 5, 11, 13, 19\}$ evaluates to: true
$t \notin S$	*non-membership*: evaluates to true if t is not in S, false if it is	$13 \notin \{0, 5, 11, 19\}$ evaluates to: true
$S_1 \subset S_2$	*strict subset*: evaluates to true if all members of S_1 are members of S_2 and S_1 is not equal to S_2; false otherwise	{'r', 'e'} ⊂ {'d', 'e', 'r'} evaluates to: true {'r', 'e'} ⊂ {'e', 'r'} evaluates to: false
$S_1 \subseteq S_2$	*subset*: evaluates to true if all members of S_1 are members of S_2; false otherwise	{'r', 'e'} ⊆ {'d', 'e', 'r'} evaluates to: true {'r', 'e'} ⊆ {'e', 'r'} evaluates to: true
$S_1 \cup S_2$	*union*: evaluates to set which is combination of S_1 and S_2	{'r', 'e'} ∪ {'d'} evaluates to: {'d', 'e', 'r'}
$\bigcup\{S_1, S_2, \ldots\}$	*distributed union*: evaluates to set which is combination of S_1, S_2, etc.	⋃{ {'r', 'e'}, {'d'}, {}, {'d', 's'} } evaluates to: {'d', 'e', 'r', 's'}
$S_1 \cap S_2$	*intersection*: evaluates to set whose elements are in S_1 and S_2	$\{1, 2, 3, 5, 7\} \cap \{2, 4, 6, 8\}$ evaluates to: $\{2\}$
$S_1 - S_2$	*set difference*: evaluates to set whose elements are in S_1 but not S_2	$\{1.5, 3.6, 7.4\} - \{3.6\}$ evaluates to: $\{1.5, 7.4\}$
$S_1 \times S_2$	*cartesian product*: evaluates to set of ordered pairs whose first element is from S_1 and second from S_2	$\{1, 2, 3\} \times \{6, 8\}$ evaluates to: $\{(1, 6), (1, 8), (2, 6), (2, 8), (3, 6), (3, 8)\}$
card S	*cardinality*: number of values in S	card$\{1, 2, 8, 9\}$ evaluates to: 4

Note that the argument to card may be included in parentheses for extra clarity; i.e. card(x) is equivalent to card x. Also, in VDM-SL tuples such as the pairs above should be preceded by *mk*- (see page 61). For example, *mk*-(1, 6).

Predefined types

In VDM types are considered to be different to sets. Essentially, sets are values and types are sets with some extra structure that allows a theoretical 'undefined' value to be included. We will usually ignore this distinction to make it easier to define types using notation strictly meant for sets. There are several useful VDM-SL types whose names are predefined. They are:

- the integers $\mathbb{Z} = \{..., -2, -1, 0, 1, 2, ...\}$;
- the natural numbers $\mathbb{N} = \{0, 1, 2, 3, ...\}$;
- the positive natural numbers $\mathbb{N}_1 = \{1, 2, 3, ...\}$;
- the real numbers $\mathbb{R}$;
- the rational numbers $\mathbb{Q}$;
- the booleans $\mathbb{B} = \{\text{true}, \text{false}\}$;
- the characters char that contain characters any of which is denoted by a symbol inside single quotes.

In VDM-SL the values of char are not explicitly given. Rather than define a new type, we find it convenient to extend the definition of char by enumerating common characters, including upper- and lower-case alphabetic characters, digits, punctuation symbols etc.:

char = { 'a', 'b', 'c', 'd', 'e', 'f', 'g', 'h', 'i', 'j', 'k', 'l', 'm',
'n', 'o', 'p', 'q', 'r', 's', 't', 'u', 'v', 'w', 'x', 'y', 'z',
'A', 'B', 'C', 'D', 'E', 'F', 'G', 'H', 'I', 'J', 'K', 'L', 'M',
'N', 'O', 'P', 'Q', 'R', 'S', 'T', 'U', 'V', 'W', 'X', 'Y', 'Z',
'0', '1', '2', '3', '4', '5', '6', '7', '8', '9', '+', '−', '=', '<>',
'>', '<', '≠ ', '×', '/', '(', ')', '[', ']', '{', '}', '.', ';', '?', '!', ...}

Furthermore, we will assume that the values are ordered according to the order they are written above and that $<, \leq, >, \geq$ are defined for char.

Relations, functions and operators

A ***relation*** between two sets A and B is a set of ordered pairs in which the first value is a member of A and the second is a member of B. Thus a relation is a subset of the cartesian product of the two sets: $A \times B$. For example if $A = \{1, 2, 3\}$ and $B = \{4, 5\}$, the relation *less-than* between A and B may be defined thus:

$$\{(1, 4), (1, 5), (2, 4), (2, 5), (3, 4), (3, 5)\}$$

It is rather cumbersome to have to write $(x, y) \in R$ to mean 'x is related to y by R' and so the relation name is used as an infix 'operator', as is $x < y$. The relations $<$, $\leq$, $>$, $\geq$ are all assumed to be defined for the numeric types $\mathbb{N}$, $\mathbb{N}_1$, $\mathbb{Z}$, $\mathbb{R}$ and $\mathbb{Q}$.

A ***function*** from A to B is a relation in which all the members of A are included in the pairs of the relation and in which for all members of A there is at most one member of B in the set of pairs. For example a function *squareof* from $A = \{-7, -8, -9, 7, 8, 9\}$ to $B = \{49, 64, 81\}$ is defined by the set

$\{ (7, 49), (-7, 49), (8, 64), (-8, 64), (9, 81), (-9, 81) \}$

As with relations, it is convenient to use more suggestive language to relate x and y in a function. We therefore speak of 'applying' a function f to x with y as a result and write $f(x) = y$.

Furthermore, it is convenient to use operators instead of function names for the common arithmetic functions for addition, multiplication, etc. Hence, $+$, $-$, $\times$, $/$, are defined for the arithmetic sets, with the expected meaning, as are $\uparrow$ (raise to the power), div (integer division), rem (remainder), mod (modulus), abs (absolute) etc. The data type $\mathbb{B}$ has the usual logical operators defined: $\wedge$, $\vee$, $\neg$, $\Rightarrow$, $\Leftrightarrow$ (see pages 13–14).

The equality and inequality operators, $=$ and $\neq$, are defined for all types; for $\mathbb{B}$ the equality operator means the same as $\Leftrightarrow$.

Set comprehension

Sets may also be denoted *implicitly* by the use of a predicate—a truth-valued expression—which describes the elements. This form of denoting a set is called a ***set comprehension***. For example (assuming a truth-valued function *is-prime*):

$$\{x \mid x \in \{1, ..., 100\} \bullet \textit{is-prime}(x)\}$$

denotes the set of all prime numbers which are less than 100.

The part of the set comprehension before the vertical bar introduces a variable; the part after the bar ***binds*** that variable to a set and gives the predicate that must be true if a value of the set is to be included in the result. In the example above x is introduced and then bound to the set $\{1, ..., 100\}$ which, with the predicate *is-prime*, specified the result of the set comprehension.

Instead of a set, a variable may be bound to a type. Strictly speaking the notation is slightly different—a colon is used in the bind instead of $\in$. The above set may also be defined using the type $\mathbb{Z}$ and using extra constraints:

$$\{y \mid y : \mathbb{Z} \bullet y \geq 1 \wedge y \leq 100 \wedge \textit{is-prime}(y)\}$$

If the predicate is true it may be omitted. Thus $\{p \mid p \in \{\text{'a'}, \text{'e'}, \text{'i'}, \text{'o'}, \text{'u'}\}\}$ is the set of vowels.

Although we tend to use the simplest form of expression to the left of the vertical bar in a set comprehension—a single variable—any expression may be used, e.g. $\{r^2 - 2 \mid r \in \{2.4, -13.6\}\}$ is the set $\{3.76, 182.96\}$.

2.2 Expressions

Formal methods involve the combination, manipulation, and analysis of symbols which represent a model of a problem. Symbols such as x, y, 32767, *SUM*, *new-account*, and *Bank-system* may be combined with other symbols (e.g. $+$, $/$, $\wedge$) to denote a value. These combinations of symbols are called ***expressions*** and are commonly said to 'evaluate to' the value they denote. Consider the following simple expression:

$4 + 7$

It denotes the combination of the values denoted by 7 and 4 with the symbol + which, assuming the usual meaning for +, denotes the value represented by the symbol 11. Lazily, we say 7 plus 4 evaluates to 11.

Frequently, in order to clarify how symbols are to be combined, punctuation symbols like parentheses are used.

$(4 + 7) \times 3$ denotes the value represented by 33

2.3 Predicate calculus

The ***predicate calculus*** is a mathematical system for expressing symbolically logical statements about objects and their properties and for reasoning about them by manipulating the symbols. This makes it essential for a formal method since it can be used in specification and proof. The predicate calculus is based on propositional logic which is outlined next.

Propositions

Propositions are statements which have a truth value: in classical logic they have either the value true, or the value false. Here are some propositions which evaluate to false (when evaluated according to an unspecified model of the world which we hopefully agree on):

England won the World Cup in 1990
The earth is a flat disc
$99 < 3$

Here are some propositions which evaluate to true:

$100.001 > 100.0009$
Belfast is in Northern Ireland
Mozart died in 1791

In the specifications of software systems many such statements are combined, often in complex combinations. (This is what makes a system specification so difficult and prone to inconsistency, contradiction and ambiguity.) To be able to analyse system specifications more effectively, we want to represent the statements symbolically, so that their combination can also be represented symbolically. This allows us to manipulate the symbols according to established rules. For example, when specifying a system for taking theatre bookings, a software developer might want to check (and agree with the client) what happens when a request for tickets is received and all seats are either provisionally booked or bought and paid for. In VDM, a model of the data would be devised:

theatre-capacity might be data which models the number of seats
bought-seats might be data which models the tickets bought and paid for
provisionals might be data which models tickets reserved but not paid for

Then the relevant statements about the data would be expressed using propositions such as:

> *number of bought-seats = theatre-capacity*
> could be a proposition to model a 'sold out' situation;
> if this proposition evaluates to true, we conclude that a performance is sold out.

To model the situation in which there are enough seats available for purchase to meet a request we might have two propositions:

> *number-of-bought-seats ≠ theatre-capacity* and
> *number-requested ≤ theatre-capacity – number-of-bought-seats*

We can, therefore, combine propositions in expressions using symbols for the logical operators *not, and, or, implies* and *equivalent.* These are represented by $\neg$, $\wedge$, $\vee$, $\Rightarrow$ and $\Leftrightarrow$ respectively, as in the following:

$$((p \wedge q) \vee (\neg r)) \Rightarrow s$$

To determine the truth of such an expression we can use ***truth tables***. A truth table is given for each operator which defines the value of the propositional expression involving it.

Note that to avoid tedious English, we often abbreviate correct statements such as 'proposition p evaluates to true' to either 'p is true' or 'p = true'. The latter is used in the truth tables below.

Not operator $\neg$

p	$\neg p$
p = true	false
p = false	true

An expression whose principal operator is $\neg$ is called a ***negation***.

And operator $\wedge$

$p \wedge q$	q = true	q = false
p = true	true	false
p = false	false	false

An expression whose principal operator is $\wedge$ is called a ***conjunction***. The sub-expressions either side of a $\wedge$ are known as ***conjuncts***.

Or operator $\vee$

$p \vee q$	q = true	q = false
p = true	true	true
p = false	true	false

An expression whose principal operator is $\vee$ is called a ***disjunction***. The sub-expressions either side of a $\vee$ are known as ***disjuncts***.

Implies operator $\Rightarrow$

$p \Rightarrow q$	q = true	q = false
p = true	true	false
p = false	true	true

An expression whose principal operator is $\Rightarrow$ is called an ***implication***; in the expression $p \Rightarrow q$, p is called the ***antecedent*** and q is the ***consequent***.

Note that $p \Rightarrow q$ is equivalent to $\neg p \vee q$.

Equivalent operator $\Leftrightarrow$

$p \Leftrightarrow q$	q = true	q = false
p = true	true	false
p = false	false	true

An expression whose principal operator is $\Leftrightarrow$ is called an ***equivalence***.

Proof for propositional logic

In order to decide that a set of propositions is a consequence of another set (a hypothesis) we can construct truth tables to show that the consequence is true in all interpretations where the hypothesis is true. However this would not be practical when large numbers of propositions are involved. Thus a set of inference rules can be used to provide the means to calculate the truth value of propositional expressions. This propositional calculus is extended for the more powerful system, the predicate calculus.

Predicates

The notation of predicate logic is an extension of the propositional logic described above. As well as the simple expressions permitted in propositional logic, predicate logic allows for variables, functions, and predicates; in addition new operators, known as quantifiers are provided (see 2.4). In this way, more powerful expressions can be written.

A ***predicate*** is a truth-valued expression containing so-called free variables; these allow the truth-valued expression to be evaluated, with different values being given to the variable.

A set of ***natural deduction rules*** for the predicate calculus has been defined, which allows the construction of formal proofs required by a method such as VDM.

2.4 Quantifiers

A ***quantifier*** is a mechanism for specifying an expression about a set of values. It is used with a predicate expressed in terms of some so-called ***bound variables*** of a specified type (these are dummy variables only used locally for expressing the predicate).

VDM-SL includes three types of quantifier: the universal quantifier $\forall$, the existential quantifier $\exists$, and the unique existential quantifier $\exists!$. The first two may be followed by a list of bound variables that are bound to either a set or type—as in set comprehension (page 11). In the descriptions below a *bind list* is a list of binds separated by commas, and the general form of a *bind* is either:

bound variable $\in$ *set specification*

or

bound variable : *type specification*

Universal quantifier $\forall$

The form of a predicate using the universal quantifier is:

$\forall$*bind list* • *predicate in terms of bound variable*

Such an expression evaluates to true if for all values of the bound variables specified in the bind list, the predicate holds. The • symbol precedes the body of this predicate.

One example is shown below:

$\forall i \in \{1, \ldots, 100\} \bullet bits\,(i) < 10$

This expression is true if for all values of i from 1 to 100, $bits(i)$ is less than 10.

In certain cases, it is necessary to use more than one bound variable in order to express the desired situation. Consider the example shown below:

$\forall i, j \in \{1, \ldots, 10\} \bullet dot\text{-}matrix\,(i)(j) = 0$

This expression evaluates to true if for every combination of values of i and j between 1 and 10, the value of $dot\text{-}matrix(i)(j)$ is zero; i.e. every element of a sequence of sequences (see Chapter 4) named *dot-matrix* is zero.

Existential quantifier $\exists$

The form of a predicate using the existential quantifier is:

$\exists$*bind list* • *predicate in terms of bound variable*

Such an expression evaluates to true if there exists at least one value in the set of bound variable values for which the predicate holds. An example of using the existential quantifier is shown below:

$\exists i \in \{1, \ldots, 100\} \bullet a(i) = 0$

This expression evaluates to true if there is at least one value i in the set of integers 1 to 100 for which $a(i)$ is zero.

Unique existential quantifier $\exists!$

The form of a predicate using the unique existential quantifier is:

$\exists!$*bind* • *predicate in terms of bound variable*

This allows you to state that *only one* value of a bound variable makes the predicate true. It is read as 'there exists a unique'. An example of its use is shown below:

$$\exists!\ no \in \{1, \ldots, 700\} \bullet a(no) = 0$$

This predicate expression evaluates to true if there is only one zero element in the first 700 elements of the sequence a (see Chapter 4) and it would not be true if there was more than one zero element in the sequence.

Multiple quantifiers

The application of a quantifier to an expression which is itself a quantified expression can be made clear using parentheses. However, these may be reduced by adopting the convention that a quantifier applies to the entire expression to its right or indented below it. For example,

$$\forall\ x \in \{1, \ldots, 100\} \bullet (\exists\ y : T \bullet p(x + y))$$

can be simplified by removing the parentheses to the following:

$$\forall\ x \in \{1, \ldots, 100\} \bullet \exists\ y : T \bullet p(x + y)$$

Indentation can be used to make the structure clear, as in:

$$\begin{array}{l} \forall\ x \in \{1, \ldots, 100\} \bullet \\ \quad \exists\ y : T \bullet p(x + y) \end{array}$$

When quantified expressions within other quantified expressions occur, they may be simplified if the quantifiers are the same. For example,

$$\forall\ i : \mathbb{N} \bullet (\forall\ j : \mathbb{N} \bullet predicate(i, j))$$

can be simplified to either of the following:

$$\forall\ i : \mathbb{N}, j : \mathbb{N} \bullet predicate(i, j)$$

$$\forall\ i, j : \mathbb{N} \bullet predicate(i, j)$$

Operator precedence

The way in which expressions are to be combined can be made explicit using parentheses, for example:

$$(a \wedge b) \vee (c) \Rightarrow (\neg d)$$

To simplify the writing of such an expression the precedence of operators is defined by the following table:

operator and quantifiers	*precedence*
$\forall, \exists, \exists!$	highest
$\neg$	
$\wedge$	
$\vee$	
$\Rightarrow$	
$\Leftrightarrow$	lowest

The expression above can be written thus:

$$a \wedge b \vee c \Rightarrow \neg d$$

2.5 Laws of predicate calculus

A set of inference rules given (known as ***natural deduction rules***) allow proofs to be formal by stating how symbols may be introduced or eliminated. Thus, proofs can be undertaken by manipulating symbols and not by informal argument based on interpretation. In this book we tend to use semi-formal and informal argument in the knowledge that formal proof can be used if required.

A few of the more commonly used rules are now given. In the following, E_1, E_2 and E_3 are expressions of predicate logic.

$\Rightarrow$ *rule of inference*

Given that expression E_1 and the implication $E_1 \Rightarrow E_2$ have been shown to be true, then it can be inferred that E_2 is true.

$$\frac{(E_1; E_1 \Rightarrow E_2)}{E_2}$$

$\wedge$ *introduction rule of inference*

Given that expressions E_1 and E_2 have been shown to be true, then it can be inferred that $E_1 \wedge E_2$ is true; i.e. a conjunction involving both can be introduced.

$$\frac{(E_1 ; E_2)}{E_1 \wedge E_2}$$

$\vee$ *introduction rule of inference*

Given that expression E_1 has been shown to be true, then it can be inferred that $E_1 \vee E_2$ is true; i.e. a disjunction involving E_1 can be introduced.

$$\frac{E_1}{E_1 \vee E_2}$$

∧ elimination rules of inference

Given that expressions E_1 and E_2 have been shown to be true, then it can be inferred that E_1 is true and E_2 is true; i.e. a conjunction involving both can be eliminated.

$$\frac{(E_1 \wedge E_2)}{E_2} \qquad \frac{(E_1 \wedge E_2)}{E_1}$$

Commutative laws

A commutative law allows the operands to be interchanged. There are three of these commutative laws in predicate calculus:

$(E_1 \wedge E_2)$	is equivalent to	$(E_2 \wedge E_1)$
$(E_1 \vee E_2)$	is equivalent to	$(E_2 \vee E_1)$
$(E_1 \Leftrightarrow E_2)$	is equivalent to	$(E_2 \Leftrightarrow E_1)$

Associative laws

Such laws allow us to dispense with brackets. In predicate calculus there are two associative laws:

$E_1 \wedge (E_2 \wedge E_3)$	is equivalent to	$(E_1 \wedge E_2) \wedge E_3$	is equivalent to	$E_1 \wedge E_2 \wedge E_3$
$E_1 \vee (E_2 \vee E_3)$	is equivalent to	$(E_1 \vee E_2) \vee E_3$	is equivalent to	$E_1 \vee E_2 \vee E_3$

Distributive laws

These laws allow one operator to be 'distributed' over another one. There are two distributive laws in predicate calculus:

$E_1 \vee (E_2 \wedge E_3)$	is equivalent to	$(E_1 \vee E_2) \wedge (E_1 \vee E_3)$
$E_1 \wedge (E_2 \vee E_3)$	is equivalent to	$(E_1 \wedge E_2) \vee (E_1 \wedge E_3)$

DeMorgan's laws

These allow the removal of brackets in negated, bracketed expressions:

$\neg(E_1 \wedge E_2)$	is equivalent to	$\neg E_1 \vee \neg E_2$
$\neg(E_1 \vee E_2)$	is equivalent to	$\neg E_1 \wedge \neg E_2$

The law of negation

This law states that a negated predicate, which is itself negated, is equivalent to the original predicate. That is, two negatives make a positive!

$\neg\neg E_1$	is equivalent to	E_1

The law of the excluded middle

This law is equivalent to saying that either a predicate is true or the negation of the predicate is true. That is, either a predicate is true, or it is false!

$E_1 \vee \neg E_1$	is equivalent to	true

The law of implication

This law expresses implication in terms of disjunction and negation. It is often used in proofs as a preliminary step to applying laws such as the laws of distribution and DeMorgan's laws:

$E_1 \Rightarrow E_2$	is equivalent to	$\neg E_1 \vee E_2$

The law of equality

This expresses equivalence in terms of implication:

$E_1 \Leftrightarrow E_2$	is equivalent to	$(E_1 \Rightarrow E_2) \wedge (E_2 \Rightarrow E_1)$

The laws of 'or' simplification

These allow expressions involving true, false and $\vee$ to be simplified:

$E_1 \vee E_1$	is equivalent to	E_1
$E_1 \vee$ true	is equivalent to	true
$E_1 \vee$ false	is equivalent to	E_1
$E_1 \vee (E_1 \wedge E_2)$	is equivalent to	E_1

The laws of 'and' simplification

These allow expressions involving true, false and $\wedge$ to be simplified:

$E_1 \wedge E_1$	is equivalent to	E_1
$E_1 \wedge$ true	is equivalent to	E_1
$E_1 \wedge$ false	is equivalent to	false
$E_1 \wedge (E_1 \vee E_2)$	is equivalent to	E_1

It is important to point out that E_1, E_2 and E_3 can stand for any predicate. For example, if E_1 is a, E_2 is $b \Rightarrow c$, and E_3 is $c \wedge d$ then the first of the distributive laws given above could be written as:

$$a \vee ((b \Rightarrow c) \wedge (c \wedge d)) \quad \text{is equivalent to} \quad (a \vee (b \Rightarrow c)) \wedge (a \vee (c \wedge d))$$

Furthermore, note that the equivalence operator $\Leftrightarrow$ has the same properties as the equality operator in algebra. The left-hand operand can be substituted for the right-hand operand in a predicate and vice versa. For example, if we knew that both the following were true:

$(a \wedge b) \Leftrightarrow (p \Rightarrow y)$
$q \vee (a \wedge b)$

we would know that $q \vee (p \Rightarrow y)$ was true.

2.6 Approaches to proof

In order to deal with complex expressions in the propositional or predicate logics, we need a proof system to allow us to deduce the truth of an expression (E_2), given the truth or falsity of other expressions (E_1). (They all assume that the expressions under consideration are defined.) There are six basic approaches to proof:

1. Direct proof—assume E_1 is true and show that E_2 must be true.
2. Contrapositive proof—assume E_2 is false and show that E_1 is false.
3. Proof by contradiction—assume E_1 is true and E_2 is false and show this leads to a contradiction.
4. Existence proof—show a claimed existence of value in E_1 to be true.
5. Proof by counterexample—to show universal quantification is false, find an example which fails to satisfy a predicate.
6. Proof by induction—for proving propositions on a range of integers greater than or equal to some value k: assume E_1 is true for value k; assume E_1 is true for value $n \geq k$ and from this deduce that E_1 is true for $n + 1$; this proves that E_1 is true for all values $\geq k$.

2.7 Fundamentals of VDM

There are a number of theoretical aspects of VDM and its specification language which we have chosen to avoid for simplicity and brevity. We will not always indicate where we have done this; many fine points of VDM-SL are due to the desire to facilitate the production of software tools for the language. However, one important deviation must be noted: in this book we rely on the classical two-valued logic given above together with its associated inference rules and proof strategies. This is not strictly correct for VDM, which requires a three-valued logic system to deal with those situations in which no real information is available, for example when a number is divided by zero, or a program loops indefinitely, or a value is not defined. These problems occur frequently in software development and the notion of a value which is itself undefined is needed.

Given the need to deal with the 'value' undefined we can revise the definitions of the operators $\neg$, $\wedge$, $\vee$, $\Rightarrow$ and $\Leftrightarrow$ as given in Appendix A.

Classical proof depends on the original definitions of these operators, particularly on $\wedge$, $\vee$ and $\Rightarrow$. These new definitions and a modified set of inference rules which make up the ***logic of partial functions*** (LPF) preclude the use of some of the classical proof strategies without careful avoidance of the undefined value. (For example, proof by contradiction cannot be used with LPF.)

If specifications and proofs avoid the undefined situation, then LPF is essentially the same as classsical two-valued logic. Therefore, for simplicity we will not use LPF in this book, and assume that our specifications and proofs avoid undefined situations. This should ensure our lack of formality does not significantly compromise the development method.

2.8 Summary of concepts

- Formal methods are based on discrete mathematics, in particular:
  - set theory;
  - propositional calculus;
  - predicate calculus.
- VDM depends on the three-valued Logic of Partial Functions, but we will use classical two-valued logic.
- Sets are unordered collections of values containing no duplicates; various functions and operators are defined for sets:
  - set membership $\in$ and set non-membership $\notin$;
  - strict subset $\subset$ subset $\subseteq$;
  - union $\cup$, distributed union $\bigcup$, intersection $\cap$, and set difference $-$;
  - cartesian product $\times$;
  - cardinality.
- Set values can be enumerated or defined using set comprehension.
- Types are different from sets; they have structured and a value undefined.
- The predicate calculus is a system based on propositional calculus for writing and evaluating expressions which are either true or false (or undefined in LPF). Its operators and quantifiers are:
  - not $\neg$, and $\wedge$, or $\vee$, implies $\Rightarrow$, equivalent $\Leftrightarrow$
  - for all $\forall$, there exists $\exists$, there exists one $\exists!$
- The natural deduction inference rules allow formal proofs by stating how symbols of predicate logic may be manipulated.

3 MODELLING DATA—SET TYPES

This chapter begins with an introduction to the concept of VDM data types and to the fundamental class of types whose values are themselves sets—***set types***. The chapter also contains a brief overview of how to specify operations on data.

3.1 Data types in VDM

The concept of type is central to VDM. In general the notion of ***data type*** involves a set of values, and a collection of operations which may be applied to those values. For example, the data type `integer` is often provided in a programming language, such as Pascal; the type consists of a range of whole number values and operations such as addition, multiplication, negation, and so on. (The range is limited owing to the limitations imposed by the way `integer` values are represented; –32768, ..., 32767 is common on micros.) We might represent the Pascal `integer` data type by Figure 3.1.

`integer`

values: `{-32768, ..., 32767}`
operations: + (identity), – (negation), + (addition), – (subtraction), `*`, **`div`**, **`mod`**, =, <>, <, >, <=, >=, ABS

Figure 3.1

From Figure 3.1 we can see that the values –5 and 65 are values in the `integer` data type. We can also see that * may be applied to integers (given some language rules) whereas / cannot, because the operation / is not defined in Pascal for integers.

In VDM a type is essentially a set of values; the associated operations are separate from the values but linked to them by the name of the type. For example the operation *ADD-TO-TRIP* (which is explained on page 29) is associated with the type *School-trip*.

ADD-TO-TRIP(*new-on-trip*: *School-trip*)

The exceptions to this rule are predefined types ($\mathbb{N}$, $\mathbb{N}_1$, $\mathbb{Z}$, $\mathbb{R}$, $\mathbb{Q}$, $\mathbb{B}$ and char, given in 2.1) whose operations are predefined, usually as infix operators, such as +.

Exercise 3.1

Using the 'box notation' of Figure 3.1 draw a diagram which depicts the type $\mathbb{Z}$. Include comparison operators (for equality, inequality, and so on) in the operations.

Solution 3.1

$\mathbb{Z}$

values: {..., –5, –4, –3, –2, –1, 0, 1, 2, 3, 4, 5, ...}
operations: + (identity), – (negation), + (addition), – (subtraction), ×, div, mod, =, ≠, >, <, ≥, ≤, abs, rem, ↑

■

3.2 Modelling data

The first phase of the classical software development process described in Chapter 1 is requirements analysis. Its primary purpose is to produce a system specification in which the functional and non-functional requirements are partitioned. The ideal is to capture the essential behaviour of the system in the functional specification and to ensure that it contains no implementation bias. In VDM terms this means capturing the essential behaviour in a mathematical model of the system: a model of its data and a model of the operations to be performed on the data.

Usually the first step in this process is to model the data. This involves analysing the statement of requirements in order to identify objects which are values of some type and classes of objects which can be modelled as types.

Consider the following fragment of a statement of requirements.

```
The new payroll system must handle different cate-
gories of staff. In our organization, the salary
scales for technical staff are different from the
scales for sales and administrative staff. Technical
staff include such people as project managers, team
leaders, analysts, designers and programmers. Although
```

```
a project team will include secretaries and clerks,
those staff are considered to be administrative rather
than technical.
```

We need to identify objects and potential types in this statement of requirements. In this case, and this is not always so, it is easier to identify the types first; they are the different categories of staff: *Technical-staff*, *Admin-staff* and *Sales-staff*. The objects are: PROJECT-MANAGER, TEAM-LEADER, ANALYST, DESIGNER, PROGRAMMER, SECRETARY, CLERK.

All but the last two objects in the example above are values of the data type *Technical-staff*. This is illustrated in Figure 3.2.

Technical-staff

values: {PROJECT-MANAGER, TEAM-LEADER, ANALYST, DESIGNER, PROGRAMMER}
operations: — not yet defined

Figure 3.2

A diagrammatic convention to specify the values and operations of a type is not provided in VDM: the values and associated operations can be defined quite separately in different parts of the specification. In VDM the information concerning values in Figure 3.2 is expressed by listing the names as follows:

types
Technical-staff = PROJECT-MANAGER | TEAM-LEADER | ANALYST |
DESIGNER | PROGRAMMER

The absence of operations is not made explicit.

The above fragment of VDM-SL actually declares six types! It implicitly defines each of the identifiers in capitals to be types that contain one value; they are called ***quote types***. This definition of the type *Technical-staff* is actually an example of a ***union type***; it is defined to be the union of the five quote types. However, to hide this complexity we will consider the identifiers in capitals to be constants and will use the following as an equivalent declaration:

Technical-staff = {PROJECT-MANAGER, TEAM-LEADER, ANALYST,
DESIGNER, PROGRAMMER}

Note that for brevity we shall usually omit the keyword types.[1]

A VDM specification contains models of both data and operations on data. Although data and operations go hand in hand, it has proved useful to focus on

[1]Similarly, we omit the keyword values which is used to introduce identifiers denoting constants.

modelling data first. Indeed it is often an advantage to postpone the specification of operations.

As well as the simple data types discussed above, we need to be able to construct new types from old. We have stated many times that a specification should be concise and understandable. VDM achieves these goals by providing only three constructors for defining new simple types—set types, sequence types and map types.

3.3 Set types

A set type is a data type whose values are sets. It is important to recognize the difference between a set and an element of the set.

To introduce a new data type in a VDM specification we must use a ***constructor***, which is a VDM language device which takes one type and creates another. The first of these is the set constructor. Given a VDM data type T, we can create a new data type, each of whose elements is a set of type T, using the following:

T-set

Hence, T-set is a set whose elements are themselves sets containing values from T.

For example, consider the type *Mode*:

Mode = {READ, WRITE, EXECUTE}

A set type based on *Mode* can be defined thus:

FileMode = *Mode*-set

This is equivalent to defining *FileMode* explicitly, thus:

FileMode =
{ { }, {READ}, {WRITE}, {EXECUTE}, {READ, WRITE}, {READ, EXECUTE}, {EXECUTE, WRITE}, {READ, WRITE, EXECUTE} }

The suffix -set is reserved for use as the set constructor. All VDM key words will be printed using a sans-serif font; all identifiers are printed in italics; all values (e.g. 1, ‘c’) are upright; where identifiers denote values they appear in capitals.

The set type constructor produces the new type whose values are *all* finite subsets of T. For example, consider the following:

Intset = $\mathbb{Z}$-set

The elements of *Intset* are *finite* sets of integers. and so the following are some possible values from *Intset* because they are elements of *Intset*, i.e. they are finite subsets of $\mathbb{Z}$.

$\{-2, 6\}$ $\qquad$ $\{n \mid n : \mathbb{N} \bullet 3 \leq n \wedge n \leq 7\}$ $\qquad$ $\{4\}$

The restriction to finite subsets is a VDM concession to computer representation; computers are finite and can store only finite sets. Therefore the -set constructor does not include infinite subsets; for example, $\mathbb{Z}$-set *excludes* the subset of $\mathbb{Z}$ which is the set of the odd integers as this is an infinite subset.

This concern for finiteness applies to the values of a VDM data type because they are possible values of a variable of a concrete implementation of the type. For example, the data type $\mathbb{Z}$ has infinitely many elements but each element is just an integer and so finite. The data type $\mathbb{Z}$-set is infinite but each element is just a finite set of integers.

Review Question 3.1

(i) Write down explicitly a non-empty element of $\mathbb{N}$-set (the natural numbers).

(ii) Write down explicitly a non-empty element of ($\mathbb{N}$-set)-set.

■

For example, a football team can be modelled as a set of players. Such a model makes sense when the important idea is whether a person is in the team or not in the team. The set model must not be used where either order or replication are important.

Exercise 3.2

Say whether the following objects can be modelled as sets. If they cannot, say why not.

(i) Passengers on a bus.

(ii) Names of people entering a lottery.

(iii) Patients waiting for an operation.

Solution 3.2

(i) Passengers on a bus can be modelled as a set.

(ii) A set cannot be used to model names in a lottery because someone can enter a lottery more than once.

(iii) A set cannot be used to model a queue because order is important.

■

Review Question 3.2

Does it make sense to model the body of a Pascal program as a set of statements?

■

Exercise 3.3

The following defines a type for modelling a school class.

Pupils = {PATRICK, CHRISTA, EMMA, PETE, FRANK, LISA, RICHARD, DAVID, DANIEL, JOHN, HELEN, PAULINE, MARK, MIKE, ELIZABETH}

Now, suppose a school trip to France is planned (and not all of the children will go on the trip). Define a type, *School-trip*, which would model all the possible groups of children who could go on a trip.

Solution 3.3

School-trip = *Pupils*-set

■

Note that the definition allows for the possibility of no children or just one or two children going on a trip. In 6.2 we show how to express practical constraints such as a minimum number for a viable trip using data type invariants.

Review Question 3.3
Using the model in Exercise 3.3 give the value of the object of type *School-trip* which includes all the girls in the class.

■

Review Question 3.4
Give an example of a subset of the real numbers, $\mathbb{R}$, that is not an element of the data type defined by $\mathbb{R}$-set.

■

3.4 Modelling operations

VDM is not just a specification language; it is a method for designing and verifying programs. It must reflect, therefore, some of the constraints on design imposed by programming languages. Although there is currently a great deal of research into programming languages in which there is no notion of computer memory or store, for the foreseeable future we shall still be using the so-called ***imperative languages*** like Pascal, Modula-2 and C in which the fundamental meaning of a program is its effect on a computer's store. This means that the language must contain an abstraction of computer store.

An abstraction of computer store

The execution of an imperative program can be thought of as causing a transformation to be made to a computer's store. The effect of a program or program fragment can therefore be specified by describing how the store should look before execution and how it should look after completion. If this were done for all configurations of the store on which a program is intended to work, the computer program would be completely specified.

The notion of what configurations of the store are valid is crucial to the specification of operations. As we shall see, we will describe the state of the store using a logical expression which evaluates to true and define an operation with an expression that must be true after the operation has completed, but only if a certain pre-condition holds before the operation.

Computer store in VDM is modelled by the notion of an ***external variable***. An external variable is just a global variable that can be modified by VDM operations. The collection of external variables in a VDM specification is called the ***state*** of the system being specified.

Operations are similar to the idea of a procedure in a programming language: they incorporate the notion of external, or global, variables and may have input parameters and a result parameter. External variables may be used or modified by an operation. Input parameters may only be used to pass values into the operation. A single result parameter may be used to output a value from an operation.

Therefore, an operation may have only two kinds of effects:

- It may affect various external variables.
- It may return a value through a result parameter.

The kind of access to an external variable which an operation requires must be declared in VDM. In an operation, an external variable must be declared to be accessible in one of the following two ways.

- It may be a read-only or rd variable. That is, the operation may read the value of the external variable but may not change that value.
- It may be a read-write or wr variable. That is, the operation may read the value of the external variable or change its value or both. There is no notion in VDM of write-only access.

We shall refer to this designation of access as the ***mode*** of the external variable. Each external variable, therefore, has a type and a mode. Access to an external variable is only permitted for those variables which are declared at the beginning of the operation with the keyword ext, followed by the mode rd or wr, and then the variable name and its type. For example, to make the variable *size* (of type $\mathbb{N}$) accessible as a read-only variable the following would be used:

ext rd $size$: $\mathbb{N}$

If more than one external variable is needed in the specification of an operation they should be listed in the ext statement. For example:

ext wr a, b: $\mathbb{N}$
rd x: $\mathbb{Z}$

General form of operations

An operation has four components:

1. operation ***header***—its name, input parameters (in parentheses) and result parameter, if any;
2. ***external clause*** (also called a ***frame***) in which external variables and their access mode are declared—the keyword ext followed by lists of variables preceded by their access mode (wr or rd);
3. ***pre-condition*** (optional)—a predicate preceded by the keyword pre;
4. ***post-condition***—a predicate preceded by the keyword post.

The general form of an operation specification with both parameters and result is as follows:

OPERATION-NAME(parameter1: Type1,
parameter2: Type2, ...) result-name: Type
ext wr *read-write variables: Type*
...
rd *read-only variables: Type*
pre *pre-condition predicate*
post *post-condition predicate*

If the operation does not return a result but has parameters then the heading is just:

OPERATION-NAME(parameter1: Type1,
parameter2: Type2, ...)

but if there is a result but no parameters then the heading is:

OPERATION-NAME( ) result-name: Type

Note that we adopt the convention of spelling operation names with capital letters.

Consider the following trivial operation to multiply the value of an external variable x by the value of the operation's argument:

MULT(factor: $\mathbb{R}$)
ext wr x: $\mathbb{R}$
pre $x < 16384$
post $x = factor \times \overleftarrow{x}$

The header tells us that the name of the operation is *MULT* and that there is one parameter, a real-number value denoted by *factor*. The external clause specifies that x may be changed. The pre-condition means that the operation is to be defined only when the state of the store is such that $x < 16384$. The post-condition states that the new value of x, which is denoted by x, is to be the old value, $\overleftarrow{x}$, multiplied by the value denoted by *factor*. Note that although the x in the pre-condition does not have a hook, it actually denotes the old value of x.

We return to operations in Chapter 7.

Review Question 3.5

Complete the following operation *ADD-TO-TRIP* by adding the post-condition which specifies that it updates an external variable *trip* of type *School-trip* (defined as in Exercise 3.3) by adding pupils from *new-on-trip*.

ADD-TO-TRIP(new-on-trip: School-trip)
ext wr *trip*: *School-trip*
pre $new\text{-}on\text{-}trip \cap trip = \{\,\}$

■

3.5 Summary of concepts

- VDM is a model-oriented formal method.
- Usually a model is constructed by devising a data model first, starting with an analysis of the statement of requirements. Data models are based on data types which are considered to be sets.
- Primitive types are provided:
  - $\mathbb{N}$, $\mathbb{N}_1$, $\mathbb{Z}$, $\mathbb{R}$, $\mathbb{Q}$, $\mathbb{B}$, char
- Set types are data types whose values are sets. Set types are defined using a set type constructor:
  - *Set-type* = *T*-set
- Operations are modelled in terms of an abstraction of computer store. They are defined in terms of external variables. An operation consists of:
  - header (name, parameters, result);
  - external (ext) variable clause including rd or wr access mode;
  - pre-condition;
  - post-condition;
- When an external variable is referred to in a pre-condition, it is its old value which is being used. In a post-condition a hook must be placed over a variable's name to show the old value (e.g. $\overleftarrow{x}$).

4 SEQUENCE TYPES

A sequence is an ordered collection of elements in which elements may occur several times. Perhaps the most commonly used sequences in computing are sequences of characters, sometimes called character strings. Every word processor deals with objects that are equivalent to character strings. However, a sequence can also be used as a model of a queue at a post office in which customers are served in the order of arrival; a list of moves in a chess game kept in the order in which the moves were made; a list of instructions in a computer program kept in the order in which they are to be executed; and any application involving order among possibly duplicate elements.

4.1 Sequence types

A ***sequence*** is a finite, *ordered* collection of zero or more objects. Sequences are collections of objects, like sets, but differ from them because they incorporate the ideas of order and repetition. Sequences are written in the same way as sets, by listing the objects separated by commas, but with square brackets '[', ']' rather than the curly brackets '{', '}' used with sets. For example:

[4, 2, 7, 1, 5, 6, 3] is a seven-element sequence of seven whole numbers

[7, 2, 1, 4, 3, 6, 5] is a different seven-element sequence of whole numbers

['C', 'O', 'N', ':'] is a sequence of characters

[42.0, 343.0, 42.0] is a three-element sequence of real numbers with 42.0 repeated

The empty sequence is written:

[ ]

As with sets, sequences are written as a list of values separated by commas, but enclosed in square brackets. Unlike sets, the order in which the objects appear in a sequence is important. For example, the sequence of characters 'a', 'b', 'c' is denoted:

['a', 'b', 'c']

Thus, because order and repetition matter in a sequence, the following sequences, which all contain members of the set of characters {'a', 'b', 'c'}, are all different although they contain the same elements:

['a', 'b', 'c'] ['a', 'c', 'b'] ['a', 'a', 'c', 'b']

A ***sequence comprehension*** construct is also available. It is similar to that for sets but is delimited by square brackets instead of braces. It also differs by requiring that the values in the set or type in the bind (to the right of the '|') be ordered. For example:

$[x \mid x \in \{1, ..., 10\} \bullet \textit{is-prime}(x)]$ evaluates to $[1, 3, 5, 7]$

Review Question 4.1

What are the two ways in which sequences differ from sets?

■

Sequences are used to model a wide variety of entities which have little in common except the attributes of order or repetition. For example, sequences can be used to model character strings, transactions on a bank account ordered by date, queues of customers at a post office, and text documents such as books.

VDM contains two sequence type constructors similar to that for sets; one allows empty sequences, which we use most, and the other does not. If T is any VDM data type then the constructions:

T^* and T^+

are the *set* of all sequences whose elements are members of T. In other words, any value of the types T^* and T^+ is a sequence whose elements are values of T. Thus, [1, 2, 3] and [4, 5, 6] are values of the type $\mathbb{N}_1{}^*$ and the elements they contain are members of $\mathbb{N}_1$. The difference between the two type constructors is that the empty sequence is a value of type T^* but not of T^+. We tend to use T^*.

The type from which a sequence is constructed is known as the ***base type***. For example, suppose *Letter* is a data type whose elements are the alphabetic characters (as might be used to model a word). Then a data type named *Word* whose elements are sequences of letters may be defined by:

$Word = Letter^*$

The base type of *Word* is *Letter*.

Exercise 4.1

Give examples of the following sequences:

(i) a list of positive integers in ascending order;

(ii) a file of withdrawals from a bank account (the withdrawals would be modelled as real numbers).

Solution 4.1

(i) [1, 2, 5, 77, 99, 256]

(ii) [20.56, 37.00, 120.61, 50.00]

■

Exercise 4.2

The following defines the data type *Smallstring*:

Smallstring = {'a', 'b', 'c'}*

Is it possible to list all the values of the data type *Smallstring*?

Solution 4.2

No, it is not possible to list all the values of *Smallstring*. The values of a data type which is defined using the sequence generator * allows unlimited repetition and will therefore be infinite. A tiny fragment of the set is given below:

Smallstring = {[ ], ['a'], ['b'], ['c'], ['a', 'a'], ['a', 'a', 'a'], ['a', 'b'], ['c', 'b'], ['b', 'a'], ['b', 'c'], ['a', 'c'], ..., ['b', 'c', 'a'], ['c', 'a', 'b'], ['a', 'a', 'b'], ['a', 'b', 'a'], ['a', 'a', 'c'], ['a', 'c', 'a'], ...}

■

Note that it is possible to define data types using nested constructors, thus:

char*-set — sets of sequences of characters

ℝ-set* — sequences of sets containing real numbers

Exercise 4.3

By modelling a word as a sequence of values of the type *Letter*, a paragraph as a sequence of words, and a chapter as a sequence of paragraphs, specify a VDM data type to model a chapter in a book. For simplicity we ignore punctuation and assume the following definition of *Letter*:

Letter = {'a', ..., 'z', 'A', ..., 'Z'}

Solution 4.3

A crude approach would be to nest sequence type constructors directly as in:

Chapter = ((*Letter**)*)*

A better, more structured approach is to name the subtypes as in:

Word = *Letter**
Paragraph = *Word**
Chapter = *Paragraph**

■

Strings

Sequences of characters, which are commonly known as strings, occur frequently in software systems. Therefore, a shorthand notation is provided for writing character string constants: the string as a whole can be enclosed in double quote marks (“ and ”) instead of quoting each character separately. For example, instead of writing a string such as:

['D', 'i', 's', 'k', ' ', 'f', 'u', 'l', 'l']

we can write:

"Disk full"

Review Question 4.2
How could the following sequence of characters be modelled as a sequence of strings?

```
Buffer overflow: file transfer aborted.
```

■

Care must be taken to distinguish between the use of double and single quotes; the latter are only used to denote values of char. For example, the following expressions are true:

'a' ∈ char
"hello" ∈ char* because "hello" is equivalent to ['h', 'e', 'l', 'l', 'o']
"a" ∈ char* because "a" is equivalent to ['a']

4.2 Functions and operators on sequences

Owing to the widespread applications of sequences in data processing, probably more sequence operators are used in modelling applications than operators on any of the other data types. We shall present the most useful operators.

Length function: len

The length of a sequence is the number of objects in the sequence. In particular the length of an empty sequence is zero. The built-in function len may be applied to any sequence to obtain its length. For example:

len ([ ]) evaluates to 0

len ([23, 44, 42, 1, 99]) evaluates to 5

It is a VDM convention that the arguments to built-in functions do not appear in parentheses unless the parentheses are needed to distinguish the argument from what follows it. Thus, the length of the sequence ['A', 'b', 'o', 'r', 't', 'e', 'd'] is given by:

len ['A', 'b', 'o', 'r', 't', 'e', 'd']

Indexing a sequence

We will use an indexing notation by which a value in a sequence can be referred to by its position: to denote the ith element of a sequence sq, we use $sq(i)$. Thus, for example, if $sq = [2, 19, 13, 5, 17]$, the element $sq(1)$ is 2 and the element $sq(4)$ is 5.

Note that indexes start at 1 and if the index i of sq is outside the range 1, ..., len sq then the result of evaluating the expression $sq(i)$ is undefined.

Exercise 4.4

What is the result of evaluating the following expressions?

(i) [‘S’, ‘y’, ‘n’, ‘t’, ‘a’, ‘x’, ‘ ’, ‘e’, ‘r’, ‘r’, ‘o’, ‘r’](4)

(ii) [43.5, 666.7647, 666.7647, 43.5, 33.14, 5334.12, 8354.89](6)

(iii) “C:\BIN\MOUSE.SYS”(2)

Solution 4.4

(i) ‘t’ (ii) 5334.12 (iii) ‘:’

■

Exercise 4.5

Write an expression which evaluates to the last element of the sequence sq.

Solution 4.5

sq(len sq)

■

Subsequences

We already know that if i is an index of a sequence sq, then $sq(i)$ is the element in the ith position of sq. We now extend the notation by applying sq to an interval of indexes. If i and j are indexes of a sequence sq and $i \leq j$, then $sq(i, \ldots, j)$ is defined as the sequence whose elements are the elements in positions $(i, \ldots, j)$ of sq. For example:

[‘a’, ‘a’, ‘d’, ‘c’, ‘a’, ‘b’](2, ..., 4)	evaluates to the sequence	[‘a’, ‘d’, ‘c’]
“C:\AUTOEXEC.BAT”(4, ..., 11)	evaluates to the sequence	“AUTOEXEC”
[201, 925, 43](2, ..., 2)	evaluates to the sequence	[925]
s(1, ..., len s)	evaluates to the sequence	s.

The result of applying s to an interval of indexes is called a ***subsequence*** of s.

If i and j are less than 1 or $i > j$, then $sq(i, \ldots, j)$ is [ ]. If i is less than 1, then $sq(i, \ldots, j)$ is the same as $sq(1, \ldots, j)$. If j is greater than the largest index of sq, then $sq(i, \ldots, j)$ is $sq(i, \ldots,$ len $sq)$.

Exercise 4.6

Write an expression which evaluates to a sequence containing the last two elements of *sq*.

Solution 4.6

$sq(\mathsf{len}(sq) - 1, \ldots, \mathsf{len}(sq))$

■

Review Question 4.3

If s = [APPEL, OLIVETY, COMPAK, FUJEE], then find

(i) $s(3, \ldots, 4)$ (ii) $s(4, \ldots, 3)$

(iii) $s(3, \ldots, 5)$ (iv) $s(1, \ldots, 1)$

■

Concatenate operator: ⁀

The second VDM function we need is the concatenation function which is denoted by the symbol ⁀. It is used as an infix operator. If s and t are both sequences then the sequence that contains all elements of s followed by all elements of t is denoted by:

$s \frown t$

For example:

[‘i’, ‘n’] ⁀ [‘f’, ‘o’, ‘r’, ‘m’] evaluates to [‘i’, ‘n’, ‘f’, ‘o’, ‘r’, ‘m’]

The concatenate operator may only be used between sequences. Thus, while the expression [‘q’] ⁀ [‘r’] is valid, ‘q’ ⁀ [‘r’] is not.

As you might expect, concatenating an empty sequence with any other sequence, s, say, will result in s, thus:

[ ] ⁀ s evaluates to s and s ⁀ [ ] evaluates to s

Note that expressions may contain several occurrences of the ⁀ operator. For example:

[12, 45, 34] ⁀ [22, 15] ⁀ [23, 109] evaluates to [12, 45, 34, 22, 15, 23, 109]

Review Question 4.4

What is [] ⁀ []?

■

Review Question 4.5

(i) Evaluate [‘a’, ‘b’, ‘a’] ⁀ [‘a’, ‘c’].

(ii) Evaluate len ([125.345, 48934.898] ⁀ [738379.8988, 829333.091, 8983.66]).

(iii) Evaluate (“USER” ⁀ “$” ⁀ “DSK” ⁀ “:”)(6, …, 8).

■

Modification operator: †

The operator † can be used to change a specific element of a sequence: a sequence is followed by † and a *map* that indicates which elements of the sequence are to be changed. A map is a set containing ordered pairs, e.g. $9 \mapsto 4.6$. Chapter 8 discusses maps in detail; in this context the first element of the map is a positive integer and the second is a value of the base type of the relevant sequence. For example [13, 2, 7, 5, 9] † {3 $\mapsto$ 11} is the sequence [13, 2, 11, 5, 9]; "mega" † {1 $\mapsto$ 'g', 2 $\mapsto$ 'i'} is the sequence "giga".

The † operator can be used to avoid complicated expressions in which a sequence is copied with an element replaced by splitting the sequence and reconstructing it with concatenation; i.e. the first example above saves one from writing [13, 2] ⁀ [11] ⁀ [5, 9] .

Head and tail functions: hd *and* tl

Every non-empty sequence can be considered to consist of a first element followed by another sequence: a head and a tail. The ***head*** is the first element in the sequence. The ***tail*** is the sequence which would remain if the head were to be removed. Therefore, the head of ['p', 'q', 'r'] is 'p'; the tail of ['p', 'q', 'r'] is ['q', 'r'].

VDM provides the function hd which returns the head of a sequence, and the function tl which returns the tail of a sequence. As for len the parentheses which enclose an argument may be omitted. For example:

hd ['p', 'q', 'r']	evaluates to	'p'
tl ['p', 'q', 'r']	evaluates to	['q', 'r']
tl [42]	evaluates to	[]

Because you cannot construct a sequence using ⁀ between an element and a sequence, you cannot reconstruct a sequence using ⁀ between its head and its tail; you must ensure that both are sequences. The following is true for any non-empty sequence:

[hd *sq*] ⁀ tl *sq* = *sq*

Note that hd [ ] and tl [ ] are undefined. You should avoid writing specifications which evaluate such expressions, but it can be difficult to see them in complex expressions and when used in recursive functions.

Exercise 4.7

Write an expression which specifies a sequence that is the last element of a sequence *sq* followed by all but the last element of *sq*.

Solution 4.7

[*sq*(len *sq*)] ⁀ *sq*(1, …, len(*sq*)–1)

■

Indexes and elements functions: inds *and* elems

In specifications involving sequences there is often a need to refer to the set of values held in a sequence; these are known as the elements of the sequence. The function elems takes a sequence as its argument and returns a set of the values held in the sequence.

Similarly, it is useful to be able to specify the set which contains the indexes of a sequence. The function inds is provided for this purpose.

The functions are specified as follows:

$$\text{inds } sq = \{1, \ldots \text{len } sq\}$$
$$\text{elems } sq = \{sq(i) \mid i \in \text{inds } sq\}$$

For example:

inds [12, 4, 6, 38, 12]	evaluates to the set	{1, 2, 3, 4, 5}
elems [12, 4, 6, 12, 4, 6, 38, 12]	evaluates to the set	{12, 4, 6, 38}

Note that inds [] and elems [] are both the empty set { }.

Review Question 4.6

Suppose $sq = [1, 3, 2, 1]$ and $t = [4]$. Which of the following are true and which are false?

(i) $\text{inds } sq = \{1, 2, 3\}$

(ii) $\text{tl } t = [\,]$

(iii) $\text{hd } t = 4$

(iv) $sq = (\text{hd } sq) \frown (\text{tl } sq)$

(v) $\text{tl}(\text{tl } t) = [\,]$

(vi) $\text{len } sq + \text{len } t = \text{len}(sq \frown t)$

(vii) $\text{len } sq = \text{len}(\text{tl } sq) + 1$

(viii) $\text{elems } t = \{4\}$

(ix) $(sq \frown t)(5) = 4$

(x) $\text{hd}(\text{tl } sq) = \text{tl}(\text{hd } sq)$

■

4.3 Specifications using sequences

We end this section by briefly demonstrating the use of the sequence data types in the specification of a text-processing system.

Documents as sequences

Suppose we are asked to develop a text-processing system. The following is a fragment of the statement of requirements.

```
The text processor considers the text file to be made
up of words. A requirement of the system is that it
must be possible to replace a word at a given position
in the file with another word....
```

Exercise 4.8

Suggest a possible (simple) model of a text file as a sequence of words.

Solution 4.8

$Text\text{-}file = Word^*$

$Word = Letter^*$

$Letter = \{l \mid l \in \{\text{'a'}, \ldots, \text{'z'}\} \cup \{\text{'A'}, \ldots, \text{'Z'}\}\}$

This is a high-level, abstract representation of a document in which we have ignored the need to model spaces and punctuation in a document. We have not yet met the appropriate notation for expressing the full model.

■

The next exercise is concerned with the *REPLACE* operation outlined in the requirements for the system.

Exercise 4.9

Write an operation, *REPLACE*, to replace the word at position *pos* with *new-word*.

Solution 4.9

REPLACE(*pos*: $\mathbb{N}_1$, *new-word*: *Word*)
ext wr *file*: *Text-file*
pre $pos \in \text{inds}\ file$
post $file = \overleftarrow{file} \dagger \{pos \mapsto new\text{-}word\}$

■

Review Question 4.7
Explain the operation *REPLACE* line by line.

■

Review Question 4.8
Express the post-condition of Exercise 4.9 using $\frown$ instead of $\dagger$.

■

4.4 Summary of concepts

- A sequence is an ordered collection of elements possibly containing multiple copies of each element.
- Sequences are denoted by a list of values in square brackets:
  - [5, 10, 15, 20, 15, 10, 5] is a seven element sequence;
  - the empty sequence is denoted by [ ];
  - character sequences (strings) can be delimited by double quotes.
- VDM provides the sequence type generators * and $^+$ which are used to define types whose values are sequences.
- The most useful functions and operators on sequences are:
  - len *sq* is the length *sq*;
  - *sq*(*i*) is the *i*th element in *sq*;
  - *sq*(*i*, ..., *j*) is a subsequence of *sq* containing the *i*th to *j*th elements;
  - *sq1* $\frown$ *sq2* is the sequence which contains the elements of *sq1* followed by those of *sq2*;
  - *sq* † $\{i \mapsto x\}$ is the same as *sq* except at position *i* where it contains *x*;
  - hd *sq* is the head of *sq*, i.e. the first element;
  - tl *sq* is the tail of *sq*, i.e. the rest of *sq* after the head;
  - inds *sq* is the set whose elements are the indexes of *sq*;
  - elems *sq* is the set whose elements are the values in *sq*.

5 SPECIFYING FUNCTIONS

This chapter introduces you to functions in VDM. Mathematically a function is a relation between two types such that each element in the first is mapped to at most one in the second. In programming terms a function may not access non-local variables; it takes an input value (in Pascal terms, no variable parameters) and returns an output value.

First, we introduce ***implicit*** specification of VDM functions as a means of describing what task a function carries out without premature inclusion of implementation details. The VDM format for ***explicit*** function definitions, which are more algorithmic in style, is given later. Recursion is an effective way to define functions explicitly and we therefore review recursion briefly.

5.1 Implicit function definition

An implicit function specification consists of the following in strict sequence:

1. a ***header***, which consists of:
   - a function name
   - a parenthesized list of parameters with their types
   - a result parameter with its type;
2. a pre-condition (optional) introduced by the keyword pre;
3. a post-condition introduced by the keyword post.

The general form of an implicit function specification is:

function-name (*parameter1*: *Type1*,
parameter2: *Type2...*) *result-name*: *Type*
pre *pre-condition*
post *post-condition*

This format of function specification is known as an implicit definition because there is no hint of how the function might be implemented or even the steps which might be required when evaluating the function.

As with an operation definition, the pre-condition states what must be true about the parameters if the post-condition is to be true; i.e. what conditions must hold for the function to produce a meaningful result. The post-condition states what the relationship is between the result and the parameters.

The following is an example of an implicit function specification:

max-of-set(s: ℕ-set) r: ℕ
pre $s \neq \{\ \}$
post $r \in s \wedge (\forall n \in s \bullet n \leq r)$

The first line is the header: *max-of-set* is the name of the function; it has one parameter, s, which is of type ℕ-set; the result parameter is denoted by r, which is of type ℕ. The pre-condition means that the function is defined only if its argument is a non-empty set.

Note that the pre-condition may simply be given as true. This means that there are no constraints on the arguments to the function. For example, consider a function, *absolute*, which returns the absolute value of an integer. The pre-condition is specified as true so as to define the post-condition for all values of the input parameter z.

absolute (z: ℤ) r: ℕ
pre true
post $(z < 0 \wedge r = -z) \vee (z \geq 0 \wedge r = z)$

If a pre-condition is true, it may be omitted.

Developing a function

We will create an implicit definition by following the three steps listed below.

- Define the function name, names and types of any arguments, and the name and type of the value returned.
- Give a pre-condition that delimits the values of the arguments for which the function is defined.
- Give a post-condition that defines the relationship between the inputs to the function and the value returned.

In order to introduce function definitions we now look at an informal description of a deceptively simple function. It is the function *location* which checks whether one string is a substring of another. As you will notice, this example deals with a fairly low-level design problem which is not what usually concerns us; it has been chosen primarily in order to shorten the discussion and to illustrate the way in which VDM may be used repeatedly to specify and design to lower levels of detail.

The function *location* is to check whether one input string, which we shall call the *pattern*, is a substring of another input string, which we shall call the *context*. If it is, the function returns the

```
position in the context string at which the pattern
begins. The pattern is just a string of characters
like the word 'the'. The context is a string such as
'other'. For these inputs the function location should
return the value 2 because the pattern ('the') begins
at the second character of the context ('other').
```

All this might seem perfectly clear. The English text above is a specification of a very small part of a system; you may think it is all we need. If you are satisfied with the specification imagine coding *location* in your favourite programming language, but keep a record of the questions that run through your mind as you think about writing the code.

Exercise 5.1

Write down some of the questions that must be answered before *location* can be implemented.

Solution 5.1

There are a number of ways in which *location* is inadequately specified. Here is a list of questions that must be answered:

- Suppose the pattern is not a substring of the context. Should *location* return some special value which would be recognized as a 'not-substring' indicator? Should it return anything at all? Should one even define *location* in this case?
- Suppose the pattern occurs twice in the context as "in" does in "innings". What should the result be?
- What is a string? Can it be empty?
- What happens if the pattern or the context is empty?
- What is a 'position' in a string? Is the first character in position 1, or position 0, or something else?
- What is a substring? Must it be contiguous or can it skip characters?

■

If *location* were specified formally we could answer all these questions and many more. The point is not that there are correct answers to the questions; it is that we have not yet even thought about what we want the answers to be. Furthermore, if we wrote the answers to the questions in English we would have a verbose specification which might very well be longer than the implementation code! And what process would we use to answer further questions that might arise?

Our specification is not precise, but, if we used English to try to correct that deficiency, our specification would not be concise. There is another serious problem: the specification is not usable in a formal development method as there is no way to verify formally that an implementation matches the specification. We require formality both to reason about the specification itself if further questions arise, and to be able to prove that an implementation conforms to the specification.

We will now show how the specification of *location* is written in VDM. First, we must find a suitable data model.

Exercise 5.2

Use the type char to suggest a simple VDM model of a string.

Solution 5.2

Order and repetition matter, so a set is inappropriate; a sequence is the simplest model we can devise. As we proceed in the specification we may have to modify the model but it is a good idea to start out by keeping it simple. We can write:

$$String = \text{char}^*$$

■

Exercise 5.3

Given the name *pt* for the pattern, and *cx* for the context, give the header of *location*. (You can use *r* for the result name.)

Solution 5.3

$$location(pt\colon String,\ cx\colon String)\ r : \mathbb{N}$$

■

The first line has the function name, *location*, followed by the argument names and types in parentheses. Function names will always be written in lower case. We have used the names *pt* for pattern and *cx* for context. At the end of the line is a variable we called *r*, which denotes the value returned by the function. It will be used in the post-condition to denote the result. Note that *r* is of type $\mathbb{N}$, denoting that the function returns a natural number.

You may have noticed that we used the variable *r* several times to refer to the value returned by a function. There is no reason for this other than that it is the first letter of 'returned' or 'returns'. If we have good reason we will deviate from this practice, but mostly when you see an '*r*' it stands for a returned value.

Now that we have a model for the data we will next decide how *location* is defined. The pre-condition will define the values of *pt* and *cx* which are valid for *location*, and it is at this point that the decisions made earlier must be recorded. Thus, if we have chosen to define the function only for non-empty inputs, we can specify the following pre-condition.

$$\text{pre } pt \neq [\,] \wedge cx \neq [\,]$$

Review Question 5.1

At what point of the specification did we indicate that strings could possibly be empty?

■

The last step in producing the specification is the post-condition which specifies precisely what *location* must do. Since we have still to answer some of the questions posed earlier, it will take some work to produce a satisfactory post-condition. First, we will make some intuitive decisions, and then we will formalize them.

Sequence indexes begin with 1; therefore if the pattern, *pt*, is not a substring of the context, *cx*, we will return, in *r*, the number zero. If it is a substring, we will return the position at which the first occurrence of the pattern begins.

Exercise 5.4

According to the preceding informal description, what must be the result of evaluating *location*, when it is used in the expression below?

location([‘i’, ‘n’], [‘b’, ‘e’, ‘g’, ‘i’, ‘n’, ‘n’, ‘i’, ‘n’, ‘g’])

Solution 5.4

The first occurrence of the pattern, [‘i’, ‘n’], begins at the fourth character of the context, [‘b’, ‘e’, ‘g’, ‘i’, ‘n’, ‘n’, ‘i’, ‘n’, ‘g’]. Hence the number 4 is returned in *r*.

■

Review Question 5.2

What is the value of the following instances of *location?*

(i) *location*([‘f’, ‘u’, ‘l’, ‘l’,], [‘p’, ‘r’, ‘i’, ‘n’, ‘t’, ‘ ’, ‘r’, ‘e’, ‘p’, ‘o’, ‘r’, ‘t’])

(ii) *location*([‘o’, ‘w’]
[‘h’, ‘o’, ‘w’, ‘ ’, ‘n’, ‘o’, ‘w’, ‘ ’,‘b’, ‘r’, ‘o’, ‘w’, ‘n’, ‘ ’, ‘c’, ‘o’, ‘w’, ‘?’])

(iii) *location*([ ], [‘a’, ‘b’, ‘c’])

■

We can state informally that a string *s* is a substring of a string *t* if there are strings *p* and *f* (meaning intuitively ‘prefix’ and ‘suffix’) such that *t* is the concatenation of *p*, *s* and *f* in that order.

Exercise 5.5

To clarify exactly the notion that one string is a substring of another, use the type *String* to write a function *is-substr* which takes two input strings *s* and *t* and returns true if *s* is a substring of *t* and false otherwise.

Solution 5.5

is-substr(*s*: *String*, *t*: *String*) $r : \mathbb{B}$
pre true
post $r \Leftrightarrow (\exists\, p, f : String \bullet t = p \frown s \frown f)$

■

The post-condition states that for *s* to be a substring of *t* there must exist (∃) a prefix, *p*, and a suffix, *f*, such that *t* is the concatenation of *p*, *s* and *f*. For example, [‘b’, ‘e’] is a substring of [‘b’, ‘e’, ‘f’, ‘o’, ‘r’, ‘e’] because the strings [ ] and [‘f’, ‘o’, ‘r’, ‘e’] can be found such that:

[‘b’, ‘e’, ‘f’, ‘o’, ‘r’, ‘e’] = [ ] ⁀ [‘b’, ‘e’] ⁀ [‘f’, ‘o’, ‘r’, ‘e’]

Note that either the prefix or the suffix may be empty.

Review Question 5.3

Is [‘u’, ‘p’] a substring of [‘u’, ‘p’]? Justify your answer using the definition of *issubstr*.

■

Now we use length and concatenation operations to define what is meant by the position of the ‘first’ occurrence of *pt* in *cx*. The idea is to look at the length of the prefixes of *pt* in *cx*.

For example, if *pt* = [‘u’, ‘k’] and *cx* = [‘m’, ‘u’, ‘k’, ‘l’, ‘u’, ‘k’], then there are two occurrences of *pt* each having a prefix. The prefixes are [‘m’] and [‘m’, ‘u’, ‘k’, ‘l’]. Their lengths are 1 and 4. The shortest prefix, [‘m’], precedes the first occurrence. The position of the first occurrence is determined by adding 1 to the length of that shortest prefix. In this example the length of the shortest prefix is 1 so the first occurrence of *pt* begins at position 2.

Exercise 5.6

Write a boolean function *is-prefix* that defines the condition for a string *p* to be a prefix of a string *s* in a string *t*.

Solution 5.6

is-prefix (*p*: *String*, *s*: *String*, *t*: *String*) *r*: $\mathbb{B}$
pre true
post $r \Leftrightarrow (\exists f: String \bullet (t = p \frown s \frown f))$

We will use this function to make the post-condition of *location* easier to read. Note that *s* is a substring of *t* if and only if there is a string *p* for which *is-prefix*(*p*, *s*, *t*) results in the value true.

■

Review Question 5.4

Find a string *p* for which *is-prefix*(*p*, [‘n’, ‘a’], [‘b’, ‘a’, ‘n’, ‘a’, ‘n’, ‘a’]) results in true.

■

We have just seen that the concept of substring can be expressed using the concept of prefix. Now we will see that it can be expressed using the concept of *shortest prefix*. To compare the concept of *prefix* with the concept of *shortest prefix* suppose there is a predicate *is-shortest*(*q*, *s*, *t*) which returns true when the string *q* is the shortest prefix of *s* in *t*.

For example, the following is true:

is-shortest([‘h’, ‘e’], [‘f’], [‘h’, ‘e’, ‘f’, ‘f’, ‘a’, ‘l’, ‘u’, ‘m’, ‘p’])

[‘f’] has two prefixes in [‘h’, ‘e’, ‘f’, ‘f’, ‘a’, ‘l’, ‘u’, ‘m’, ‘p’]. These are [‘h’, ’e’] and [‘h’, ’e’, ’f’]. The former is clearly the shortest.

Review Question 5.5
What is the value of the following?

is-shortest(['a', 'c', 'a', 'b'], ['c', 'a'], ['a', 'c', 'a', 'b', 'c', 'a'])

■

Review Question 5.6
Explain in your own words why the two statements below, which are equivalent for given strings s and t are true in the same situation:

$\exists p : String \bullet is\text{-}prefix(p, s, t)$

$\exists q : String \bullet is\text{-}shortest(q, s, t)$

■

Defining the post-condition

Recall the header of the function *location*:

$location(pt\text{: } String, cx\text{: } String)\ r\text{: } \mathbb{N}$

The value returned by *location* depends on whether or not *pt* is a substring of *cx*. In what we term an implicit specification, such a dependence on various cases of the parameters shows up as a disjunction (i.e. an 'or' statement) in the post-condition.

The post-condition of *location* is such a disjunction. It can be expressed in words as follows: either 'there is a shortest prefix p of *pt* in *cx* and the result is $1 + \text{len}\, p$', or '*pt* is not a substring of *cx* and the result is 0'.

Expressed in symbols we have:

$$\begin{aligned}\text{post}\ & (\exists\, p : String \bullet is\text{-}shortest(p, pt, cx) \wedge r = (1 + \text{len}\, p)) \vee \\ & (\neg is\text{-}substr(pt, cx) \wedge r = 0)\end{aligned}$$

The function *is-shortest* can be defined using *is-prefix*. The idea is simply to say that a shortest prefix is first of all a prefix, and secondly that it is as short as any prefix.

The definition of *is-shortest* (p, s, t) is as follows:

$$\begin{aligned}& is\text{-}shortest\ (p\text{: } String, s\text{: } String, t\text{: } String) \\ & \text{post}\ \ is\text{-}prefix(p, s, t) \wedge \forall q : String \bullet (is\text{-}prefix(q, s, t) \Rightarrow \text{len}\, q \geq \text{len}\, p)\end{aligned}$$

The definition in words says p is a prefix of s in t and all prefixes, q, of s in t have a length greater than or equal to that of p.

The entire specification of *location* is as follows.

$$\begin{aligned}& location(pt\text{: } String, cx\text{: } String)\ r\text{: } \mathbb{N} \\ & \text{pre}\ \ pt \neq [\,] \wedge cx \neq [\,] \\ & \text{post}\ (\exists\, p : String \bullet is\text{-}shortest(p, pt, cx) \wedge r = (1 + \text{len}\, p)) \vee \\ & \qquad (\neg is\text{-}substr(pt, cx) \wedge r = 0)\end{aligned}$$

The specification is precise, concise, usable and has one more important property: it is implicit. It says nothing about how to calculate the value of *location*.

result

r

An implementor is free to use any algorithm that returns values which satisfy the post-condition. You must be careful not to think of a post-condition as a recipe for calculation: it is only a description of the relationship between input and output.

5.2 Explicit function definitions

In the previous subsection we presented the VDM format for implicit function specifications. Implicit functions are preferred because an implicit definition draws attention to the description of what a function does and it does not suggest any implementation details; i.e. any implementation of the specification is acceptable. Nevertheless, explicit definitions of very simple functions may sometimes be more concise and easier to read than implicit definitions.

An ***explicit definition***, which is also known as a ***direct definition***, is a specification of a function which is algorithmic in style. An explicit definition does not use pre- and post-conditions, but it uses control constructs like those of programming languages to show how the function *might* be computed. Whereas an implicit definition expresses that *any* value meeting the post-condition is acceptable, an explicit definition expresses a single value.

The form of explicit (or direct) function specification used is:

1. a ***signature***, which consists of:
   - a function name
   - a colon
   - a specification of the types of the function's parameters, separated by $\times$ (i.e. the domain of the function as a cartesian product);
   - the symbol $\rightarrow$ (which separates types of parameters from the type of the result);
   - a specification of the type of the function (i.e. the range of the function);
2. a header, which consists of:
   - the function name
   - a parenthesized list of parameter names;
3. the symbol $\triangleq$ (the 'is defined as' symbol);
4. an expression.

The general format of an explicit definition is given below.

function-name: *parameter-types* $\rightarrow$ *result-type*
function-name(*parameter-list*) $\triangleq$
    expression

Note that in the case of explicit definitions, type names and parameter names are usually separated on two lines and are associated by position. The first line contains the names of the parameter types as a cartesian product; i.e. each type is separated by a $\times$. Then follows an arrow and the result type; if there is more than one a cartesian product may be used. The second line repeats the function name and the names of the arguments in parentheses. The first parameter denotes a value of the first domain type; the second parameter is of the second domain type, and so on. The parameters are followed by the symbol $\triangleq$ which is read 'is defined as'. Then the result of the function is given as an expression.

An example of an explicit definition is the function *add*, which takes two real numbers and returns the sum as a real number:

$$
\begin{aligned}
&add: \mathbb{R} \times \mathbb{R} \rightarrow \mathbb{R} \\
&add(x, y) \triangleq \\
&\quad x + y
\end{aligned}
$$

The first line is the signature: it declares the name of the function to be *add*, the type of its first argument to be $\mathbb{R}$, the type of the second argument to be $\mathbb{R}$, and the type of the result to be $\mathbb{R}$. The header repeats the function name and declares that the arguments will be denoted by x and y. The function is defined as the addition of the values denoted by x and y.

There are two important differences between specifying the value of a function implicitly using a post-condition and defining the value directly.

- In an explicit definition no name is given to the result, whereas in an implicit definition the result has a name like r.
- A post-condition is a predicate that has the value true or false: it says something about the value of the function. An explicit definition just gives the value of the function: it does not describe it in a predicate.

Inevitably, the implicit style is more general and less specific than the explicit. The latter looks more algorithmic but similarly specifies a function; it may be convenient to read or discuss VDM-SL specifications as if they are programs (as if they are executed), but you must remember that they are specifications. Each style has its own advantages and disadvantages in terms of ease of expression. We shall use explicit definitions of functions where they are more concise and understandable than implicit specifications. When in doubt, a good rule is to use implicit specifications.

VDM contains several constructions for writing expressions in explicit definitions: the first we present is the if-then-else construct.

if-then-else *expression*

The if-then-else expression consists of an if keyword, followed by a boolean expression (a condition), a then keyword and an expression and an else keyword and an expression. When the if-then-else expression is evaluated, the result of the then expression is returned if the condition is true and the result of the else expression is returned otherwise. For example, the following expression evaluates to 3 if the variable *size* is 1 or evaluates to 999 otherwise:

if *size* = 1
then 33
else 999

If-then-else expressions may be nested.

We now compare the formats of explicit and implicit definition by defining the absolute value function *absolute* for integers using both styles. First, recall the implicit version of *absolute*:

$absolute\ (z{:}\ \mathbb{Z})\ r{:}\ \mathbb{N}$
pre true
post $(z < 0 \wedge r = -z) \vee (z \geq 0 \wedge r = z)$

The explicit alternative uses the if-then-else construct, which specifies which value is to be returned:

$absolute : \mathbb{Z} \rightarrow \mathbb{N}$
$absolute(z) \triangleq$
if $z < 0$ then $-z$ else z

In the case of the *absolute* function, the explicit definition is probably simpler to express and understand. This is not the case in general. Indeed, it is probably more common to find that an implicit definition is more succinct.

There is an important difference between the if-then-else *expression* of VDM-SL and the **`if-then-else`** *statement* of a programming language like Pascal. In a programming language, a statement is meant to be executed. It makes sense to ask questions about how it is executed and to query its efficiency. For example, we could ask why, in defining *absolute*, was the test $z < 0$ made? Why not test $z \leq 0$, or $z > 0$? Do these affect the efficiency of the calculation? Such questions do not apply to a specification. A specification is *not* a calculation. Its 'efficiency' is measured by its clarity. In VDM-SL the if-then-else construct means only that there are two alternatives under consideration. In the case of *absolute*, the alternatives are z is negative and z is non-negative. Any other concise way of specifying *absolute* is equally acceptable if it is equally understandable.

When a function requires several arguments its domain is, technically speaking, a single argument drawn from a cartesian product. For example, the function *is-prefix* of the previous subsection was defined with three strings as arguments. In an explicit definition its heading would include a single argument whose type is the cartesian product, *String* × *String* × *String*, as shown below:

$is\text{-}prefix{:}\ String \times String \times String \rightarrow \mathbb{B}$

The cartesian product notation × here indicates that the inputs to the function are ordered triples of *String*. This is a fine point which does not usually need to be considered.

Exercise 5.7

Write a direct definition of a function *max* which takes two integers as input and returns the larger.

Solution 5.7

$max: \mathbb{Z} \times \mathbb{Z} \rightarrow \mathbb{Z}$
$max(a, b) \triangleq$
  if $(a > b)$ then a else b

■

The following exercise illustrates that explicit definitions do not always require the use of if-then-else when a condition determines a result.

Exercise 5.8

Give an explicit definition of the function *is-prefix* defined in Exercise 5.6.

Solution 5.8

$is\text{-}prefix: String \times String \times String \rightarrow \mathbb{B}$
$is\text{-}prefix(p, s, t) \triangleq$
  $\exists f : String \bullet (t = p \frown s \frown f)$

■

cases *expression*

The cases expression allows a number of conditions to be specified as prerequisites to different results to an expression. It takes the form of a cases keyword, an expression (called the cases index), a colon, and then a list of *case alternatives* separated by a comma and terminated by the keyword end. Each case alternative consists of a list of index values, followed by an arrow and the matching result expression for the preceding index values. Optionally, an alternative to the other index values may be specified using the keyword others.

The general format is:

cases *index* :
  value1, *value2* → *result1*,
  value3, *value4*, *value5* → *result2*,
  ...
  valuen → *resultm*,
others
  resultx
end

For example, instead of using nested if-then-else expressions, a cases expression can be used, as in the following function which returns an integer in the range 0, ..., 3 depending on the value of the parameter *col*:

brightness: *Colour* $\rightarrow$ {0, ..., 3}
brightness(*col*) $\triangleq$
cases *col* :
BLACK $\rightarrow$ 0,
RED, GREEN, BLUE $\rightarrow$ 1,
YELLOW, CYAN, MAGENTA $\rightarrow$ 2,
WHITE $\rightarrow$ 3
end

5.3 Auxiliary functions

A specification can be made more readable if some ***auxiliary functions*** are introduced. An auxiliary function is just a function used in the specification of something else. We have already used auxiliary functions in the definition of *location—is-prefix* and *is-shortest*. The use of *is-prefix* and *is-shortest* as auxiliary functions reduces the complexity of the definition. Now we shall illustrate the use of auxiliary functions in a manner analogous to local definitions of functions and procedures in a programming language, that is, as a means of systematically structuring specifications.

Let us examine the problem of specifying a function to compute the greatest common divisor (*gcd*) of two natural numbers. The greatest common divisor is the largest natural number that divides exactly into the two given numbers. For example, the *gcd* of 60 and 84 is 12.

The first step in developing an implicit definition is to write the header:

gcd(x: $\mathbb{N}$, y: $\mathbb{N}$) r: $\mathbb{N}$

The second step is to consider the pre-condition: since there is no further restriction on the domain of the function (other than that the arguments be of the type $\mathbb{N}$), the pre-condition is true.

The third step is usually the hardest. A good way to create the post-condition is to think of the properties of the function result rather than of algorithms for its computation. The properties we require are that:

- the *gcd* divides the two numbers without a remainder, and
- any other divisor of the two numbers is smaller than the *gcd*.

The idea of one number being the divisor of two others seems to be important in both properties of the *gcd* function, so the next step is to encapsulate this idea. This will be done by defining a function *is-common-divisor*, which returns the value true when a number n is a common divisor of numbers x and y. For the moment all we will do is to name the function and decide on the order in which its arguments appear. We will postpone its formal specification until later.

For example, *is-common-divisor*(2, 4, 224) = true because 2 is a divisor of both 4 and 224.

We can now restate the properties of the result r returned by *gcd*(x, y) in a semi-formal way:

- *is-common-divisor*(r, x, y) evaluates to true;
- for all natural numbers n, *is-common-divisor*(n, x, y) implies $n \leq r$.

The conjunction of these two properties is the post-condition for *gcd*.

Exercise 5.9

Use *is-common-divisor* as an auxiliary function to give an implicit specification of *gcd*.

Solution 5.9

$gcd(x: \mathbb{N}, y: \mathbb{N})\ r: \mathbb{N}$
pre true
post $is\text{-}common\text{-}divisor(r, x, y) \wedge$
$\forall n : \mathbb{N} \bullet (is\text{-}common\text{-}divisor(n, x, y) \Rightarrow n \leq r)$

■

You should notice two features of the process so far:

- It was much easier to describe the properties of *gcd* implicitly in a post-condition than it would be to give an algorithmic style of definition.
- The post-condition is much easier to read because of the auxiliary function.

We can complete the specification by defining *is-common-divisor*. We shall follow the three steps of implicit definition (given on page 42).

In the first step we name the function, its arguments, and the value returned—either true or false:

$is\text{-}common\text{-}divisor(n: \mathbb{N}, x: \mathbb{N}, y: \mathbb{N})\ r: \mathbb{B}$

In the second step we define the pre-condition; we wish to state that the function is defined for all triples of natural numbers. Since this is represented by a true pre-condition, it can be omitted.

The third step is to define the post-condition, which involves examining the properties of a common divisor of two numbers.

Exercise 5.10

List the properties that n must have in order to be a common divisor of x and y.

Solution 5.10

The properties required are merely:

- n divides x without a remainder, and
- n divides y without a remainder.

■

We can use another auxiliary function, *divides*(n, x), to indicate whether a natural number n divides a natural number x exactly.

The post-condition of *is-common-divisor* may now be written using *divides*:

is-common-divisor(n: $\mathbb{N}$, x: $\mathbb{N}$, y: $\mathbb{N}$) r: $\mathbb{B}$
post $r \Leftrightarrow divides(n, x) \land divides(n, y)$

The function *divides* can now be defined by noting that n divides x if there is a natural number m such that x is the product of m and n.

Exercise 5.11

Give a direct definition of the function *divides*.

Solution 5.11

$divides: \mathbb{N} \times \mathbb{N} \rightarrow \mathbb{B}$
$divides(n, x) \triangleq \exists\, m : \mathbb{N} \cdot x = m \times n$

■

5.4 Explicit definition of recursive functions

A recursive definition of a function includes a use of the function itself without the definition being totally circular. Here is a recursive definition of the function len which returns the length of a sequence of values of type T (we will substitute a specific type for T when needed). We shall use len to explain recursion in explicit definitions of functions.

len: $T^* \rightarrow \mathbb{N}$
len(s) $\triangleq$
  if s = [ ]
  then 0
  else 1 + len(tl s)

Generally, a recursive definition contains a selection among alternative values of the defining arguments. A value (or collection of values) is given for which the function is defined without reference to itself. We will call this the ***base part*** of the definition and refer to the argument values as ***base values***. In the definition of len the base part defines the length of the empty sequence to be zero. The base value in the definition of len is the empty sequence. The other part of a recursive definition contains a collection of values for which the function is defined in terms of itself. This is the ***recursive part*** of the definition.

In a recursive definition of a function the function name always appears in the recursive part; it is said to be a ***recursive reference*** to the function. For len the recursive reference occurs in the form of len (tl s). The arguments in the recursive reference are never identical to the arguments in the header (the arguments appearing before the $\triangleq$ symbol). This prevents the definition from being circular. Notice that s is the argument used in the header of len but that tl s is the argument of the recursive reference. Furthermore, the arguments of the recursive reference must in some way be 'closer' to the base values than the arguments of the definition. This last property is very important because it is essential that the definition reduces to a base value in a finite number of steps.

Exercise 5.12

In what way is tl s closer to [ ] than the sequence s?

Solution 5.12

The sequence tl s has one value fewer than s. Therefore tl s reduces s towards [ ]. The length of a sequence is one plus the length of the tail of the sequence. The length of the tail is one plus the length of the tail's tail, and so on until the definition reduces to the length of the empty sequence.

■

For example, the length of the sequence ['a', 'b', 'c'] can be determined from the definition of len by reducing the sequence to the base value—the empty sequence:

$$
\begin{aligned}
\text{len}([\text{'a'}, \text{'b'}, \text{'c'}]) &= 1 + \text{len}([\text{'b'}, \text{'c'}]) \\
&= 1 + (1 + \text{len}([\text{'c'}])) \\
&= 1 + (1 + (1 + \text{len}([\,]))) \\
&= 1 + (1 + (1 + 0)) \\
&= 3
\end{aligned}
$$

The first three equalities are justified by the recursive reference in the definition of len. The length of a sequence is 1 + the length of its tail. (We have inserted parentheses to encapsulate the result of each recursive reference.) The tl function eventually reduces the sequence to [ ] whose length is 0.

Again, it is worth emphasizing that recursive definitions are not intended as algorithms for implementation. They are precise, concise and, with experience, understandable definitions of functions. And, of course, an implementation of len does not have to be recursive; it merely has to return values which agree with the definition.

To construct a recursive function you must first have some notion, however informal, of what the function does; then you need to identify some base values for which the function can be defined without recursion. In the case of len its purpose is to return the number of elements in a sequence, and we can identify the base value as [ ] for which len must return zero.

The next step is the most difficult: we try to find a reduction of a typical argument towards a base value and then try to relate the value of the function on the reduced argument to the value on the typical argument. The reasoning is as follows: if we knew the value of the function using the reduced argument, we could use that value to determine the value of the function using the original argument; if so, we have a recursive definition.

In the example of len we tried reducing s to tl s. If we knew the length of tl s, how could we find the length of s? Since tl s is obtained from s by throwing away the first item we just have to add 1 to the length of tl s in order to obtain the length of s. That relationship is expressed symbolically in the recursive part of the definition which was given above.

Earlier in the chapter we compared the implicit and explicit styles of definition. The contrast can be striking when recursion is used in an explicit definition. Consider, for example, the function *max-num*, which returns the largest integer in a non-empty sequence. First the implicit version:

$max\text{-}num(s: \mathbb{Z}^+)\ r : \mathbb{Z}$
post $\exists r \in$ elems $s \bullet \forall i \in$ elems $s \bullet i \leq r$

In this definition there is no suggestion of searching the sequence and no question of the function returning a particular occurrence of the largest value (if there is more than one occurrence). Contrast this with the explicit version.

Exercise 5.13

Write an explicit, recursive version of *max-num*.

Solution 5.13

$max\text{-}num: \mathbb{Z}^+ \rightarrow \mathbb{Z}$
$max\text{-}num(s) \triangleq$
if tl s = [ ]
then hd s
else
if hd $s \geq max\text{-}num($tl $s)$
then hd s
else $max\text{-}num($tl $s)$

Notice how this version of *max-num* seems algorithmic: it would appear that the function must be coded as a recursive subroutine. This is an incorrect way of interpreting the explicit definition, albeit a natural one for a programmer.

■

The let-in *notation*

It is often the case that expressions in VDM specifications can become long and complex. Therefore, it is convenient to be able to structure the expressions by introducing local names for common sub-expressions. We use the key words let-in as a way of making local definitions of variables in a VDM expression. There are several forms of the notation. The simplest form defines an identifier to be equivalent to an expression; its general form is:

let *identifier* = *expression1* in *expression2*

The meaning of this construct is that every occurrence of the identifier in *expression2* stands for the value of *expression1*. For example, consider the following:

$cos(sin(x) - 1)/(sin(x) - 1)$

It can be structured, and hence simplified, by using y to denote $sin(x) - 1$:

let $y = sin(x) - 1$ in $cos(y)/y$

Exercise 5.14

Use the let-in construction to rewrite the explicit definition of *max-num* from the solution to Exercise 5.13.

Solution 5.14

max-num: $\mathbb{Z}^+ \rightarrow \mathbb{Z}$
max-num(s) $\triangleq$
  if tl s = [ ]
  then hd s
  else
    let *max-in-tail* = *max-num*(tl s) in
    if hd $s \geq$ *max-in-tail*
    then hd s
    else *max-in-tail*

■

A list of expressions can precede the in symbol as an abbreviation for consecutive let constructs. For example

let *max-in-tail* = *max-num*(tl s), *head* = hd s in
if *head* ≥ *max-in-tail*
then *head*
else *max-in-tail*

may be used instead of

let *max-in-tail* = *max-num*(tl s) in
let *head* = hd s in
...

Another form of let construct allows the selection of a value from a set, either of an arbitrary member or one satisfying some condition. The most common form of this type of let construction is:

let *bind list* in *expression*

or with a condition preceded by be st (for 'be such that'):

let *bind list* be st *boolean-expression* in *expression*

These two forms are particularly useful in expressions in which elements of a set or type are extracted recursively, as in the following function to return the sum of all values in a set:

sum-set: $\mathbb{R}$-set $\rightarrow \mathbb{R}$
sum-set(s) $\triangleq$
  if s = { }

then 0
else
let $x \in s$ in
$x + sum\text{-}set(s - \{x\})$

In effect, the let in *sum-set* selects an arbitrary value from the set s and makes x this value; the value of x is then added to the sum of the set with x removed $(s - \{x\})$.

5.5 Summary of concepts

- A function is a relation between two types such that each element in the first is mapped to at most one in the second. The use of a function in a VDM expression denotes the result of evaluating the function with the given arguments; no change occurs to the arguments.
- Two styles of function definitions are provided, implicit and explicit:
  - implicit definitions are expressed in terms of a pre-condition on the parameters and a post-condition which expresses the relation between the parameters and an identifier denoting the function result;
  - explicit definitions use an algorithmic style in which the result is denoted by an expression;
  - if-then-else and cases expressions are common in the explicit style;
  - recursive functions are frequently expressed using explicit definitions.
- Various forms of the let-in construct are provided to structure and simplify functions.
- Auxiliary functions are frequently used to structure and simplify other functions (and operations).
- The development of a function can often clarify vague requirements.

6 COMPOSITE OBJECT TYPES

In the specification of software systems, there is a need to define types whose values are composite objects which consist of several components of different types. For example, in a banking system there might be a need to define an object *Customer* which may have the components of *name*, *addr*, and *phone-num*. VDM offers us the facility to define such an object as a value of a composite object type. In this chapter we present several ways to decompose a composite object into its constituent fields and show how operators on the field data types can be used to modify the composite object as a whole.

6.1 Specifying composite object types

The specification of a ***composite object type*** has the form:

Composite-name ::
  fieldname1: *Type1*
  fieldname2: *Type2*
  ...

A composite object type is similar to a Pascal record type: its values are a combination of values of other types. These may be elementary types (like $\mathbb{N}$, char, etc.) sets, sequences, maps (see Chapter 8), or further composite object types.

For example, suppose *Name*, *Address*, and *Phone* are each data types. We can construct a new data type named *Customer* as follows:

Customer ::
  name: *Name*
  addr: *Address*
  phone-num: *Phone*

There are several things to notice: the equals symbol, used with the set and sequence type constructors to introduce a type is replaced by a double colon; each ***component name***, or ***field***, of the composite object type appears before its type, and, by convention, the field names are written in lower case.

Furthermore, a composite object type defined using the above syntax must have a name. This is in contrast to the other data types which can be referred to anonymously. Whereas we can refer to the type '*X*-set' without needing a name for *X*-set we can only refer to a composite object type by its name, as in 'values of type *Customer*' and 'the data type *Customer*'.

As with the other data types, *Customer* is a set of values. Each value in the type *Customer* has three fields. In VDM the component names are used to select component values from a composite object. For example, if *cust* is a value of the composite type *Customer* defined above, then *cust.name* is the value of the name field of *cust*. Similarly *cust.addr* and *cust.phone-num* are the values of the address and telephone number fields of *cust* respectively.[1]

Exercise 6.1

Write a VDM specification of a composite object type called *StockItem* with three components which represent a product code for an item of stock, the price of an item, and the names of the item's suppliers.

Solution 6.1

The first component, *product-code*, is a character string (for which a type name is given), the second, *price*, is a real number, the third, *suppliers*, is a set of supplier names (where the names are character strings). Thus *StockItem* can be defined as follows.

$String = \mathsf{char}^*$
$StockItem$ ::
  $product\text{-}code$: $String$
  $price$: $\mathbb{R}$
  $suppliers$: $String\text{-}\mathsf{set}$

■

Many of the examples of operations up to now have had simple external variables; in practice most operations are defined in terms of external variables of a composite object type. For example, the operation *CHANGE-PRICE* is defined to change the price of a variable of type *StockItem* and to leave the other fields unchanged:

$CHANGE\text{-}PRICE(p: \mathbb{R})$
ext wr s: $StockItem$
pre $p \geq 0.0$
post $s.price = p \wedge s.product\text{-}code = \overleftarrow{s}.product\text{-}code \wedge s.suppliers = \overleftarrow{s}.suppliers$

---

[1] In some dialects of VDM, selector functions are used to select fields of a composite object; e.g. *s-name*(*cust*) or simply *name*(*cust*).

Review Question 6.1

A composite object type is defined by

Ship ::
  name: char*
  tonnage: $\mathbb{R}$
  takes-passengers: $\mathbb{B}$

If *s* is a value of the composite object type *Ship*, show how the value of each component of *s* is denoted.

■

Make functions

We need to be able to represent a value of a composite object type such as *StockItem*. Unlike for sets and sequences, there are no special brackets provided for enclosing the components of a value of a composite object type. Instead of brackets, functions are used to construct values of composite object types. Such functions are called ***make functions***.

Each composite object type has a make function associated with it which takes field values as arguments and returns an object of the composite data type having as its fields the arguments supplied. These field-value arguments must appear in the same order as the fields are listed in the composite object type. The make function is named *mk-* followed by the type name. For example, *mk-StockItem* is the make function for the type *StockItem*. It takes three arguments whose types are, in order, char*, $\mathbb{R}$, and char*-set. The function *mk-StockItem* can be used as follows:

mk-StockItem("TV/521-89", 269.99, {"Ferkusson", "Fillipz", "Soknee"})

When evaluated, this expression returns a composite object of type *StockItem*, with field values "TV/521-89" for *product-code*, 269.99 for *price*, and {"Ferkusson", "Fillipz", "Soknee"} for *suppliers*.

Using *String* for char* the signature of the function *mk-StockItem* is:

mk-StockItem : *String* $\times \mathbb{R} \times$ *String* -set $\rightarrow$ *StockItem*

Note that, as for all VDM functions, the order of the arguments is important; the types of the arguments must correspond exactly to the types of the composite object type.

Exercise 6.2

Rewrite the post-condition of *CHANGE-PRICE* using a make function.

Solution 6.2

The relevant make function is *mk-StockItem*. Its first argument must be the product code of the old value of the external variable *s* (denoted in the post-condition by $\overleftarrow{s}$*.product-code*); its second argument must be new price *p*; the third argument must be the *suppliers* field of the old value of the external variable s (denoted by $\overleftarrow{s}.suppliers$). This is given below:

post $s = mk\text{-}StockItem(\overleftarrow{s}.product\text{-}code, p, \overleftarrow{s}.suppliers)$

■

Exercise 6.3

Consider the following requirements:

```
The management is interested in two pieces of
information regarding committees: the people on the
committee and the date when the committee reported on
its work or is to report on its work. The name and
department of a committee member is sufficient to
identify a person, and we are only interested in work
since the beginning of the century.
```

Write a VDM specification of a composite object type which models a committee.

Solution 6.3

You must first decide on some names. In the context of a real application you will probably use names from the customer's statement of requirements. The composite object should have two fields: the first models the committee membership; the second models the report date for the committee. The first field is to be modelled as a set of persons (with a person being modelled as a composite of name and department name). The second field should be modelled as a *Date* (a composite of day, month and year fields which you should define using set comprehension).

Committee ::
  members: *Person*-set
  report-date: *Date*

Person ::
  name: char^*
  department: char^*

Date ::
  day: $\{d \mid d : \mathbb{N}_1 \bullet d \leq 31\}$
  month: $\{m \mid m : \mathbb{N}_1 \bullet m \leq 12\}$
  year: $\{y \mid y : \mathbb{N}_1 \bullet y \geq 1900\}$

It does not matter if you defined the type *Date* before *Committee* or if you used a different order for the fields of *Date*. VDM is not a programming language and there is plenty of freedom to organize specifications as you like.

■

Exercise 6.4

Suppose *transport-group* is an object of type *Committee* as defined in the solution to Exercise 6.3. How is the value of the month of the *report-date* field of *transport-group* denoted?

Solution 6.4

The names of the components are used to select the values. Hence *transport-group.report-date* gives the value of the second component of *transport-group*. Since it too is a composite object, the field name *month* is used to extract the value of the month. Therefore the answer is:

transport-group.report-date.month

■

The let construction introduced at the end of Section 5.2 is extremely useful in simplifying references to fields of composite object types. Our answer to Exercise 6.4 may be rewritten as:

let *rep* = *transport-group.report-date* in *rep.month*

Review Question 6.2

(i) Use a make function to create an object of type *Date* corresponding to 26 April 1943.

(ii) Use a make function to create an object of type *Date* having *month*, *day* and *year* equal to *m*, *d* and *y* respectively. (The identifiers *m*, *d*, and *y* denote values of the appropriate types.)

■

6.2 Data type invariants

A typical (but simple) example of a composite object is a date. Consider the specification in the solution to Exercise 6.3:

Date ::
  day: $\{d \mid d : \mathbb{N}_1 \cdot d \leq 31\}$
  month: $\{m \mid m : \mathbb{N}_1 \cdot m \leq 12\}$
  year: $\{y \mid y : \mathbb{N}_1 \cdot y \geq 1900\}$

Do all values of the type *Date* correspond to calendar dates? For instance, is it sensible for a type which models dates to contain the object with field values *year* = 1910, *month* = 2, and *day* = 31? In other words, is the type *Date* an adequate model given that *mk-Date*(31, 2, 1910) is a value of the type? The date does not correspond to a 'real' one because February had only 28 days in 1910. Therefore, the model is not adequate: it does not capture the essence of real calendar dates.

What has happened is that we have defined the components of a date—the day, the month, the year—independently of each other and have consequently lost an important aspect of calendar dates: different months have different numbers of days, and one month, February, has an extra day on leap years. We need to capture this subtlety in the formal model by relating the components to each other. We do this by adding a predicate called a ***data type invariant*** to the specification. The data type invariant (or just ***invariant*** for short) appears after the definition of a type as a boolean-valued function whose argument is of the data type. The general form of a type definition which includes an invariant is:

$T = \ldots$
$inv\text{-}T\,(t) \triangleq \ldots$.

The meaning is that T is a set of possible values for a data type defined by whatever is to the right of the '=', but that T consists only of those values which satisfy the predicate *inv-T*. That predicate is called a data type invariant and is always named *inv-* followed by the name of the type. For a type T it is as if a function with signature $inv\text{-}T: T \to \mathbb{B}$ has been defined. In fact *inv-* functions are provided automatically (like *mk-* functions) so there is no need to provide a signature. The argument to *inv-T* represents an instance of T and is used in the predicate by some boolean-valued expression following the '$\triangleq$'. Thus, the invariant is expressed as an explicit function definition with a single parameter—a value of the type to which the invariant applies.

We can use a data type invariant to restrict the definition of *Date* so that only real calendar dates are defined. We do so by specifying *inv-Date* and appending to the definition of date, thus:

$Date ::$
$\quad day\!: \{d \mid d : \mathbb{N}_1 \bullet d \leq 31\}$
$\quad month\!: \{m \mid m : \mathbb{N}_1 \bullet m \leq 12\}$
$\quad year\!: \{y \mid y : \mathbb{N}_1 \bullet y \geq 1900\}$

$inv\text{-}Date(da) \triangleq$
$\quad (da.month \in \{1, 3, 5, 7, 8, 10, 12\} \wedge da.day \in \{1, \ldots, 31\}) \vee$
$\quad (da.month \in \{4, 6, 9, 11\} \wedge da.day \in \{1, \ldots, 30\}) \vee$
$\quad ((da.month = 2) \wedge (\neg is\text{-}leap\text{-}year(da.year)) \wedge (da.day \in \{1, \ldots, 28\})) \vee$
$\quad ((da.month = 2) \wedge (is\text{-}leap\text{-}year(da.year)) \wedge (da.day \in \{1, \ldots, 29\}))$

Note the use of the auxiliary function *is-leap-year*. In complex specifications, data type invariants will often rely heavily on auxiliary functions.

Review Question 6.3
What is the value of *inv-Date*(*mk-Date*(29, 2, 1940))?

■

Review Question 6.4
Use the let construction to simplify the date invariant.

■

Exercise 6.5

Give an explicit definition of *is-leap-year*. Define it on the natural numbers and remember that leap years are multiples of 4 but years that are multiples of 100 are only leap years if they are also multiples of 400; for example 2000 is a leap year but 1900 is not.

Solution 6.5

is-leap-year: $\mathbb{N} \rightarrow \mathbb{B}$
is-leap-year(*y*) $\triangleq$ (y mod $4 = 0 \wedge y$ mod $100 \neq 0) \vee y$ mod $400 = 0$

■

The date invariant *inv-Date* may appear over-complex (invariants on composite object types tend to become complex); you might find a cases expression clearer:

inv-Date(*da*) $\triangleq$
cases *da.month* :
1, 3, 5, 7, 8, 10, 12 $\rightarrow$ *da.day* $\in \{1, ..., 31\}$,
4, 6, 9, 11 $\rightarrow$ *da.day* $\in \{1, ..., 30\}$,
2 $\rightarrow$
if *is-leap-year*(*da.year*)
then *da.day* $\in \{1, ..., 29\}$
else *da.day* $\in \{1, ..., 28\}$
end

This version is simpler largely because the number of field selections has been reduced. They can be eliminated altogether by using a let construct to introduce the names *d*, *m* and *y* which can then be used instead of *da.day*, *da.month* and *da.year*.

Review Question 6.5
Use the let construction to simplify the cases version of the *date* invariant.

■

Exercise 6.6

Specify a composite object type which has two fields: the first is sequences of up to 1000 integers which are in ascending order; the second is a count of the number of negative integers in the first field.

Solution 6.6

AscendingList ::
list: $\mathbb{Z}^*$
num-of-negs: $\mathbb{N}$

inv-AscendingList(*l*)$\triangleq$
let *lst* = *l.list*, *negs* = *l.num-of-negs* in
len *lst* $\leq 1000 \wedge$
$\forall i, j \in$ inds *lst* $\bullet$ $i > j \Leftrightarrow lst(i) > lst(j) \wedge negs =$ card $\{n \mid n \in$ elems $lst \bullet n < 0\}$

■

While it might be preferable to express a data type without a data type invariant, one is frequently needed to capture 'real-world' attributes in a formal model. However, since it is a goal of formal specification that a model be as concise and as simple as possible, invariants should be used as precisely as possible. Consider a composite object type, *Phone-no*, which models telephone numbers in the UK. A telephone number consists of an area code and a local number. Local numbers consist of a sequence of digits of length between 2 and 8; the first digit is never zero. Area codes are sequences of digits of length between 2 and 6 and begin with zero. The following specification captures these properties:

Phone-no ::
  ac : {'0', ..., '9'}* — *the area code*
  no : {'0', ..., '9'}* — *the local number*

$inv\text{-}Phone\text{-}no(p) \triangleq$
  $2 \leq \mathsf{len}(p.ac) \wedge \mathsf{len}(p.ac) \leq 6 \wedge p.ac(1) = \text{'0'} \wedge$
  $2 \leq \mathsf{len}(p.no) \wedge \mathsf{len}(p.no) \leq 8 \wedge p.no(1) \neq \text{'0'}$

However, the specification is deficient in two respects: it models the attributes of local numbers and area codes as a property of phone numbers rather than identifying local numbers and area codes. It therefore overcomplicates the definition of *Phone-no*. A better approach is to not use anonymous types for the fields but to use named types with their own invariants.

Exercise 6.7

Define the types *Area-code* and *Local-no* with suitable data type invariants and redefine the composite object type *Phone-no* in terms of these two.

Solution 6.7

Area-code = {'0', ..., '9'}*

$inv\text{-}Area\text{-}code(ac) \triangleq 2 \leq (\mathsf{len}\ ac) \wedge (\mathsf{len}\ ac) \leq 6 \wedge ac(1) = \text{'0'}$

Local-no = {'0', ..., '9'}*

$inv\text{-}Local\text{-}no(n) \triangleq 2 \leq (\mathsf{len}\ n) \wedge (\mathsf{len}\ n) \leq 8 \wedge n(1) \neq \text{'0'}$

Phone-no ::
  ac : *Area-code*
  no : *Local-no*

■

6.3 Creating a modified composite object

Composite objects are often used as models in data processing applications. For example, an *Employee* record containing an identifying *number*, *name*, *address*, *department*, and *salary* might be modelled as a composite object. After a worker receives a salary rise we need a new value of *Employee* which is the same for the worker except that the *salary* component is at the new level; all other fields remain the same. It is useful to have a function which makes a modified copy of a value without requiring redefinition of the values of all fields. That is, we want an operator which creates a composite object from another with the component values remaining the same except for a particular field or fields.

The μ function (the Greek letter 'mu') creates a modified copy of a composite object. In its simplest form the μ function has two arguments. The first is a value of a composite object type; the second is a pair consisting of the name of a field (of the first argument) and a new value for that field. The pair is shown separated by the symbol $\mapsto$. The function returns a composite object of the same type as the first argument with the field value changed. For example, suppose:

$$da = mk\text{-}Date(27, 3, 1975).$$

Then $\mu(da, month \mapsto 1)$ evaluates to the value $mk\text{-}Date(27, 1, 1975)$.

Note that it is always possible to construct an updated value of a composite type using its make function. For example, consider an operation to change the area code of a telephone number as defined in the solution to Exercise 6.7.

CHANGE-AREA(newarea: Area-code)
ext wr *ph: Phone-no*
post $ph = mk\text{-}Phone\text{-}no(\overleftarrow{ph}.no, newarea)$

Using the μ function the post-condition would be:

post $ph = \mu(\overleftarrow{ph}, ac \mapsto newarea)$

Review Question 6.6

Suppose *da* has the value $mk\text{-}Date(3, 3, 1976)$. Use the μ function on *da* to create the date 3–3–1977.

■

Exercise 6.8

Consider the following model of an entry in a simple file system:

File-entry ::
  name: char*
  size: $\mathbb{N}$
  type: {TEXT, CODE, DATA, GRAPHICS}
  created: *Date-and-time*
  modified: *Date-and-time*

Write a function *newname* which takes as arguments a value of type *File-entry* and a string and returns a *File-entry* value which is the same as the first argument but with the name field changed to the value of the string.

Solution 6.8

$newname: File\text{-}entry \times \text{char}^* \rightarrow File\text{-}entry$
$newname(f, s) \triangleq \mu(f, name \mapsto s)$

■

The μ function allows more than one field to be replaced by including several field-value pairs in the argument list. For example, the function *copyfile* creates a new version of a *File-entry* value but with the *created* and *modified* fields set to the current date and time, *now*.

> *copyfile*: *File-entry* × *Date-and-time* → *File-entry*
> *copyfile*(*f*, *now*) $\triangleq$
> μ(*f*, *created* ↦ *now*, *modified* ↦ *now*)

Review Question 6.7
Rewrite the *CHANGE-PRICE* operation on page 60 using the μ function.

■

6.4 Pattern matching with make functions

Specifications involving composite object types are often rather complex, because they either use field selection throughout an expression or use many let constructs to introduce local variables as synonyms for field values.

Pattern matching provides an alternative, more compact way of introducing local variables as synonyms for field values. A composite value is equated to a make function whose arguments are all undefined variables which can be used locally as the values of fields of a composite object. The pattern match makes the equality true by giving the undefined variables the values of the corresponding fields. For example, if *al* is a value of the type *AscendingList* defined below:

> *AscendingList* ::
> *list*: $\mathbb{Z}^*$
> *num-of-negs*: $\mathbb{N}$

then:

> let *mk-AscendingList* (*l*, *n*) = *al* in ...

is equivalent to

> let *l* = *al.list*, *n* = *al.num-of-negs* in ...

To compare the different styles of representing a specification, consider a function *in-summer-76* which takes a value of the type *Date* and returns true if the date occurs during the summer of 1976. We have to indicate that the year must be 1976, and the month and day must be summer-time (in the northern hemisphere). We define summer to last from 21 June to 20 September.

> *in-summer-76* : *Date* → $\mathbb{B}$
> *in-summer-76* (*da*) $\triangleq$
> (*da.year* = 1976) ∧
> ((*da.month* ∈ {7, 8}) ∨
> (*da.month* = 6 ∧ *da.day* ≥ 21) ∨
> (*da.month* = 9 ∧ *da.day* ≤ 20))

As we have seen, a let clause may be use to bind values to variables which appear after an in. Thus, in the following version of *in-summer-76* the expressions *da.day*, *da.month*, and *da.year* are evaluated and their values are bound to *d*, *y* and *m*.

$$
\begin{array}{l}
\textit{in-summer-76} : \textit{Date} \rightarrow \mathbb{B} \\
\textit{in-summer-76}\ (\textit{da}) \triangleq \\
\quad \text{let } d = \textit{da.day},\ m = \textit{da.month},\ \ y = \textit{da.year} \text{ in} \\
\quad (y = 1976) \wedge ((m \in \{7, 8\}) \vee (m = 6 \wedge d \geq 21) \vee (m = 9 \wedge d \leq 20))
\end{array}
$$

Using the make function, *mk-Date* allows the evaluation of the components of *da* to be implicit, thus:

$$
\begin{array}{l}
\textit{in-summer-76} : \textit{Date} \rightarrow \mathbb{B} \\
\textit{in-summer-76}\ (\textit{da}) \triangleq \\
\quad \text{let } \textit{mk-Date}(d, m, y) = \textit{da} \text{ in} \\
\quad (y = 1976) \wedge ((m \in \{7, 8\}) \vee (m = 6 \wedge d \geq 21) \vee (m = 9 \wedge d \leq 20))
\end{array}
$$

In this version of the function, *mk-Date* is used in a let clause to define a pattern using the symbols *y*, *m*, and *d*. This pattern is matched to the structure of *da* and the component values of *da* are bound to the variables *d*, *m* and *y* for use in the expression in the last line.

This pattern matching can be made even more succinct when used with parameters; instead of using a let construct, the parameter can be replaced by the make function:

$$
\begin{array}{l}
\textit{in-summer-76} : \textit{Date} \rightarrow \mathbb{B} \\
\textit{in-summer-76}\ (\textit{mk-Date}(d, m, y)) \triangleq \\
\quad (y = 1976) \wedge ((m \in \{7, 8\}) \vee (m = 6 \wedge d \geq 21) \vee (m = 9 \wedge d \leq 20))
\end{array}
$$

6.5 Summary of concepts

- Composite objects are structures analogous to Pascal records in that they contain fields of various types.
- A composite object can be built from field values by using a make function. Make functions are named by prefixing the name of the composite object type with *mk-*.
- A composite object can be decomposed into its individual field values by using field selection.
- Constraints on data types often need to be imposed in order adequately to model reality. These are expressed using data type invariants which are specified as boolean-valued functions on the type to be constrained.
- The μ function is an operator which creates a copy of a value of a composite object type except that specified fields are changed.
- The make function of a composite object type can be used to match the structure of a value of the type and to bind variables to the component values.

7 SPECIFICATION WITH OPERATIONS

In this chapter we concentrate on operations in VDM. These differ from functions in that they involve the notion of state, which is analogous to the set of global variables in a procedural programming language. More detail is given here on external variables, which were first introduced in Chapter 3. The preservation of data type invariants is also discussed, followed by an explanation of the implementability of operations.

7.1 External variables

We will revisit the syntax for specifying operations and illustrate the use of external variables to model the state. Recall from Chapter 3 that the state is the abstract model of computer store which the operations may change by accessing external variables. Consider the following extract from a statement of requirements for a computerized security system.

```
Access to a high-security building is to be controlled
by a password system. To gain admittance to the
building a member of staff will type in a code at a
keypad next to the main entrance. She will be
permitted access to the system if the code is one of
the registered codes stored in a central computer.
Each code is unique and consists of 8 characters.

When the system is first installed the security
manager will register only one code—his own.
Thereafter, unique codes may be added to or deleted
from the register by that manager.
```

An analysis of these requirements leads to a formal model involving a data type to model codes, a representation of a register, of codes and operations to initialize the register, to add or delete a code and to check if a code is registered. The type *Code* can be modelled as an eight-character string (the length being imposed by the invariant) as in the following type definition:

$Code = \mathsf{char}^*$

$inv\text{-}Code(c) \triangleq \mathsf{len}\ c = 8$

The statement of requirements describes a register of codes; clearly there is a need to store values in what is known as the state in VDM. Thus, to model the state for this system (i.e. the register of password codes) we use an external variable in the operations suggested by the statement of requirements: initializing the register, adding a code, etc. The operation to initialize the register follows. It includes a clause which declares write access (wr) to the external (ext) variable *register*, thus implicitly defining it as the state. Since order is not significant and the uniqueness of registered codes is required, the register is modelled as a variable whose type is a set—*Code*-set:

INIT-REGISTER(first-code: Code)
ext wr *register*: *Code*-set
pre true
post $register = \{first\text{-}code\}$

Exercise 7.1

Write an operation *ADD-NEW* to place a new code into the set of registered codes. The operation should only work for codes which are not already present in the register.

Solution 7.1

Since *register* is to be modified by the inclusion of the new code, *ADD-NEW* must have read-write access. Thus, the mode of *register* is wr:

ADD-NEW(c: Code)
ext wr *register*: *Code*-set
pre $c \notin register$
post $register = \overleftarrow{register} \cup \{c\}$

■

We shall use either of the terms ***new value*** or ***output value*** to refer to the value of an external variable after an operation and use ***old value*** or ***input value*** to refer to its value before the operation. Recall that variables representing old values have a hook placed over them; thus, the post-condition of *ADD-NEW* says that the output value of *register* is the union of the input value of *register* ($\overleftarrow{register}$) and the singleton set containing the new code *c*. (We had to enclose *c* in the braces { } because the set union operator requires two sets and *c* is a single code, not a set of codes.)

Here is a specification of an operation *IS-REGISTERED* which can be used to check if a code is stored in the register. Again, the abstraction of storage, the state (which here is the set of registered codes), is represented as an external variable to the operation.

IS-REGISTERED(c: *Code*) r : $\mathbb{B}$
ext rd *register*: *Code*-set
pre true
post $r \Leftrightarrow (c \in register)$

Notice that, unlike *ADD-NEW*, *INIT-REGISTER* does not modify the state but 'reads' its value and returns a result; it does not modify an external variable. Not only does *IS-REGISTERED* have a parameter c of type *Code*, it has been defined in such a way that it returns a boolean value (via r): true if c is in a set of registered codes, *register*, and false if not. Compare this with *ADD-CODE* which has write access to the state and does not return a result value. Generally, operations which return a result value do not access their external variables in wr mode, although it is sometimes convenient to change the state and return a result.

7.2 Constructing a VDM specification

This section looks in detail at a small example of a VDM specification. The example has a state with several component variables. A composite object type is used to define the system state and a variety of VDM constructs are used to simplify specification. Finally, a review of techniques for writing VDM specifications is given at the end of the section.

Case-study: the Acme stock-control system

The requirement is for a point-of-sale system (an 'intelligent' cash register) which will carry out stock control for the Acme Kite Company. The company sells a single type of product, kites. The following is an extract from the company's statement of requirements.

```
The selling price of kites fluctuates from day to day
due to fluctuations in the price of raw materials.
There is a discount for those customers who buy their
kites in bulk and the point-of-sale terminal needs to
store the discount level and the minimum purchase
order required to obtain a discount. There is only one
discount level. The system will need to be able to do
the following:

1. Reset the point-of-sale system every day.

2. Set the selling price of a kite.

3. Record any sale – the number of kites and
   their cost.

4. Record the receipt of a number of kites at
   the warehouse.
```

```
5. Calculate the total cash taken at the end of
   the day.
6. Monitor stock-level.
```

We have to write a specification to show to the company before we proceed with the design and implementation of the system. After lengthy discussions, the company has confirmed that the following operations of an electronic cash register with stock-control functions are to be supplied with the first release of the system.

- *START-DAY*: sets the cash received to zero at the start of each day's trading.
- *TOTAL*: return the total amount of cash received so far today.
- *RECORD-SALE*(k): record the sale of k kites.
- *SET-PRICE*(p): set the price of a kite to p.
- *ADD-TO-STOCK*(k): record the receipt of k kites to be added to stock.
- *STOCK-LEVEL*: return the number of kites in stock.
- *SET-DISCOUNT*(d, m): set the discount to d per cent for a minimum purchase of m kites.

The first step in VDM is to model the state by defining an appropriate data type. As part of this we will outline the necessary operations together with a brief description of what they do. We need to get some better idea of the system before writing the formal specification using a mathematical notation.

Exercise 7.2

Study the statement of requirements above and write down what values will have to be recorded by the system.

Solution 7.2

We need to record the number of kites in stock at the present time, the selling price of a kite, the total cash received during the day, the discount on bulk purchase (held as a percentage), and the discount threshold—the minimum number of kites that need to be bought before the discount level applies.

■

The state for this system consists of the following composite object type. Each field is given with its type and a comment (preceded by --) which describes its purpose. Comments are not part of a formal specification but they should be used to enhance understanding when the situation is complex.

Stock-sys ::
  price: $\mathbb{R}$ -- *selling price of a kite*
  stock: $\mathbb{N}$ -- *number of kites in stock*
  cash: $\mathbb{R}$ -- *amount of cash taken that day*
  discount: $\mathbb{R}$ -- *discount level*
  threshold: $\mathbb{N}$ -- *minimum order to obtain discount*

Exercise 7.3

You may have noticed that we decided to use $\mathbb{R}$ as the type of *price* and *cash*, and not $\mathbb{N}$ which could have allowed the values to have been recorded in pence. Why might it have been wrong to have chosen $\mathbb{N}$ for these variables?

Solution 7.3

Choosing $\mathbb{N}$ is a temptation for programmers because it is often more convenient and more accurate to use whole numbers in a programming language. To choose $\mathbb{N}$ would, therefore, admit an implementation bias into the specification. Also, because discounts could include fractions of a percentage point, small amounts of money could be lost on large transactions.

Now that we have specified the state of the system we will outline the operations on it. All we will do is name the operations, include any parameters or returned values, and describe the operation in words. For example, *TOTAL* would be:

TOTAL( ) *r*: $\mathbb{R}$
  -- *return the total amount of cash r received so far during the day*

We have chosen to model *TOTAL* as an operation which has no input parameters but returns a value. As we proceed we shall include the external variables which represent the state of the system and the pre- and post-conditions.

■

Exercise 7.4

Write similar outline specifications for the other operations.

Solution 7.4

START-DAY
  -- *set the cash received to zero*

RECORD-SALE(*k*: $\mathbb{N}$) *r*: $\mathbb{R}$
  -- *record the sale of k kites and return the total selling price r*
  -- *accumulate day's total cash*

SET-PRICE(*p*: $\mathbb{R}$)
  -- *set the selling price of a kite to be p*

ADD-TO-STOCK(*k*: $\mathbb{N}$)
  -- *record the receipt of k kites in stock*

STOCK-LEVEL( ) *r*: $\mathbb{N}$
  -- *return the number of kites in stock*

SET-DISCOUNT(*d*: $\mathbb{R}$, *m*: $\mathbb{N}$)
  -- *set the discount level to d*
  -- *set the minimum order which qualifies for a discount to m*

■

Having produced an outline of each operation in the form of a heading and a comment, we will proceed to complete them by specifying the external variables and the pre- and post-conditions for each operation.

Exercise 7.5

Write a specification for *START-DAY*.

Solution 7.5

START-DAY -- *this operation is used at the start of each day*
ext wr *sys*: *Stock-sys*
pre true
post $sys = \mu(\overleftarrow{sys}, cash \mapsto 0)$ -- *set the cash received to zero*

■

Exercise 7.6

Write a specification for the operation *TOTAL*.

Solution 7.6

TOTAL( ) *r*: $\mathbb{R}$ -- *return the total amount of cash r received so far during the day*
ext rd *sys*: *Stock-sys*
pre true
post $r = sys.cash$

■

Next, we consider how the operation *RECORD-SALE* should be specified. This is a complicated operation and it is worth noting again how the use of a formal specification forces us to resolve ambiguities that might not be obvious in an informal description. The concept of returning the total selling price seems clear enough although we have to account for the possible discount. But what exactly does it mean to record a sale?

VDM gives us a framework for answering that question. The meaning of an operation is the relationship between its inputs and its outputs. The inputs are its parameters and the state of the system before the operation. The outputs are the state of the system after the operation and the value returned, if any. We have already specified for *RECORD-SALE* the parameter and returned value. So the next step in deciding what *RECORD-SALE* means is to look at the state variables and decide which are read and which are modified by *RECORD-SALE*.

Exercise 7.7

Does *RECORD-SALE* require access to any of the components of the state—*price*, *stock*, *cash*, *discount*, or *threshold*? If so, what kind of access and why?

Solution 7.7

In order to return the total price *RECORD-SALE* needs to have read-only access to *price*, *discount*, and *threshold*. This is sufficient because none of those three variables will be modified by *RECORD-SALE*. *RECORD-SALE* must adjust the values of *cash* and *stock* to reflect the increase in *cash* and the decrease in *stock* due to the sale, so it requires read-write access to those variables.

■

In the first two operations, *START-DAY* and *TOTAL*, we have made explicit the state of the system (the collection of component variables) by including the variable *sys* in the external clause of each operation. However a particular operation will often use only some of the components of the state variable and neither read from nor write to the others. Therefore, we could include in the external clause of an operation only those component variables of the state which are used in the operation (i.e. only those that appear in pre- and/or post-conditions).

For example, we could express the ext clause of *RECORD-SALE* as follows:

ext rd *price*: $\mathbb{R}$
 wr *stock*: $\mathbb{N}$
 wr *cash*: $\mathbb{R}$
 rd *discount*: $\mathbb{R}$
 rd *threshold*: $\mathbb{N}$

However, for uniformity we will include the entire state variable in external clauses. Consequently, we make explicit the assumption that if components of an external variable do not appear in a post-condition, we shall assume that they are unchanged by the operation. This assumption may have to be made explicit later by adding clauses such as, for example, $sys.cash = \overleftarrow{sys}.cash$ during proofs.

To construct the pre-condition of *RECORD-SALE* we must determine if there are any constraints on selling kites, and what they are. At some point in analysis we may ask what to do if a customer tries to buy more kites than are in stock. Acme have decided not to back-order kites so *RECORD-SALE* will be defined only if the customer's order can be satisfied from existing stock. Furthermore, it makes no sense to 'sell' zero kites. Consequently the pre-condition is:

$$0 < k \ \wedge \ k \leq sys.stock$$

The post-condition has three properties, as follows:

- The value *r* returned is the total selling price.
- The value of *cash* is increased by the total selling price.
- The value of *stock* is decreased by the number sold.

Review Question 7.1

Use VDM notation to express the relationship between the input and output values of *stock*.

■

There are two cases to consider for the total selling price because of discount pricing. The first case is when the number of kites in an order qualifies for a discount. The second case is when the number of kites does not qualify for a discount. In the first case, the number sold must be at least equal to the minimum qualifying order and the actual discount must be calculated and subtracted from the *price*. The two cases are reflected in a disjunction which specifies *r*:

RECORD-SALE(k: $\mathbb{N}$) r: $\mathbb{R}$
  -- *If the number of kites sold is enough to qualify for a discount, then r is*
  -- *the discounted total. If the number does not qualify for discount, then r is*
  -- *the non-discounted total.*
  -- *Operation increases the cash level by the amount of the sale, and*
  -- *decreases the stock level by the number sold.*
ext wr *sys*: *Stock-sys*
pre $0 < k \wedge k \leq sys.stock$
post let $thresh = \overleftarrow{sys}.threshold$, $pr = \overleftarrow{sys}.price$, $disc = \overleftarrow{sys}.discount$ in
  $((k \geq thresh \wedge r = k \times pr \times (1.0 - disc)) \vee (k < thresh \wedge r = k \times pr)) \wedge$
  $sys = \mu(\overleftarrow{sys}, cash \mapsto \overleftarrow{sys}.cash + r, stock \mapsto \overleftarrow{sys}.stock - k)$

Exercise 7.8

Specify *SET-PRICE*. Include a descriptive comment.

Solution 7.8

SET-PRICE(p: $\mathbb{R}$) -- *set the new price for kites*
ext wr *sys*: *Stock-sys*
pre $p \geq 0.0$
post $sys = \mu(\overleftarrow{sys}, \overleftarrow{sys}.price \mapsto p)$

■

All the remaining operations are straightforward to specify.

ADD-TO-STOCK(k: $\mathbb{N}$) -- *increase the stock levels on the delivery of some kites*
ext wr *sys*: *Stock-sys*
pre true
post $sys = \mu(\overleftarrow{sys}, stock \mapsto \overleftarrow{sys}.stock + k)$

STOCK-LEVEL( ) r: $\mathbb{N}$ -- *return the number of kites currently in stock*
ext rd *sys*: *Stock-sys*
pre true
post $r = sys.stock$

SET-DISCOUNT(d: $\mathbb{R}$, m: $\mathbb{N}$)
  -- *Set the discount rate and the minimum order size that qualifies for discount*
ext wr *sys*: *Stock-sys*
pre $d \geq 0.0 \wedge m \geq 0$
post $sys = \mu(\overleftarrow{sys}, discount \mapsto d, threshold \mapsto m)$

There are two points which arise from these specifications. First, many of the operations have a pre-condition of true which means that input parameters to these operations are not constrained. Second, the specifications include a description of each operation in English; this habit should be cultivated as specifications are much easier to read and check if there is an accompanying commentary. However, we should stress that the role of this commentary is to provide a guide to reading the mathematics and an informal check of it. The mathematics specifies the required software function and if a difference exists between the mathematics and the English you should believe the mathematics because of the vagueness of natural language.

Exercise 7.9

Consider the effect of a change of mind by Acme. The company might realize that cash should be put in the till at the start of each day so the till operator could give change. The amount might vary from day to day depending on experience. Modify *START-DAY* to take as a parameter the size of the float (the amount of cash in the till at the start of a day).

Solution 7.9

START-DAY(f: $\mathbb{R}$)
  -- *set the cash received to the float.*
  -- *this operation is run at the start of each day's trading*
ext wr *sys*: *Stock-sys*
pre $f \geq 0.0$
post $sys = \mu(\overleftarrow{sys}, cash \mapsto f)$

■

At another meeting Acme requested that the system keep track of the total number of kites sold during a day. This involves adding a new component to the state of the system, we will call it *kites-today*, and a new operation, *SOLD-TODAY*, to return the number of kites sold during the day.

We can add the following field to the state type:

kites-today: $\mathbb{N}$ -- *number of kites sold today*

The specification of the operation to enquire about the number sold during the day is shown below:

SOLD-TODAY( ) r: $\mathbb{N}$ -- *return the number of kites sold today*
ext rd *sys*: *Stock-sys*
pre true
post $r = sys.kites\text{-}today$

Simply defining the component *kites-today* and providing an operation to return its value is not enough. All previously defined operations must be examined to see if they affect *kites-today*. When operations were specified, one of the steps was a check of each component of the state to see if the operation required access. Now that the state has changed that check should be made for the new component.

Exercise 7.10

Which of the other operations should be modified to keep *kites-today* accurate?

Solution 7.10

Plainly *RECORD-SALE* should be changed to update *kites-today*. Perhaps it is not so obvious that *START-DAY* should also be changed: it should set the value of *kites-today* to zero at the start of each day. None of the other operations needs to be modified.

■

The new specifications for the modified operations can now be written.

Exercise 7.11

Write the new specifications for *START-DAY* and *RECORD-SALE*.

Solution 7.11

START-DAY(f: $\mathbb{R}$)
-- *set the cash received to the float and the number of kites sold today to zero*
-- *this operation is run at the start of each day's trading*
ext wr *sys*: *Stock-sys*
pre $f \geq 0.0$
post $sys = \mu(\overleftarrow{sys}, cash \mapsto f,. kites\text{-}today \mapsto 0)$

RECORD-SALE(k: $\mathbb{N}$) r: $\mathbb{R}$
ext wr *sys*: *Stock-sys*
pre $0 < k \;\wedge\; k \leq sys.stock$
post let $thresh = sys.threshold, pr = sys.price, disc = sys.discount$ in
$((k \geq thresh \;\wedge\; r = k \times pr \times (1.0 - disc)) \;\vee\; (k < thresh \wedge r = k \times pr)) \wedge$
$sys = \mu(\overleftarrow{sys}, cash \mapsto \overleftarrow{sys}.cash + r, stock \mapsto \overleftarrow{sys}.stock - k,$
$kites\text{-}today \mapsto \overleftarrow{sys}.kites\text{-}today + k)$

■

Writing specifications

This subsection contains a review of the process of writing specifications.

When trying to write formal specifications for the first time the beginner often has difficulties with both the ideas and the notation. To write a specification, the first thing to tackle is the data model. This is the best starting point because you cannot specify the properties you require if you do not have some understanding of the data to be transformed. Without necessarily completing the specification of the data types needed you should tackle the operations; you will often find that your data model is flawed when attempting to write the operations for a system. For example, you may find that your operations on the state are very difficult to express because of your data model and that changes to it makes the operations simpler and so increases your confidence in their correctness. You will often find that realizing the need for an operation exposes an omission from the data model (e.g. the need for *TOTAL* exposed the need for the state component *cash*).

For large specifications, deriving the data model can take several weeks, but for these small problems minutes should do. In either case, the first thing to write down is the state. Next comes the heading of each operation. Some decision needs to be made about whether the operation requires arguments and/or returns a value. After that, you can decide what kind of **ext** declaration is needed; if an operation without access to external variables is to be specified, there will be no **ext** line.

The pre-condition is the next thing to write down; this is in some ways easy, as the developer need 'only' ask what are the valid inputs to an operation—i.e. what are the input values for which the operation is to be defined. The pre-condition should be as *restrictive* as possible, typically including many conjuncts. By restrictive we mean that you should not make an operation more general than it needs to be. This is not only good business sense (only providing what the customer has paid for) but it makes proof easier.

Finally you must tackle the post-condition; this is often more difficult than writing down the pre-condition as it should be as *weak* as possible (having few conjuncts). Having a weak post-condition means not having to restrict the output values; if a customer is content to have an operation produce a number between 1 and 100, why restrict the output to even numbers or prime numbers?

One approach to constructing a post-condition is to try to write down briefly the list of properties the post-condition should have. Each element in this list can then be translated into a predicate. Careful consideration of the problem may produce a list of properties such as:

- property 1
- property 2
- property 3

A good starting point for the post-condition is often the conjunction of the required properties. For example, the following might be a good attempt at a post-condition:

property 1 $\wedge$ property 2 $\wedge$ property 3

Sometimes it is not immediately obvious what the properties of the required post-condition are. The tactic then is to try a few examples. Write down some possible inputs and their corresponding outputs. Try the sort of values one might have problems with in an implementation when first testing it: choose a couple of simple values whose answer is obvious and one or two more difficult cases. It may be possible to generalize from the answers the properties that are required.

Finally, do not expect to be able to write a correct specification on the first attempt. You will find that you often have to respecify operations. Once a reasonable list of properties for the post-condition has been derived, you can try the test cases again. If these work we are probably on the right track, if they do not it is worth reconsidering both the properties and the test cases.

7.3 Preservation of invariants and implementability

We have seen that constraints may have to be applied to a VDM model by defining an invariant on a type. The following example shows how such a constraint may arise and how it is incorporated in a specification.

Suppose a computerized flight reservation system is to store data about a number of flights and about passengers who have booked on flights. We might model the type of a flight by:

$Flight = Passenger$-set

where values of the type *Passenger* represent people who might book the flight. (We can leave *Passenger* unspecified until it is necessary to decide if it is a code, a composite object containing name, address and telephone number, or whatever.)

The use of a set to model the group indicates that we regard the flight passengers as an unordered collection of distinct elements.

There is an important aspect of airline seating that is not reflected in this model: an aeroplane has a fixed number of seats. To be specific, suppose a flight is limited to at most 150 passengers; we need a way to incorporate the constraint that *Flight* consists only of those sets of *Passenger* which have at most 150 elements. In other words, we need to respecify *Flight* by defining its invariant *inv-Flight* to restrict the maximum cardinality of sets of passengers. This is shown below:

$Flight = Passenger$-set

$inv\text{-}Flight(f) \triangleq \mathrm{card}\, f \leq 150$

Preservation of data type invariants

When a data type is specified using a data type invariant, a ***proof obligation*** is incurred for each operation in which a variable of that data type appears as an external read-write variable. The reason is that an operation can affect the state of a system only by changing the values of external read-write variables. If a variable belongs to a type defined with an invariant and an operation changes the value of that variable, then it must be proved that the new value satisfies the invariant.

We shall use the example of *Flight* to illustrate this concept of ***invariant preservation***. Suppose the state of our system consists of a variable *fl* of type *Flight* and an operation *ADD-PASS* is defined to add a new passenger to the flight.

Exercise 7.12

Write a specification of *ADD-PASS*. Use an argument *p* to represent the passenger to be added.

Solution 7.12

ADD-PASS(p: Passenger)
  -- adds a new passenger p to the flight fl providing it is not already full
ext wr *fl*: *Flight*
pre $(p \notin fl) \wedge (\mathrm{card}\, fl < 150)$
post $fl = \overleftarrow{fl} \cup \{p\}$

■

The pre-condition is the conjunction of two clauses: the first says that *p* is a new passenger (i.e. not already a member of *fl*) and the second specifies that the flight is not full (i.e. card *fl* is less than 150). We shall see that *ADD-PASS* preserves the invariant, and we shall see how the obligation to prove invariant preservation would have helped to catch the omission of the second conjunct (card $fl < 150$) had we failed to include it in the pre-condition.

Pre- and post-conditions as predicates

Before continuing with this specific example (in Exercise 7.13) we shall first state what must be proved for a general operation. A general operation, *OP*, may have several arguments and return a result. We shall assume *OP* is defined on a state *s* of type *T* and that *T* has a data type invariant. Thus, the form of *OP* is:

OP(*parameter1*: *Type1*, *parameter2*: *Type2*...) *res*: *Type-of-result*
ext wr *s* : *T*
pre ...
post ...

The names in the parameter list denote all of the arguments which are passed to an operation and *res* denotes the variable which contains the result.

Now the pre-condition is a function of the types of the parameters, *parameter1*, *parameter2*, etc., and the input value of the state, *s*. That is, the pre-condition gives a condition that must be satisfied by the arguments and the input value of the state (i.e. the external variable) in order that the operation be defined. For convenience we will denote the pre-condition function of an operation, *OP*, by *pre-OP*. Since *pre-OP* does not depend on the output value of the operation, we have not needed to use a hooked variable in defining a pre-condition. Thus, it is understood that the state value in a pre-condition refers to the input value. However, in expressing the proof obligation of invariant preservation we will need to combine pre- and post-conditions. When we do so we will write the pre-condition using a hooked variable so that it is clear that the pre-condition applies to the input value of the state.

On the other hand, the post-condition is a function of *parameter1*, *parameter2*, ..., $\overleftarrow{s}$, *s*, and *res*. It expresses a relation between the input and output values of the state along with the arguments and the result. We will denote the post-condition of an operation *OP* as *post-Op*. Here is the proof obligation in both words and symbols:

If the value of the state before the operation satisfies the invariant	$(inv\text{-}T(\overleftarrow{s})$
and	$\wedge$
the operation is defined for the given values of the state and the arguments,	$pre\text{-}Op(parameter1, parameter2, ..., \overleftarrow{s})$
and	$\wedge$
the post-condition is true,	$post\text{-}Op(parameter1, parameter2, ..., \overleftarrow{s}, s, res))$
then	$\Rightarrow$
the invariant still holds.	$inv\text{-}T(s)$

Notice that we wrote *pre-OP(parameter1, parameter2, ...,* $\overleftarrow{s}$) to indicate that the pre-condition applied specifically to the input value of the state. That is, whenever *OP* is validly applied to a state when the invariant holds, it will still hold after *OP*.

Exercise 7.13

Write the proof obligation for *ADD-PASS* in terms of the invariant on *Flight* and the pre- and post-condition functions of the operation.

Solution 7.13

$$(\textit{inv-Flight}(\overleftarrow{fl}) \wedge \textit{pre-ADD-PASS}(p, \overleftarrow{fl}) \wedge \textit{post-ADD-PASS}(p, \overleftarrow{fl}, fl)) \Rightarrow \textit{inv-Flight}(fl)$$

■

Exercise 7.14

Now write the proof obligation replacing *pre-ADD-PASS*, *post-ADD-PASS*, and *inv-Flight* by the logical expressions given in their definitions.

Solution 7.14

$$(\textit{inv-Flight}(\overleftarrow{fl}) \wedge \textit{pre-ADD-PASS}(p, \overleftarrow{fl}) \wedge \textit{post-ADD-PASS}(p, \overleftarrow{fl}, fl)) \Rightarrow \textit{inv-Flight}(fl)$$

↓ ↓ ↓ ↓

i.e. $((\text{card}\,\overleftarrow{fl} \leq 150) \wedge (p \notin \overleftarrow{fl}) \wedge (\text{card}\,\overleftarrow{fl} < 150) \wedge (fl = \overleftarrow{fl} \cup \{p\})) \Rightarrow \text{card}\,fl \leq 150$

■

Review Question 7.2

(i) Which part of the rewritten proof obligation in Solution 7.14 corresponds to the words 'the flight is not full'?

(ii) Which part corresponds to 'the flight is not overbooked'?

■

It is easy to discharge this proof obligation informally: the previous line can be simplified to:

$$((\text{card}\,\overleftarrow{fl} < 150) \wedge (p \notin \overleftarrow{fl}) \wedge (fl = \overleftarrow{fl} \cup \{p\})) \Rightarrow \text{card}\,fl \leq 150$$

Adding a new member ($fl = \overleftarrow{fl} \cup \{p\}$) to a set *fl* with less than 150 members ($\text{card}\,\overleftarrow{fl} < 150$) results in a set with at most 150 members ($\text{card}\,fl \leq 150$).

It is often possible to prove invariant preservation by informal arguments. But sometimes we are unable to prove that an operation preserves an invariant. This can happen for one of two possible reasons: either we erred in specifying the operation and for some valid inputs it violates the invariant, or, even though the operation does not violate the invariant, its specification may not contain enough conditions to allow a proof.

We shall now show how the VDM process helps to distinguish between the causes of failing to prove that a data type invariant is preserved.

Strengthening the post-condition

It is always possible to redefine an operation using a stronger post-condition in such a way that the proof of invariant preservation is obvious. All that is necessary is to add the data type invariant to the post-condition by conjunction.

For example, suppose an earlier version of *ADD-PASS* called *ADD-PASS0* had been specified with a pre-condition which omitted the constraint that the flight must not be full:

ADD-PASS0(p: Passenger)
-- adds a new passenger p to the flight fl providing it is not already full.
ext wr *fl*: *Flight*
pre $p \notin fl$
post $fl = \overleftarrow{fl} \cup \{p\}$

In this case the informal argument we gave of invariant preservation is no longer valid, because it is certainly not true that adding a new member *p* to a set with at most 150 elements results in a set with at most 150 elements; if the input value of *fl* contains exactly 150 elements, adding a further element *p* would increase its cardinality to 151.

Exercise 7.15

Write out the proof obligation for *ADD-PASS0* symbolically using the new pre-condition.

Solution 7.15

$$((\text{card}\,\overleftarrow{fl} \leq 150) \wedge (p \notin \overleftarrow{fl}) \wedge (\overleftarrow{fl} = fl \cup \{p\})) \Rightarrow \text{card}\,fl \leq 150$$

■

Since we cannot prove this statement, we can attempt to correct *ADD-PASS0* by conjoining the invariant to its post-condition. We call the new version *ADD-PASS1*:

ADD-PASS1(p: Passenger)
ext wr *fl*: *Flight*
pre $p \notin fl$
post $(fl = \overleftarrow{fl} \cup \{p\}) \wedge \text{card}\,fl \leq 150$

Now it is very easy to prove invariant preservation because the post-condition contains the invariant! The proof obligation for the revised *ADD-PASS0* is met as a result of the operation itself: the post-condition already states that the flight is not overbooked which certainly implies that the flight is not overbooked.

However, there is a difficulty with *ADD-PASS1* which we shall now investigate: the operation does preserve the invariant *inv-Flight* but contains an inconsistency.

Exercise 7.16

Describe an inconsistency in the specification of *ADD-PASS1*.

Solution 7.16

Even if a flight is fully booked *ADD-PASS1* is apparently still defined to add a new passenger. This is because the output value of the external variable *fl* is constrained to be no greater than 150 by the second conjunct in the post-condition, even though it is impossible to achieve if the input value of *fl* already contains 150 members, which is permitted by the invariant on the type of *fl*.

■

This inconsistency is analogous to the more obvious one in this operation:

$NEW\text{-}Y(x: \mathbb{Z})$
ext wr $y: \mathbb{Z}$
pre $x > 10$
post $y = x \wedge y < 0$

Clearly, it is valid that y takes the value of x, but it cannot be valid that y is also less than 0.

Implementability

VDM imposes another proof obligation to trap inconsistencies like the one above. Every operation must be shown to be 'implementable'. Implementability is the VDM term for the following proof obligation. We express it in terms of a general operation, *OP*. *OP* is said to be ***implementable*** if for every valid input (*parameter1*, *parameter2*, ... and $\overleftarrow{s}$), there is at least one output (s and *res*) which satisfies the post-condition. In symbols:

$$\forall \overleftarrow{s} : T \bullet pre\text{-}OP(parameter1, parameter2, ..., \overleftarrow{s}) \Rightarrow$$
$$\exists s : T, res : Result\text{-}type \bullet post\text{-}OP(parameter1, parameter2, ..., \overleftarrow{s}, s, res)$$

If this proof obligation cannot be satisfied, there is no possibility of implementing the operation because, quite simply, there will be situations in which both the invariant and pre-condition are satisfied for which there is no result satisfying the invariant and post-condition.

Note that it still must be proved that the post-condition preserves any invariant.

Exercise 7.17

Write down what must be proved to show that *ADD-PASS1* is implementable using the logical expressions which define the pre- and post-conditions. (Since *ADD-PASS1* does not have a result parameter you need only be concerned with the output value of the external variable.)

Solution 7.17

$$\forall \overleftarrow{fl} : Flight \bullet p \notin \overleftarrow{fl} \Rightarrow \exists fl : Flight \bullet (fl = \overleftarrow{fl} \cup \{p\}) \wedge (\text{card}\, fl \leq 150)$$

■

Review Question 7.3

Say why we cannot prove the expression in the solution of Exercise 7.17, both in terms of the mathematics and of the flight booking system.

■

If an operation is not implementable, then we must change the specification, possibly by amending both the pre- and post-conditions. We have made a logical error and we must modify the specification of the operation. Usually, identifying the reason for lack of implementability is an aid when modifying the operation. In the case of *ADD-PASS1*, the pre-condition was too weak. Without weakening the post-condition to allow an unlimited number of people, the pre-condition had to be strengthened by including the constraint that the flight must not be full. Once that change is made, the operation is both implementable and preserves the invariant.

Implementability is a proof obligation that must be discharged for every operation regardless of whether any data type invariant is involved. It is a consistency check on the specification. If an operation is not implementable, it must be respecified or eliminated.

The following steps are recommended for an operation that changes a state having a data type invariant. We assume that it has been shown to be implementable.

1. Try to prove that the data type invariant is preserved. No further action need be taken if you succeed.
2. If the proof cannot be carried out, redefine the operation by conjoining the invariant to the post-condition and check implementability. No further action need be taken if the amended operation is implementable.
3. If the amended operation is not implementable, then rethink the operation from the beginning using the reason for lack of implementability as a guide.

7.4 Declaring the state

So far we have implicitly introduced the names of variables which represent the state of the system being specified by referring to them in the external clauses of operations. One problem with this approach is that considerable effort is needed to establish just what variables make up the system by examining all operation specifications. Therefore, VDM-SL has introduced facilities to declare type names and variable names in a manner similar to the type and variable declarations of a language like Pascal. For example, consider again the security code system from section 7.1; the type name *Code* and the variable *register* can be explicitly declared using the types keyword and state...end construct as follows:

types
    Code = char*
state *Security-system* of
    register: *Code*-set
end

As well as providing an explicit declaration that *Security-system* is the name of the state and that it has one component (*register*), the state construct allows a state invariant to be specified (using the keyword inv) and provides a succinct way of specifying the initial value of the state (using the keyword init). If we wanted the password register to be initialized to the empty set and for all passwords to begin with one of the characters $, %, *, @, !, £ and #, we could specify the state thus:

$$\begin{array}{l}
\text{state } \textit{Security-system} \text{ of} \\
\quad \textit{register}\text{: } \textit{Code}\text{-set} \\
\text{inv } \textit{mk-Security-system}(\textit{register}) \triangleq \\
\quad \forall pw \in \textit{register} \bullet pw(1) \in \{\text{'\$'}, \text{'\%'}, \text{'*'}, \text{'@'}, \text{'!'}, \text{'£'}, \text{'\#'}\} \\
\text{init } \textit{mk-Security-system}(\textit{register}) \triangleq \\
\quad \textit{register} = \{\ \} \\
\text{end}
\end{array}$$

Note that when declaring the invariant and initial value a make function should be used to denote the collection of state component variables.

The use of a state declaration also allows component variables to be listed separately and to be accessed by operations separately instead of using a composite object type (even though the latter may better capture the link between the components).

Exercise 7.18

Express the stock system discussed in section 7.2 using a state declaration and rewrite the *RECORD-SALE* operation to use the declaration.

Solution 7.18

The *Stock-sys* composite object type can be split into its component parts:

$$\begin{array}{ll}
\text{state } \textit{Stock-sys} \text{ of} & \\
\quad \textit{price}: \mathbb{R} & \text{-- } \textit{selling price of a kite} \\
\quad \textit{stock}: \mathbb{N} & \text{-- } \textit{number of kites in stock} \\
\quad \textit{cash}: \mathbb{R} & \text{-- } \textit{amount of cash taken that day} \\
\quad \textit{discount}: \mathbb{R} & \text{-- } \textit{discount level} \\
\quad \textit{threshold}: \mathbb{N} & \text{-- } \textit{minimum order to obtain discount} \\
\quad \textit{kites-today}: \mathbb{N} & \text{-- } \textit{number of kites sold today} \\
\text{end} &
\end{array}$$

The revised *RECORD-SALE* simply refers to the individual components and their access modes and does not refer to components of a composite type:

$$\begin{array}{ll}
\multicolumn{2}{l}{\textit{RECORD-SALE}(k: \mathbb{N})\ r: \mathbb{R}} \\
\text{ext} & \text{wr } \textit{stock}: \mathbb{N} \\
 & \text{wr } \textit{cash}: \mathbb{R} \\
 & \text{wr } \textit{kites-today}: \mathbb{N} \\
 & \text{rd } \textit{price}: \mathbb{R} \\
 & \text{rd } \textit{discount}: \mathbb{R} \\
 & \text{rd } \textit{threshold}: \mathbb{N} \\
\text{post} & \text{let } \textit{thresh} = \textit{threshold}, \textit{pr} = \textit{price}, \textit{disc} = \textit{discount} \text{ in} \\
 & ((k \geq \textit{thresh} \ \wedge\ r = k \times \textit{pr} \times (1.0 - \textit{disc}))\ \vee\ (k < \textit{thresh} \wedge r = k \times \textit{pr}))\ \wedge \\
 & (\textit{cash} = \overleftarrow{\textit{cash}} + r) \wedge (\textit{stock} = \overleftarrow{\textit{stock}} - k) \wedge (\textit{kites-today} = \overleftarrow{\textit{kites-today}} + k)
\end{array}$$

■

Review Question 7.4

An operation is required which merges two sequences of natural numbers. Each of the two sequences is ordered and may only contain a number once, and the resulting sequence is also ordered and has any duplicate elements removed. So, for example, if 5 occurs in both sequences it will not appear in the final sequence twice. Write a VDM model including any data type invariant and the operation to carry out the merging.

■

7.5 Summary of concepts

- Operations on the model of store – the state – are expressed in terms of external variables (often composite objects) whose access modes are specified as wr or rd (write/read or read only).
- Variable names for components of the state may be collected with any state invariant or initial value specification using a state...end construct.
- When specifying a complex system it is usual to attempt to define the data model first and then attempt to define the operations. However, the process is inherently iterative and:
  - in (re-)defining operations deficiencies in the data model may be exposed;
  - in (re-)defining data model deficiencies in the operations may be exposed.
- An operation must preserve any relevant data type invariant. When we are unable to prove that an operation preserves a data type invariant, we conjoin the invariant to its post-condition.
- All operations must be shown to be implementable. For each valid input there must exist an output which satisfies the post-condition. This guarantees that there is no logical conflict among the pre-condition, post-condition, and type definitions. Being implementable does not guarantee that the operation can be coded in a particular programming language on a particular computer. It is intended as a logical check of consistency, not as an assurance that a computer implementation is possible.
- Failure to satisfy proof obligations may be the result of an interaction between failure to preserve an invariant and unimplementability. If an implementable operation cannot be shown to preserve an invariant then the invariant may be conjoined to the post-condition. If the resulting operation is not implementable then there is an inconsistency in the operation and it must be rethought.

8 MAP TYPES

Maps are generalizations of programming constructs for representing associations such as dictionaries, lookup tables, arrays and functions. In this chapter we will explore both the concept of map data types and introduce a constructor for specifying mappings between one data type and another.

8.1 Maps

In specifications we often want to say that two sets are ***associated***; that is, elements of the first set are associated with elements of the second. For example, a statement of requirements for a chemical monitoring system may contain the following sentence:

```
Each reactor is connected to a thermocouple which is
used to sense the temperature of the reactor.
```

This describes an association between the set of reactors and the set of thermocouples. VDM uses ***maps*** in order to specify this form of association. For the reactor example, the following map might be a valid value:

$$\{\text{MAIN-REACTOR} \mapsto \text{THERMO1}, \text{EAST-REACTOR} \mapsto \text{THERMO2}\}$$

The map concept

We start by assuming the existence of two sets, A and B. We shall define the notion of a map from A to B by making use of the cartesian product $A \times B$.

The ***cartesian product*** of two sets, A and B, is the set of all ordered pairs where the first element of the pair is a member of A and the second element is a member of B. Using standard mathematical notation to denote an ordered pair by (a, b) we have

$$A \times B = \{(a, b) \mid (a \in A) \wedge (b \in B)\}$$

Assuming $A = \{a1, a2, a3, a4, ...\}$ and $B = \{b1, b2, b3, ...\}$, then the following set would be a subset of $A \times B$:

$$\{(a1, b1), (a2, b2), (a3, b1), (a4, b3)\}$$

A map m from A to B is a *finite* subset of $A \times B$ with the property that no two distinct pairs in m have the same first element. We regard an ordered pair in a map as denoting an association between the elements of the pair. In VDM a special notation is used to designate an ordered pair in a map. Instead of writing (a, b), we write $a \mapsto b$. The subset of $A \times B$ would therefore be written as:

$$\{a1 \mapsto b1, a2 \mapsto b2, a3 \mapsto b1, a4 \mapsto b3\}$$

The pair $a \mapsto b$ is called a ***maplet*** in VDM. For example, the following is a map from $\mathbb{N}$ to $\mathbb{B}$ which contains three maplets:

$$\{3 \mapsto \text{true}, 0 \mapsto \text{false}, 4 \mapsto \text{true}\}$$

Exercise 8.1

Write the set of maplets which define a map from temperatures in Celsius to temperatures in Fahrenheit for Celsius temperatures from –10° to 30° in steps of 10°.

Solution 8.1

$$\{-10 \mapsto 14, 0 \mapsto 32, 10 \mapsto 50, 20 \mapsto 68, 30 \mapsto 86\}$$

■

It is important to emphasize that the values on the left of each maplet in a map must be unique, and so we think of a map as having a direction from A to B. The maplet notation uses an arrow $\mapsto$ to indicate the direction.

We shall refer to the first element of a maplet as the ***key***. Owing to the way that maps are defined each key can appear in only one maplet of a given map. Hence the mapping {"Programs" $\mapsto$ "C:", "Programs" $\mapsto$ "D:"} is not valid; {"C:" $\mapsto$ "Programs", "D:" $\mapsto$ "Programs"} is valid. The empty map $\{\mapsto\}$ is also valid.

Review Question 8.1

Determine which of the following are maps from $\mathbb{Z}$ to $\mathbb{N}$.

(i) $\{-3 \mapsto 0, 3 \mapsto 0\}$

(ii) $\{0 \mapsto 4, 1 \mapsto 1, 0 \mapsto 3\}$

(iii) $\{\ \}$

■

Review Question 8.2

Write the set of keys which appear in the following map from $\mathbb{N}$ to $\mathbb{N}$.

$$\{2 \mapsto 4, 3 \mapsto 0, 4 \mapsto 1\}$$

■

The map data type constructor

In VDM a map data type is constructed from a set A and a set B by the constructor $\xrightarrow{m}$ (map to). For example:

$$A \xrightarrow{m} B$$

is the type which includes the set of all maps from A to B.

A map data type is not a single map. Rather, it is the *set* of all possible values for the data type it defines. For example, the following are all elements of the map type $\mathbb{N} \xrightarrow{m} \mathbb{N}$:

$$\{\mapsto\} \qquad \{1 \mapsto 42\} \qquad \{1 \mapsto 0, 4 \mapsto 0\}$$

There are infinitely many other maps from $\mathbb{N}$ to $\mathbb{N}$.

Exercise 8.2

Define a data type to model the accounts in a bank in which each customer has a single account which is identified by a unique account number. You should assume that the types *Name*, *Acc-no* and *Account* have already been defined to model customer name, account numbers and account details (such as transactions and balance).

Solution 8.2

The system will need to define two map types to associate customer names with sets of account numbers (the *custs* field below) and account numbers with actual account details (the *accs* field).

Acc-system ::
  custs: *Name* $\xrightarrow{m}$ *Acc-no*
  accs: *Acc-no* $\xrightarrow{m}$ *Account*

■

It is often helpful to think of maps as tables. For example, assuming that *Name* is defined as a string and *Acc-no* as an 8-character string of digits, the following is a value of the *custs* map in the solution to Exercise 8.2:

{"Ms J. Bloggs" ↦ "71068927", "Dr H. Hughes" ↦ "82569010",
"Mr J. Dowe" ↦ "72068277", "Mr P. Revere" ↦ "21678809"}

This value can be displayed as in Table 8.1:

custs	Ms J. Bloggs	↦	71068927
	Dr H. Hughes	↦	82569010
	Mr J. Dowe	↦	72068277
	Mr P. Revere	↦	21678809

Table 8.1

Note that the representation used in Table 8.1 is not part of VDM and not indicative of any implementation; it is simply a useful diagram.

Map comprehension

A succinct way to define a map is to use map comprehension (similar to set comprehension). The most usual form is shown below:

$\{x \mapsto y \mid$ *bind list including x and y* $\bullet$ *predicate involving x and y*$\}$

The first part of this expression introduces local variable names (x and y in this case) for use in the predicate in the second part; if the predicate is simply true, it is usually omitted. The value defined by the map comprehension contains all maplets containing all x and y pairs for which the predicate evaluates to true. For example:

$\{p \mapsto q \mid p \in \{0, 1\}, q\text{: } String \bullet (p = 1 \wedge q = \text{“YES”}) \vee (p = 0 \wedge q = \text{“NO”})\}$

evaluates to:

$\{0 \mapsto \text{“NO”}, 1 \mapsto \text{“YES”}\}$

(See the definition of the map overwrite operator for a more complex example.)

8.2 Map functions and operators

In this section we define the most useful functions and operators for map types.

Domain and range functions: **dom** *and* **rng**

Several map operators come from the notion of a map as a function and others come from the notion of a map as a table. It is not really necessary to make any distinction in the origin of the operator definitions but it can help you to develop an intuition concerning the use of maps. First, here are some operators and notation that are related to the idea of a map as a function.

Suppose m is a map from type A to type B. Then the ***domain*** of m is the set of elements of A which occur as the first elements of maplets in m—in other words, the set of keys of m. We define the function dom by:

$\text{dom}: (A \xrightarrow{m} B) \to A\text{-set}$
$\text{dom}(m) \triangleq \{a \mid a : A, b : B \bullet a \mapsto b \in m\}$

Similarly the ***range*** of m is the set of distinct second elements of maplets in m. The function rng is defined by:

$\text{rng}: (A \xrightarrow{m} B) \to B\text{-set}$
$\text{rng}(m) \triangleq \{b \mid b : B, a : A \bullet a \mapsto b \in m\}$

For an element $a \in \text{dom}(m)$, we use the function notation $m(a)$ to denote the second element of the maplet in m which contains a. We say that m is ***applied*** to a with ***result*** $m(a)$. If $a \in A$, but $a \notin \text{dom}(A)$ then $m(a)$ is undefined.

The domain and range of the empty map are just empty sets.

Note that, in common with other built-in functions in VDM, dom and rng are often used as prefix operators without parentheses (e.g. dom *m1*, rng *m2*).

Exercise 8.3

In most British and American computer systems character values are represented in a coding system known as the ASCII code set. The ASCII representation of 'A' is the bit pattern 1000001, which can be interpreted as the binary representation of decimal 65; 'B' is 1000010 (66); 'C' is 1000011 (67); and so on. Thus, the following map models the association between capital vowel letters and integers:

$\{\text{'A'} \mapsto 65, \text{'E'} \mapsto 69, \text{'I'} \mapsto 73, \text{'O'} \mapsto 79, \text{'U'} \mapsto 85\}$

Assuming the variable *vowels* has as its value the map on the previous line, list the following:

(i) dom *vowels* (ii) rng *vowels* (iii) *vowels*('O')

Solution 8.3

(i) {'A', 'E', 'I', 'O', 'U'} (ii) { 65, 69, 73, 79, 85} (iii) 79

■

The domain of a map *m* is just the set of keys in the map. It is important to understand that the domain of a map from *A* to *B* is a subset of *A* and not necessarily all of *A*. In the last exercise, the map *vowels* would have been a value of the map type char $\xrightarrow{m}$ $\mathbb{N}$, but dom *vowels* is {'A', 'E', 'I', 'O', 'U'}, not the whole of char.

Review Question 8.3

Suppose $m \in \mathbb{N} \xrightarrow{m} \mathbb{N}$.

(i) Find dom *m*, rng *m*, and *m*(12) for $m = \{1 \mapsto 0, 12 \mapsto 0, 13 \mapsto 0\}$.

(ii) Find the domain and range of $m = \{\mapsto\}$

■

Map overwrite operator: †

One of the most useful map operators is the ***map overwrite*** operator (which is also called the map *override* operator). If we think of a map as a table, then the idea behind the overwrite operator can be expressed by thinking of 'overwriting' one table *m*, with a second table *n* of the same type. The result of the overwrite is a new table containing all the maplets in *n* but only those maplets in *m* whose keys are not in *n*. The result of overwriting *m* with *n* is written as:

$m \dagger n$

The following are examples of the use of the overwrite operator:

$\{2 \mapsto 4, 1 \mapsto 3\} \dagger \{3 \mapsto 5, 1 \mapsto 2\}$ evaluates to $\{1 \mapsto 2, 2 \mapsto 4, 3 \mapsto 5\}$

$$\{3 \mapsto 5, 1 \mapsto 2\} \dagger \{2 \mapsto 4, 1 \mapsto 3\} \text{ evaluates to } \{1 \mapsto 3, 2 \mapsto 4, 3 \mapsto 5\}$$

The overwrite operator is formally defined as shown below. The definition is given in a style which is similar to the explicit style of function definition; for an operator the position of its operands are shown using underscores:

$$\_ \dagger \_ : ((A \xrightarrow{m} B) \times (A \xrightarrow{m} B)) \to (A \xrightarrow{m} B)$$
$$m \dagger n \triangleq$$
$$\{a \mapsto b \mid a : A, b : B \cdot ((a \in \text{dom } n) \wedge (b = n(a))) \vee ((a \in (\text{dom } m - \text{dom } n)) \wedge (b = m(a)))\}$$

Exercise 8.4

Consider a model of a handicap sheet for a sport in which players are assigned handicaps according to some scheme. For simplicity we suppose, as in golf, that the handicaps are integers; we leave the definition of a player for this exercise.

$$Hsheet = Player \xrightarrow{m} \mathbb{N}$$

If hs is a value of type $Hsheet$, then state in words what dom hs and rng hs are. If $p \in Player$, then state what $hs(p)$ is.

Solution 8.4

dom hs is the set of players who are listed on the handicap sheet and rng hs is the set of handicaps that are assigned to players on the sheet. If $p \in$ dom hs, then $hs(p)$ is the handicap assigned to player p. Otherwise $hs(p)$ is undefined.

■

Exercise 8.5

(i) Does the model in Exercise 8.4 permit a player to have more than one handicap at a time?

(ii) May several players have the same handicap?

(iii) Suppose a list of corrections, cs, of type $Hsheet$, is published. The corrections include some new players and their handicaps, and some corrected handicaps for existing players. Use the overwrite operator to model a new sheet containing the updated information based on hs.

Solution 8.5

(i) No, a player appears as a key in at most one maplet by the definition of maps.

(ii) Yes, because there is no restriction on the number of times an integer may appear as the second entry in a maplet.

(iii) $hs \dagger cs$ is the corrected map from players to their handicaps. The overwriting map is always the second argument.

■

Domain restriction and deletion operators: $\lhd$, $⩤$

There are two other useful map operators that can be used in map-valued expressions. They are ***domain restriction*** ($\lhd$) and ***domain deletion*** ($⩤$). Intuitively, domain restriction can be regarded as selecting some of the entries (maplets) in a table according to a set of keys which restrict our attention. Domain deletion can be thought of as returning a copy of a table with some of the entries removed—those which have keys matching a given set.

Both the domain restriction and domain deletion operators are infix. Given sets A and B, the left argument of each is of type A-set and the right argument is of type $A \xrightarrow{m} B$. The result of these operators is a value of $A \xrightarrow{m} B$.

If s is a subset of A and m is a map from A to B, then domain restriction is written:

$$s \lhd m$$

and is defined to be the set of maplets in m which have keys that are in s. For example:

$\{2, 3, 4\} \lhd \{1 \mapsto 3, 4 \mapsto 7, 3 \mapsto 3\}$ evaluates to $\{4 \mapsto 7, 3 \mapsto 3\}$
$\{\ \} \lhd m$ evaluates to $\{\ \}$

Domain restriction can be formally defined thus:

$$\_ \lhd \_ : (A\text{-set} \times (A \xrightarrow{m} B)) \to (A \xrightarrow{m} B)$$
$$s \lhd m \triangleq \{a \mapsto m(a) \mid a{:}\ A \bullet a \in ((\mathsf{dom}\ m) \cap s)\}$$

Domain deletion is written:

$$s ⩤ m$$

and is defined to be the set of maplets in m which have keys that are not in s. For example:

$\{2, 3, 4\} ⩤ \{1 \mapsto 3, 4 \mapsto 7, 3 \mapsto 3\}$ evaluates to $\{1 \mapsto 3\}$
$\{\ \} ⩤ m$ evaluates to m

Domain deletion can be formally defined thus:

$$\_ ⩤ \_ : (A\text{-set} \times (A \xrightarrow{m} B)) \to (A \xrightarrow{m} B)$$
$$s ⩤ m \triangleq \{a \mapsto m(a) \mid a{:}\ A \bullet a \in ((\mathsf{dom}\ m) - s)\}$$

Review Question 8.4

Suppose in the preceding exercise that a certain set *sp* of players is determined to be 'special' for some reason.

(i) Give an expression for the handicap sheet that would be used in an event where only special players who already have a handicap listed on the sheet *hs* are invited to participate.

(ii) Give an expression for the handicap sheet that would be used in an event where players are invited if they already have a handicap listed in *hs* and they are not special.

■

Exercise 8.6

(i) Express dom $(s \lhd m)$ in terms of s and dom m.

(ii) Express dom $(s ⩤ m)$ in terms of s and dom m.

Solution 8.6

(i) (dom m) $\cap s$. The domain of m is restricted to s.

(ii) (dom m) $- s$. s is deleted from the domain of m.

■

8.3 Specifications using maps

We now present a specification which uses maps, composite objects, and data type invariants to model an application.

A team management system

A system will be specified to record information about a league of football teams. The specification involves sets, maps, and composite objects. It provides practice in using several different types together and in reasoning about specifications.

To begin, we need some requirements. We shall imagine that the customer for the system has presented these in some informal description. As specification proceeds we may have to consult with the customer to clarify what is needed. Here are the initial requirements.

```
The league consists of a collection of teams. Each team
must register with the league; on doing so the team is
assigned a unique identifier by the league office. A
team must be registered before it can officially invite
players to join as members. For each team, the team
members are to be recorded. Members of a team must be
players who are registered with the league.

Each player must also register with the league and may
not join a team without being registered. A player who
registers with the league is assigned a unique
identifier. If a player becomes a member of a team the
league records the player's team affiliation.

The league would like the system to support the
following operations.

  Register a new team in the league.

  Deregister a team from the league.

  Register a new player.

  Deregister a player.

  Add a registered player to a registered team.
```

```
Remove a player from a team.

Initialize the league.
```

The first step in producing a VDM specification is to model the state of the system. Then the operations can be specified. We begin by naming the data type.

The entire system will be modelled by a data type called *League*. A league has two kinds of objects, *teams* and *players*. This suggests that a league is a composite object type consisting of teams and players. As is common practice, we will avoid considering detail too early by postponing the definition of the types of these components, but rather than denote this with a comment we now introduce a new symbol sequence: is not yet defined. So we begin by writing:

League ::
  teams: is not yet defined
  players: is not yet defined

We now proceed to consider how to specify the types which are not yet defined. The types of *teams* and *players* will almost certainly involve the team identifiers and player identifiers mentioned in the statement of requirements. It would appear sensible to develop a specification of a team type using types for the unique identifiers.

Exercise 8.7

Suppose *Team-id* and *Player-id* are types whose details are deliberately postponed. Record this fact and define a composite type called *Teamtype* which has two fields, one containing a team identifier, and the other a collection of players.

Solution 8.7

Team-id = is not yet defined
Player-id = is not yet defined
Teamtype ::
  tm-id: *Team-id*
  tm-plrs: *Player-id*-set

■

A composite object model of a single team is satisfactory but if we consider the more likely situation of a system with many teams, there is a relationship between teams and their identifiers that we have failed to capture: each team must have a unique identifier. Therefore, the specification must ensure that different teams are assigned different identifiers. The same is true of players and their identifiers.

To capture the uniqueness property using a composite object model would require a data type invariant. However, map types have an inherent property of uniqueness which we can exploit—the keys of a map must be unique. By using map types we can avoid an explicit invariant. We therefore abandon our *Teamtype* specification and complete our attempt to specify a league by representing teams and players in the system using maps:

League ::
  teams: *Team-id* $\xrightarrow{m}$ *Player-id*-set
  players: *Player-id* $\xrightarrow{m}$ *Team-id*

These have the extra benefit of clearly exposing the relationships between teams and players via their ranges and domains. For example, *teams* is specified to be a map type whose domain contains values of *Team-id* (still not yet defined) and whose range contains values which are sets (of *Player-id* values) that represent the membership of a team. [1]

Table 8.2 shows possible values of a variable of type *League*. The maps are shown as tables. For the purposes of the figure, team identifiers are shown as 3-digit numbers and player identifiers as 4-digit numbers.

teams	210	$\mapsto$	{3040, 2213}
	123	$\mapsto$	{6220}
players	2213	$\mapsto$	210
	3040	$\mapsto$	210
	6220	$\mapsto$	123

Table 8.2

Review Question 8.5

Using Table 8.2:

(i) list the identifiers of the registered teams;

(ii) list the identifiers of the players on team 123;

(iii) list the identifiers of the registered players.

■

There is one serious problem with the model so far. There is no provision for representing a newly registered player who is not yet affiliated with a team. To record a player in a variable of type *League*, a value of the field *players* must be given. What is required is a value in *Team-id* to indicate lack of affiliation. We introduce another VDM feature to achieve this.

The constant nil

If *X* is any VDM type, then the notation [*X*] denotes the type whose values are the elements of *X* together with one additional element called nil. The identifier nil is a constant in VDM which can only be used as part of a type declared in square brackets. That is, nil is never an element of a type *X*, but always an element of a type [*X*]. The intuition behind the use of nil is that it can be used in situations where a value is optional.

---

[1] In fact, to expose ideas later we have over-specified the model by allowing information to be held in more than one place, as can be seen from the tables. Normally such redundancy should be avoided.

The element nil will be incorporated into the specification of *League* as part of the type of the field *players*. In this context we interpret a value of nil as an indicator that a player is not affiliated with any team. The modified specification is:

League ::
  teams: *Team-id* $\xrightarrow{m}$ *Player-id*-set
  players: *Player-id* $\xrightarrow{m}$ [*Team-id*]

The only change is brackets around *Team-id* in the definition of the type of *players*.

Review Question 8.6

(i) Why were brackets not put around *Team-id* in the line defining *players* in the specification of *League* above?

(ii) Is a nil value needed to indicate that a registered team has no players?

■

Table 8.3 is a modification of Table 8.2 in which a team with no players, and an unaffiliated player, have been included: team 100 is the newly registered team because it is mapped to the empty set representing no players; player 4200 is the newly registered player, which can be seen from the nil value for his team.

teams	210	↦	{3040, 2213}
	123	↦	{6220}
	100	↦	{ }
players	2213	↦	210
	3040	↦	210
	6220	↦	123
	4200	↦	nil

Table 8.3

The specification of *League* is not yet sufficiently restrictive. There is nothing that reflects the relationship between the value of *teams* and that of *players*.

Exercise 8.8

Describe in words a data type invariant that could be defined for *League* which captures the relationship between *players* and *teams*.

Solution 8.8

A player is recorded as affiliated with a team if and only if the team is recorded as having the player as a member.

■

An example of this relationship can be seen in Table 8.3, where player 2213 is in team 210. The player identifier 2213 is mapped to 210 and the team identifier 210 is mapped to a set containing 2213.

Before we write the data type invariant we will recall the notation (from Chapter 6) for referring to the different parts of a variable of type *League*. Suppose we have a variable *le*, of type *League*, and that the component values of *le* are as depicted in Table 8.3. Then the team identifier (or possibly nil value) associated with player 2213 is denoted by *le.players*(2213). That is because *le.players* is the *players* field of *le* which is defined as a map. The player identifier 2213 is in the domain of the map, and *le.players*(2213) is the value which results from applying the map to 2213.

Exercise 8.9

This exercise refers to the value of *le* depicted in Table 8.3.

(i) Find the value of *le.players*(4200).

(ii) How do we refer to the collection of players in the team identified by 123?

(iii) What is the value of rng *le.players*?

(iv) What is the set of identifiers of registered teams?

(v) What is the value of *le.teams*?

Solution 8.9

(i) nil (ii) *le.teams* (123) (iii) {210, 123, nil} (iv) {210, 123, 100}
(v) $\{210 \mapsto \{3040, 2213\}, 123 \mapsto \{6220\}, 100 \mapsto \{\}\}$

■

Review Question 8.7
How do we refer to the set of players in team 210?

■

Now we will define *inv-League*:

$$\begin{array}{l} inv\text{-}League(le) \triangleq \\ \quad \forall tid \in \mathsf{dom}\ le.teams \ \bullet \\ \quad\quad \forall pid \in \mathsf{dom}\ le.players \bullet (pid \in le.teams(tid)) \Leftrightarrow (tid = le.players(pid)) \end{array}$$

In other words, satisfying the invariant means that a player identifier is mapped to a team identifier if and only if the team identifier is mapped to a set containing the player identifier.

The invariant can be verified as being true for the particular values in Table 8.3 just by observation. For instance, team 210 contains players 2213 and 3040 and they are the only players who are recorded as being affiliated with team 210. Similarly, the other teams and players also stand in the relationship required by the invariant.

Defining and checking operations

We have just completed the most difficult part of this specification. In this example, the operations are much easier to specify than the state. The state of the system is an external variable of type *League*.

An operation to register a new player can be defined as follows:

$REG\text{-}PL()\ r\text{: } Player\text{-}id$

-- *returns a new id and registers a new player as unaffiliated*

ext wr $le\text{: } League$

pre true

post $(r \notin \text{dom } \overleftarrow{le}.players) \wedge (le. = \mu(\overleftarrow{le}, players \mapsto \overleftarrow{le}.players \dagger \{r \mapsto \text{nil}\}))$

The post-condition indicates that the identifier is new and that the new unaffiliated player identifier is added to the *players* map as unaffiliated (i.e. mapped to nil).

We must now check that *REG-PL* is implementable (as described in 7.3). Recall that for an operation to be implementable for every valid input there must be an output which satisfies the post-condition. In this example we will usually give informal statements and informal proofs. If we become confused by possible ambiguity, then we can resolve it by increasing the level of formality. Since this is the first proof obligation to be stated for *League*, we will give a formal statement by way of illustration. Then an informal statement and proof will be given.

The general rule for implementability was formalized in Chapter 7 (page 85) thus:

$$\forall \overleftarrow{s} : T \bullet pre\text{-}OP(parameter1, parameter2, ..., \overleftarrow{s}) \Rightarrow$$
$$\exists\, s : T, res : Result\text{-}type \bullet post\text{-}OP(parameter1, parameter2, ..., \overleftarrow{s}, s, res)$$

Making appropriate substitutions (there are no parameters to *REG-PL* and its pre-condition is true), the statement that *REG-PL* is implementable is:

$$\forall \overleftarrow{le} : League \bullet pre\text{-}REG\text{-}PL\,(\overleftarrow{le}) \Rightarrow$$
$$\exists\, le : League, r : Player\text{-}id \bullet post\text{-}REG\text{-}PL\,(\overleftarrow{le}, le, r)$$

Replacing the pre- and post-conditions by the definitions above, and making explicit the requirement that the *teams* component of *le* be unchanged, gives:

$$\forall \overleftarrow{le} : League \bullet \text{true} \Rightarrow$$
$$\exists\, le : League,\ r : Player\text{-}id \bullet$$
$$(r \notin \text{dom } \overleftarrow{le}.players) \wedge (le.players = \overleftarrow{le}.players \dagger \{r \mapsto \text{nil}\}) \wedge$$
$$(le.teams = \overleftarrow{le}.teams)$$

Exercise 8.10

State the implementability proof obligation in words.

Solution 8.10

For every input value of type *League*, there is a new player identifier and there is an output value of type *League* which is the same as the input value except that the *players* map has a new association between the new player identifiers and the value nil. That is, it is always possible to obtain a new identifier and to add the new association to the *players* map leaving everything else unchanged. ■

An informal proof of implementability might start out as follows:

One can always add a new maplet to a map; since the new maplet has a new key the rest of the map is unchanged.

The proof would be complete if one could always obtain a new player identifier. However, this is only possible if the type *Player-id* has a sufficient number of elements. For example, if *Player-id* is defined as the set of numbers between 1 and 100, then it might be possible to run out of new player identifiers if there were many registered players. This may be an obvious point in retrospect, but it showed up in this specification only during a proof obligation. Uncovering deficiencies such as this is one reason why we insist on carrying out proofs, however informally.

In order to remove the difficulty we should consult with the customer to find out whether there are any estimates of the number of possible registered players. Then we can record a comment with *Player-id* that the number of possible player identifiers must be at least the customer's estimate and can add an invariant to show that the system is defined only up to the estimated maximum number of players. When *Player-id* is defined (later during design or implementation) the comment can help to ensure that there will always be new player identifiers available to register new players. We shall assume from here on that *Player-id* and also *Team-id* are large enough to supply new identifiers whenever required.

Now we must prove that *inv-League* is preserved by *REG-PLR*. The proof obligation will be stated formally and then informally. A formal statement is:

$$\begin{array}{l} \mathit{inv\text{-}League}(\overleftarrow{le}) \wedge \\ \mathit{pre\text{-}REG\text{-}PLR}(\overleftarrow{le}) \wedge \\ \mathit{post\text{-}REG\text{-}PLR}(\overleftarrow{le}, le, r) \;\Rightarrow\; \mathit{inv\text{-}League}(le) \end{array}$$

We restate the proof obligation informally as follows:

If the *players* and *teams* maps satisfy the invariant in the input state, and if the pre- and post-conditions of the operation hold, then the maps will satisfy the invariant in the output state.

Exercise 8.11

Give an informal proof that *REG-PL* preserves the invariant.

Solution 8.11

Since nothing changes except for the addition of a new player identifier to the *players* map, the only possible inconsistency would occur if the new player was recorded as affiliated with a team. In that case, the set of team members would have to be updated. But the post-condition ensures that the player is recorded as unaffiliated. Therefore, the invariant is preserved.

■

An operation *REG-TM* can now be defined to register a new team.

Exercise 8.12

Specify *REG-TM* so that the new team is given a new identifier and the set of team members is empty.

Solution 8.12

> *REG-TM*( ) *r*: *Team-id*
> -- *returns a new team id and registers the new team as having no players*
> ext wr *le*: *League*
> post $(r \notin \text{dom } \overleftarrow{le}.teams) \wedge (le = \mu(\overleftarrow{le}, teams \mapsto \overleftarrow{le}.teams \dagger \{ r \mapsto \{ \} \})$

■

Exercise 8.13

Give informal statements and proofs that *REG-TM* is implementable and that it preserves the invariant.

Solution 8.13

A statement that *REG-TM* is implementable is as follows:

> For every input value of type *League* there is a new team identifier and an output value of type *League* such that the output value is the same as the input except for the inclusion of a new maplet in teams.

An informal proof is given below:

> We have previously agreed that *Team-id* is a large enough set to provide new team identifiers whenever they are needed. Adding a maplet with a new key to a map leaves the other maplets unchanged.

Preservation of the invariant can be stated thus:

> Consistency of the maps in the input state together with the pre- and post-conditions guarantees consistency of the maps in the output state.

An informal proof is given below:

> The only inconsistency that can arise from adding a new team occurs if the team has a non-empty set of players. In that case the *players* map would have to be changed. However, the post-condition ensures that the new team has no players.

■

We can define *ADD-PL* to add an unaffiliated player to a team.

> *ADD-PL*(*pid*: *Player-id*, *tid*: *Team-id*) -- *adds an unaffiliated player to a team*
> ext wr *le*: *League*
> pre $(pid \in \text{dom } le.players) \wedge (le.players(pid) = \text{nil}) \wedge (tid \in \text{dom } le.teams)$
> post $(le.teams = \overleftarrow{le}.teams \dagger \{tid \mapsto (\overleftarrow{le}.teams(tid) \cup \{pid\})\}) \wedge$
> $(le.players = \overleftarrow{le}.players \dagger \{pid \mapsto tid\})$

The pre-condition says that the player and the team are registered and that the player is unaffiliated. The post-condition says that the player is made a member of the team and is recorded as affiliated with the team.

We leave it as a mental exercise to prove that *ADD-PL* is implementable and preserves the invariant. However, we point out that the pre-condition plays an important role in the proof of implementability. It ensures that the expression $\overleftarrow{teams}(tid)$ is defined.

Review Question 8.8

Specify an operation *REM-PL* which removes a player from a team and records the player as unaffiliated. The pre-condition must guarantee that the player is on the team and that both are registered. The post-condition should specify the updating of the set of team members and the player's affiliation.

■

The domain deletion operator can be used in the specification of *DEREG-PLR* which deregisters an unaffiliated player.

DEREG-PLR(*pid*: *Player-id*) -- *deregisters an unaffiliated player*
ext wr *le*: *League*
pre $(pid \in \text{dom } le.players) \wedge (le.players(pid) = \text{nil})$
post $le = \mu(\overleftarrow{le}, players \mapsto \{pid\} \ntriangleleft \overleftarrow{le}.players)$

The domain deletion operator is used to indicate that the *players* map is changed only by removing the maplet with key equal to *pid*.

The other operations on *League* can be specified in a similar way to the operations specified above. No new ideas are involved so we will not go through the specifications. However, there is one more task for you to do that illustrates how specifications must be altered when the reality they model changes.

Exercise 8.14

The league authority has instituted a new regulation. No team may have more than 20 players. Modify *inv-League* and change any of the operations specified above so that the new regulation is enforced. For any operations that are changed, give informal proofs of implementability and invariant preservation. For those that are unchanged, give a brief argument to show that the modified invariant is preserved. Your arguments may refer to the proofs given before.

Solution 8.14

We will conjoin a statement of the new regulation to *inv-League*. It uses the function card to say that the set of players in a team has at most 20 members.

$$
\begin{aligned}
&inv\text{-}League(le) \triangleq \\
&\quad (\forall tid \in \text{dom } le.teams\ , \\
&\qquad \forall\ pid \in \text{dom } le.players \cdot (pid \in le.teams\ (tid)) \Leftrightarrow (tid = le.players\ (pid))) \wedge \\
&\quad (\forall tid \in \text{dom } le.teams \cdot (\text{card}(le.teams\ (tid)) \leq 20))
\end{aligned}
$$

■

The only operation that requires modification is *ADD-PL*. None of the others increases the size of a team. The only modification to *ADD-PL* is a conjunct in its pre-condition to ensure that the team is not full.

ADD-PL(*pid*: *Player-id*, *tid*: *Team-id*)
  -- *adds an unaffiliated player to a team that is not full*
ext wr *le*: *League*
pre $(pid \in \text{dom } le.players) \wedge (le.players(pid) = \text{nil}) \wedge$
  $(tid \in \text{dom } le.teams) \wedge (\text{card}(le.teams(tid)) < 20)$
post $(le.teams = \overleftarrow{le}.teams \dagger \{tid \mapsto (\overleftarrow{le}.teams(tid) \cup \{pid\})\}) \wedge$
  $(le.players = \overleftarrow{le}.players \dagger \{pid \mapsto tid\})$

We will now give a proof of implementability that relies on a general logical principle: making a pre-condition more restrictive reduces the set of valid inputs.

Implementability says that for every valid input there is an output satisfying the post-condition. If an operation is implementable for a large set of valid inputs, it remains implementable when that set is reduced. Since *ADD-PL* was changed only by making the pre-condition more restrictive, and since we proved it implementable before the change, *ADD-PL* remains implementable after the change.

To prove the invariant is preserved we will refer to the proof given for *ADD-PL* before modification. The only change to the invariant is the addition of another condition, that there are at most 20 players in any team. If this is true in the input state to *ADD-PL*, then it remains true for every team except possibly team *tid*. The reason is that the other teams are unchanged. However, *tid* is changed only by the addition of one more player. The pre-condition says that *tid* had fewer than 20 players as input to *ADD-PL*, and therefore *tid* has at most 20 players after the addition of the new player. Therefore, the invariant is preserved.

Each of the other operations preserves the modified invariant because none of them adds a player to a team. Therefore, if the team had at most 20 players as input to the operation, it has at most 20 players as output.

8.4 Summary of concepts

- A map expresses a many-to-one relationship from the elements in its domain, called keys, to the elements in its range. That is, each key is mapped to only one element in the range (even though many elements of the range may have different keys). This situation arises often in data processing applications and so map data types are used frequently in the specification of such systems.
- In VDM-SL map is represented by a set of pairs of values called maplets (e.g. {2 ↦ "erase"}) which can be thought of as a table.
- The data type $X \xrightarrow{m} Y$ consists of all the maps from the type X to the type Y.
- The most useful functions and operators on maps are:
  - dom a is the set whose elements are the elements of the domain of a (i.e. the

keys of a);
- rng a is the set whose elements are the elements of the range of a;
- $a \dagger b$ is the map equivalent to a with the maplets of b added or with the maplets of b replacing those of the same key in a;
- $s \lhd a$ is the map which only contains maplets from a whose keys equal the elements of s;
- $s \ntriangleleft a$ is the map which only contains maplets from a whose keys are not equal to the elements of s.

- The constant nil may be used to denote 'no value' of a type where a value is optional (e.g. $[X]$).
- A specification consisting of data types and operations on the types requires proofs that each operation is implementable and that each preserves data type invariants.

9 REIFYING ABSTRACT DATA TYPES

Chapters 9 and 10 show how using VDM enables the software designer to produce an accurate specification of a software system. The specification of a system in the specification language VDM defines what the software functions are in terms of abstract data types, operations and functions.

In specifying abstract data types, operations, and functions, we can use the full apparatus of set theory and predicate logic. However, if this approach is to be of full use, then we will need to be able to demonstrate that a given implementation is a valid reflection of a specification.

What we will describe in the next two chapters is a technique which enables the developer to replace abstract data types and operations on abstract data types by more concrete data types and operations on such concrete data types. This is generally called ***refinement***.

9.1 Reification and decomposition

Ultimately, the concrete data types will be the actual data structures of a particular programming language; by the end of a software development abstract data types, such as those defined using maps and sequences, will have been transformed into concrete data structures such as arrays, records and linked lists. However, during development it may be judicious to refine an abstract specification to a more concrete one, still expressed in VDM-SL. This process of replacing abstract data types with more concrete data types is known in VDM as ***data type reification*** or just ***data reification***. Since abstractly specified data types must eventually be implemented as the concrete data types of a programming language, reification is an important part of the VDM.

We have already seen how specifying operation gives rise to proof obligations: predicates that the developer has to demonstrate to be true in order to verify the development process. Similarly, data reification gives rise to proof obligations. In this chapter we discuss the process of data reification and place some emphasis on the proof obligations that reification requires of the software developer. The proof obligations come in the form of rules that the concrete data types and operations on them must satisfy in relation to the original abstract data types and operations: the proof obligations demand that a reification of a type is an adequate representation for it.

Later we will discuss the process of refining operations on concrete data types into algorithms expressed in a programming language. This process is known as ***operation decomposition***. Through the process of operation decomposition, concretely defined operations are transformed into lines of code of the target programming language. We discuss operation decomposition in full in Chapters 11 and 12.

We deal with three proof obligations for reification here:

- proving ***adequacy***: that a concrete type is an adequate representation of an abstract type;
- proving the ***domain rule***: that the pre-condition of a concrete operation on a concrete type is not too restrictive, so that it is at least as widely applicable as the abstract operation;
- proving the ***result rule***: that the result of an operation, as expressed by its post-condition, is compatible with that expected by the abstract operation.

When a software developer specifies a software system using VDM, the initial step is to define the abstract data types together with the operations and functions on those data types. Of course a VDM specification is not itself a piece of software: it is not executable. A VDM specification is a relatively high-level description of what a piece of software should do. It does not necessarily prescribe how the software should execute on a machine, although it does specify the functionality of the software; it specifies what the software does, not how it is to do it. Thus, when developing software using VDM the next task after writing a specification is to convert it into executable software (code) written in a programming language, e.g. Pascal.

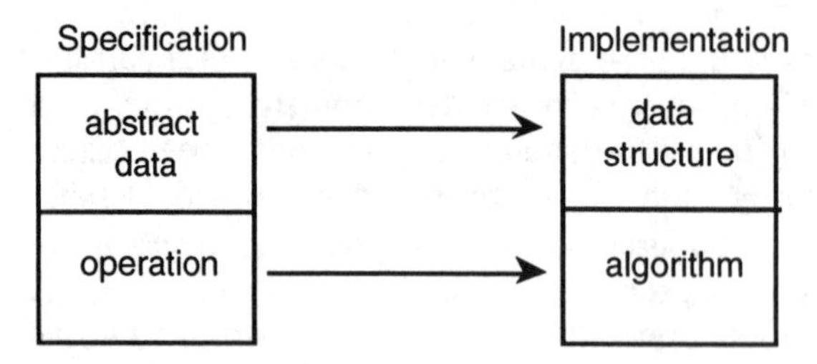

Figure 9.1

When moving from VDM to a program written in Pascal we are really developing another specification, one that can be compiled into a sequence of instructions which a real machine executes. Because different constructs are provided in VDM and Pascal, with different meanings, we need a method of showing that the code we develop satisfies the specification from which it was derived. In other words, we need a software development method: a technique which will enable us to prove that the software we write satisfies its specification.

Since program source code is really just one form of very detailed specification, we will consider the relationships which hold between specifications in general rather than just those which hold between a VDM specification and a source code in a programming language. We can picture the end-product of reification and decomposition as shown in Figure 9.1.

Thus the *development* part of VDM consists of two elements: the reification of data types and the decomposition of operations, both of which generate proof obligations.

Review Question 9.1

Why do data reification and operation decomposition generate proof obligations?

■

The basic abstract data types of the VDM specification language are sets, sequences and maps as described in Chapters 3, 4 and 8. In addition, VDM allows us to specify composite types, each element of which consists of a pre-determined number of components of fixed (but usually different) types. In most programming languages, such as Pascal, Ada or Modula-2, data is represented using scalars,[1] arrays, records and pointers; see Figure 9.2.

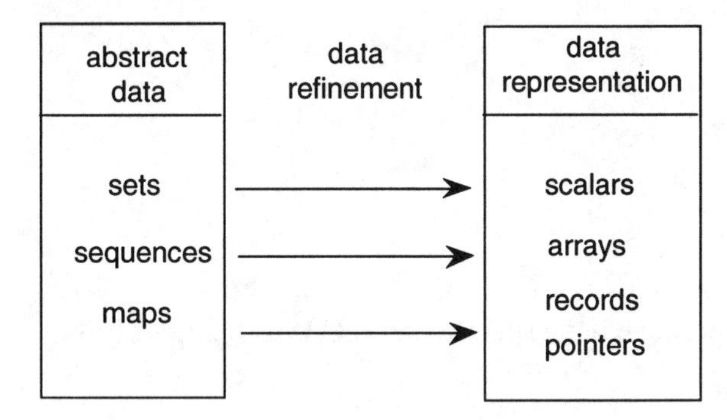

Figure 9.2

Usually, complex data structures are needed to implement VDM data types, but sometimes a VDM data type can be almost trivially implemented in a programming language, e.g. composite objects can be represented in Pascal by records. It is for the more complex reifications that we need a development method to guide us and help us in checking our work.

To illustrate the point, we will work 'backwards' from an implementation to the corresponding VDM. You will notice that different implementations are possible for the same abstract specification and that different specifications can lead to the same concrete data structure. A variety of data structures can usually be

[1] Scalar types are the simple programming language types such as integers, real numbers, characters and enumeration types.

constructed which are reifications of an abstract data type. The following discussion about which data structure to use illustrates this point. For example, a set of numeric identifiers in the range from 200 to 299 can be represented in Pascal by an array, thus:[1]

```
type
   presence = (absent, present);
   setasarray  = array [ 200..299 ] of presence;
var
   idset: setasarray;
```

The set is represented here by an array each of whose components contain a value, `present` or `absent`, which indicates whether the integer equal to the array index is present or absent in the set. Thus if `idset[159] = present`, `159` is a member of the set.

However, if the set were sparse (i.e. likely to contain far fewer than 100 possible members), it might be more appropriate to represent it as a linked list, thus:

```
type
   id = 200..299;
   listptr = ^listnode;
   listnode =  record
                  value : id;
                  next : listptr;
               end;
   setaslist = ^listnode;
var
   idset: setaslist;
```

Exercise 9.1

The set implemented above might have been specified in VDM as being of type

$$SetOfIds = \{200, ..., 299\}\text{-set}$$

How would you specify *SeqOfIds* as an ordered sequence of natural numbers in the range 200 to 299?

Solution 9.1

$$SeqOfIds = \{200, ..., 299\}^*$$

$$inv\text{-}SeqOfIds\ (s) \triangleq \forall i, j \in \text{inds}\ s \bullet (i < j \Rightarrow s(i) \leq s(j))$$

■

From the preceding fragments of Pascal and Exercise 9.1 you should see that both data structures `setasarray` and `setaslist` are potential implementations of the VDM data type *SeqOfIds*. Besides representing sets, the same Pascal data

---

[1] Many implementations of Pascal will not permit set types of more than a few hundred elements. Hence an array type is frequently used for implementing sets.

structures might also be chosen to represent VDM sequences. Therefore one abstract structure can have various different concrete representations, and a particular concrete representation may represent different abstract structures. Figure 9.3 shows the typical situation where both sets and sequences may be implemented as either arrays or linked lists.

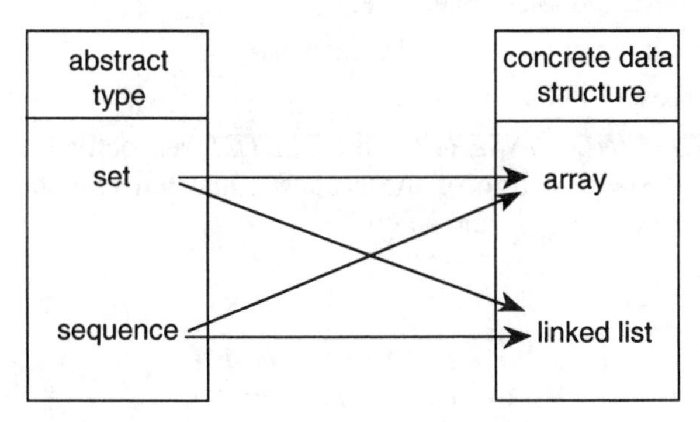

Figure 9.3

9.2 The implementation process

Implementing a specification is a process which involves many stages during each of which we transform an abstract type into another more concrete type. Eventually we terminate the process with the data structures of a programming language.

Let us illustrate this idea of data reification by considering a very simple database. Here are some of the requirements:

```
The database consists of a collection of natural
numbers, with no two the same. The system should
include an operation to initialize the database to be
empty, an operation to insert a number in the
database, one to delete it, and an operation to
discover if a particular number is already in the
database.
```

Exercise 9.2

Specify the database as a set of natural numbers. Call the data type *Nbase1*.

Solution 9.2

We specify the type of such a database as *Nbase1* thus:

$Nbase1 = \mathbb{N}\text{-set}$

A particular database variable will at all times contain some value of the type *Nbase1*.

■

Exercise 9.3

Specify the operations on a database to:

(i) Initialize that database to the empty set.

(ii) Find a natural number in the database; this is an operation which yields true if the number is in the database and false otherwise.

(iii) Insert a natural number which is not present in the database.

(iv) Delete a number which is present in the database.

Call the operations *INITIALIZE1*, *FIND1*, *INSERT1* and *DELETE1*, respectively. The suffix '*1*' refers to the first specification of these operations. Subsequent more concrete ones will have suffixes '*2*', '*3*' and so on.

Solution 9.3

INITIALIZE1
ext wr db: $Nbase1$
pre true
post $db = \{\ \}$

FIND1(n: $\mathbb{N}$) *found*: $\mathbb{B}$
ext rd db: $Nbase1$
pre true
post $found \Leftrightarrow (n \in db)$

INSERT1(n: $\mathbb{N}$)
ext wr db: $Nbase1$
pre $n \notin db$
post $db = \overleftarrow{db} \cup \{n\}$

DELETE1(n: $\mathbb{N}$)
ext wr db: $Nbase1$
pre $n \in db$
post $db = \overleftarrow{db} - \{n\}$

■

Note that throughout this part of the book we will adopt the following convention: successive reifications of a data type T will be called *T1*, *T2*, etc., and an operation *OP* on T will be respecified as *OP1*, *OP2*, and so on.

In the solution to Exercise 9.3, *INITIALIZE1* sets the database to be the empty set. Its pre-condition is true no matter what the value of the current state. The particular database operated on is given by the external variable *db*.

FIND1 returns a boolean value, which is true if its argument is present in the database and false otherwise.

INSERT1 adds its argument to the database if it is not already there. This prerequisite is made explicit by the pre-condition $n \notin db$. If it is already in the database, *INSERT1* is undefined.

DELETE1 removes its argument from the database if it is present. If it is not in the database, the result of *DELETE1* is undefined.

The specification of *Nbase1* gives us a very high-level specification of the database. However, the specifications of the operations are not executable: *FIND1* contains no clue about how to determine whether or not its argument is in the database. In other words, the specification of the database is relatively abstract, just as it should be. To implement a database we must be more concrete: we will therefore develop a specification of the database which is intermediate in 'concreteness' between our very high-level specification and the sort of code one might expect to find in a programming language like Pascal.

For example, *FIND1*, when implemented in a programming language, would probably execute a search algorithm. Therefore, in order to get closer to an executable program, we should respecify the database so that a search mechanism is made explicit. (The end-product of the reification process is eventually a specification in the form of code. The implementation of *FIND1* in a programming language will certainly be explicit.)

One possibility is to respecify the database as a sequence of natural numbers. This might be to allow for a more efficient search algorithm, which could make use of the order. We will call the new database *Nbase2*:

$$Nbase2 = \mathbb{N}^*$$

This definition specifies that every database of the type *Nbase2* (i.e. every element *s* of the set of all possible values of the type *Nbase2*), is a sequence of natural numbers. By using a data invariant at this point we could have guaranteed the requirement that no two values in the database be the same, but this would have unnecessarily restricted our design possibilities which we discuss after Exercise 9.5.

Review Question 9.2

Is the empty sequence [ ] a member of *Nbase2*?

■

Now we can respecify *FIND1* for *Nbase2*, calling it *FIND2*.

In fact, we shall specify *FIND2* in two different ways, called *FIND2A* and *FIND2B*. The first is similar in spirit to the specification of *FIND1*. The second makes more explicit the search mechanism that the final implementation of *FIND* might be expected to execute.

Here, first, is a relatively high-level specification:

FIND2A(n: $\mathbb{N}$) *found*: $\mathbb{B}$
ext rd *db*: *Nbase2*
pre true
post *found* $\Leftrightarrow$ ($n \in dbvalues(db)$)

The post-condition has been written in terms of an auxiliary function *dbvalues* which is intended to return the set of all numbers in the database. Because the database is a sequence, it would have been as easy to write the condition directly, but the use of the auxiliary function has some merit in not making every line of the specification dependent on the fact that the database is a sequence. If other information is subsequently stored in the database, such as access controls, this will require the definition of *dbvalues* to be changed, but nothing else.

Exercise 9.4

(i) Give an explicit definition of the auxiliary function *dbvalues*.

(ii) What is the value of *dbvalues*(*db*) for the following values of *db* ?
(a) [2,1,3] (b) [2, 2, 1, 3, 1, 2] (c) [ ]

Solution 9.4

(i) $dbvalues: Nbase2 \rightarrow \mathbb{N}\text{-set}$
$dbvalues(db) \triangleq \text{elems } db$

(ii) (a) $\{1, 2, 3\}$ (b) $\{1, 2, 3\}$ (c) $\{\,\}$

■

From a sequence of natural numbers the function *dbvalues* produces the set of all the different natural numbers in the sequence. Because its result is a set it throws away any information represented by order or repetition in the sequence.

Exercise 9.5

Specify *INITIALIZE2A*, *INSERT2A* and *DELETE2A*.

Solution 9.5

INITIALIZE2A
ext wr db: *Nbase2*
pre true
post $db = [\,]$

INSERT2A(n: $\mathbb{N}$)
ext wr db: *Nbase2*
pre $n \notin dbvalues(db)$
post $dbvalues(db) = dbvalues(\overleftarrow{db}) \cup \{n\}$

DELETE2A(n: $\mathbb{N}$)
ext wr db: *Nbase2*
pre $n \in dbvalues(db)$
post $dbvalues(db) = dbvalues(\overleftarrow{db}) - \{n\}$

■

This first approach to respecifying *FIND2* offers relatively little gain in concreteness. It has still left enormous latitude as to which sequences represent a set. For example, the set {3, 5, 7} could be represented by any of the sequences [3, 5, 7], [5, 3, 7] or [3, 3, 5, 3, 5, 7, 3]. All that is demanded is that all the different elements in the sequence form the elements of the database set. Similarly, the operation *INSERT2A* has not specified where in the database sequence the new element is to be inserted. It could even be inserted multiple times, and the database re-ordered. For example, *INSERT2A*(5) in the database [1, 2, 3] might result in the database [5, 1, 3, 2, 1, 3, 2, 5]. All that is required is that the values in the new database include all those in the old sequence as well as the new element. This latitude has both advantages and disadvantages. It leaves many choices open to the implementor, to be made in the light of considerations such as efficiency or ease of implementation, but equally it has not really made any use of the structure of sequences.

An important feature of a sequence is that it consists of a head followed by a tail, which is also a sequence. This similarity of structure of the tail to the whole is what allows iterative and recursive programs to be constructed. Performing an operation on a sequence often involves doing something to the head of the sequence and then performing the operation on the tail of the sequence. The post-condition of the operation applied to a sequence is related to the same post-condition of the operation applied to the tail of the sequence. We see that it may prove useful to be able to re-use a post-condition within the post-condition itself.

Review Question 9.3

There are many ways of representing sets as sequences. Define possible invariants on *Nbase2* which would:

(i) constrain the sequence to contain no duplicates;

(ii) constrain the sequence to contain no duplicates and be in ascending order;

(iii) constrain the sequence to contain duplicates and be in ascending order.

■

Quoting post-conditions

The post-condition of an operation is really a boolean expression which might in various circumstances evaluate to true or false. The implication of using an expression as a post-condition is that when it is evaluated after a correct application of the operation, it must evaluate to true. The boolean expression will include references to the arguments of the operation, the external variables, and the operation result. It could therefore be considered as a boolean function with these values as arguments. For example, the post-condition of *DELETE2A* could be considered as a function, thus:

$$post\text{-}DELETE2A: \mathbb{N} \times Nbase2 \times Nbase2 \rightarrow \mathbb{B}$$

$$post\text{-}DELETE2A(n, olddb, newdb) \triangleq$$
$$\quad dbvalues(newdb) = dbvalues(olddb) - \{n\}$$

In general, the post-condition of an operation is a boolean function of the following arguments:

- the arguments of the operation;
- the original values of any external variables;
- the final values of any writeable external variables, if they are not read-only;
- the result variable, if any.

Very often, post-conditions in different operations contain very similar parts, and it would be convenient if one could make use of the post-condition of one operation when defining another. Suppose an operation *ROLLRED* is defined which simulates the rolling of two red dice by setting the sequence *red-dice* to contain two numbers in the range 1, ..., 6. It might be defined as follows:

ROLLRED
ext wr $red\text{-}dice : \mathbb{N}_1^*$
pre len $red\text{-}dice = 2$
post $1 \leq red\text{-}dice\,(1) \wedge red\text{-}dice\,(1) \leq 6 \wedge$
$\quad 1 \leq red\text{-}dice\,(2) \wedge red\text{-}dice\,(2) \leq 6$

The post-condition can be thought of as a boolean function *post-ROLLRED(old-red-dice, new-red-dice)*. This captures the relationship between dice before and after being rolled, whatever variable they are stored in. Suppose later one is about to define an operation which rolls two black dice until one of them is a six. The action of rolling any dice is already captured by *post-ROLLRED*. We can make use of this by invoking it with arguments representing the black dice:

ROLLBLACKFOR6
ext wr *black-dice*: $\mathbb{N}_1^*$
pre len *red-dice* $= 2$
post *post-ROLLRED*($\overleftarrow{black\text{-}dice}$, *black-dice*) $\wedge$ $6 \in$ elems *black-dice*

The commonest form of quoting of post-conditions is when a post-condition quotes itself. This recursive quoting is useful when an operation has a natural recursive structure. For instance, adding up all the elements in a sequence between positions i and j is closely related to adding up the elements between positions $i + 1$ and j.

SUM(i: $\mathbb{N}$, j: $\mathbb{N}$) r: $\mathbb{N}$
ext rd $s : \mathbb{N}^*$
pre $(1 \le i \wedge i \le$ len $s) \wedge (1 \le j \wedge j \le$ len $s) \wedge (i \le j)$
post $i = j \wedge r = s(i) \vee$
$\exists\, t : \mathbb{N} \cdot$ *post-SUM*$(i+1, j, s, t) \wedge r = t + s(i)$

Here, *post-SUM* is the relationship that must hold between i, j, s and r for r to be the sum of elements i to j in the sequence s. It is as though we had defined a boolean function:

post-SUM (*indexlo*, *indexhi*, *sequence*, *total*)

The relationship can be easily expressed recursively in terms of the element $s(i)$ and the sum of the elements between $i + 1$ and j. The variable t is needed only to give a name to this intermediate sum.

We will make use of the ability to invoke the post-condition of an operation in order to write recursive post-conditions which will lead naturally to recursive and iterative programs.

FIND2 with quoted post-conditions

We now respecify *FIND2*, and the other operations on *Nbase2*, using recursive post-conditions. The new versions will have '*2B*' suffixes. The post-conditions will themselves express the idea of sequencing down a list, so we will eventually substitute the higher level function *dbvalues* which previously hid the internal structure of the list.

These '*2B*' specifications are considerably more difficult to read than the '*2A*' ones, both because they are more detailed and more algorithmic in character. They are closer in structure to executable programs. In practice, specifications as complex as these would not be produced until the higher level specification had been shown to be entirely satisfactory, as considering low-level specifications can waste a lot of time. However, they do illustrate the fact that one can specify operations in a variety of different ways. Showing that differently specified operations are really the same is not always trivial.

$FIND2B(n\colon \mathbb{N})\ found\colon \mathbb{B}$
ext rd $db\colon Nbase2$
pre true
post $db = [\,] \wedge found = \text{false} \vee$
$\quad n = \text{hd}\ db \wedge found = \text{true} \vee$
$\quad n \neq \text{hd}\ db \wedge post\text{-}FIND2B(n, \text{tl}\ db, found)$

Here the post-condition is a boolean function relating an integer value, a sequence and a boolean search result. Because the external variables are read-only, the initial and final values do not both occur as parameters. The post-condition constrains *found* to be the value false if the sequence is empty, and to be true if the integer value occurs at the head of the sequence. If neither of these cases holds, the post-condition constrains the value, the tail of the sequence and the search result to be related by a recursive call of itself.

The function *post-FIND2B* can be used in any boolean expression. For example, *post-FIND2B*(3, [2, 3, 4], true) and *post-FIND2B*(3, [7, 8], false) both evaluate to true; *post-FIND2B*(3, [2,3,4], false) and *post-FIND2B*(3, [7,8], true) both evaluate to false.

Exercise 9.6

By using recursive post-conditions, specify *INSERT2B* and *DELETE2B*.

Solution 9.6

$INSERT2B(n\colon \mathbb{N})$
ext wr $db\colon Nbase2$
pre $n \notin dbvalues(db)$
post $(\overleftarrow{db} = [\,] \wedge db = [n]) \vee$
$\quad n < \text{hd}\ \overleftarrow{db} \wedge db = [n] \frown \overleftarrow{db} \vee$
$\quad n > \text{hd}\ \overleftarrow{db} \wedge$
$\qquad (\exists\, t \in Nbase2 \cdot post\text{-}INSERT2B(n, \text{tl}\ \overleftarrow{db}, t) \wedge db = [\text{hd}\ \overleftarrow{db}] \frown t)$

INSERT2B uses a writeable external variable, so both input and output values of the variable occur as arguments in *post-INSERT2B* which is therefore a boolean function of the integer value, the sequence before the operation and the sequence afterwards. The variable t is needed just to give a name to the sequence which results from inserting n in the tail of db. The post-condition of *INSERT2B* asserts that if n is greater than the first element of the existing database, there exists another database t resulting from inserting n into the tail of the database, (expressed by the recursive call of the post-condition), and the new database is this other database with the old first element prefixed to it.

$DELETE2B(n\colon \mathbb{N})$
ext wr $db\colon Nbase2$
pre $n \in dbvalues(db)$
post $\overleftarrow{db} = [n] \wedge db = [\,] \vee n = \text{hd}\ \overleftarrow{db} \wedge db = \text{tl}\ \overleftarrow{db} \vee$
$\quad n \neq \text{hd}\ \overleftarrow{db} \wedge$
$\qquad (\exists\, t : Nbase2 \cdot post\text{-}DELETE2B(n, \text{tl}\ \overleftarrow{db}, t) \wedge db = [\text{hd}\ \overleftarrow{db}] \frown t)$

The function *post-DELETE2B* is a boolean function with three arguments, the value, the old sequence and the new one. It evaluates to true if $\overleftarrow{db}$ is just $[n]$ and db is $[\,]$. It also evaluates to true if n is not the first element of db and there is a database t such that deleting n from the tail of $\overleftarrow{db}$ gives t and the new db is the old first element of $\overleftarrow{db}$ prefixed to t.

■

We now have two different specifications of the numerical database, viz. *Nbase1* and *Nbase2*, and each has a set of operations associated with its own representation of the data type. We even have two different versions of the operations for the second representation of the database as a sequence (the '*2A*' and '*2B*' versions). These differ in being far more explicit as to the details of how the operations should behave.

How can we check that the second representation really is a more concrete version of the first? How can we check that the second set of operations has the right properties and that the latter set of operations do the same sort of jobs on the latter representation as the former set do on the former representation?

In the next sections we focus on these questions and discuss the proof obligations they generate.

9.3 Proof obligations for reification

When reifying data types, we need to check that the transformation from the abstract data type to a more concrete one is correct. But what do we mean by correct?

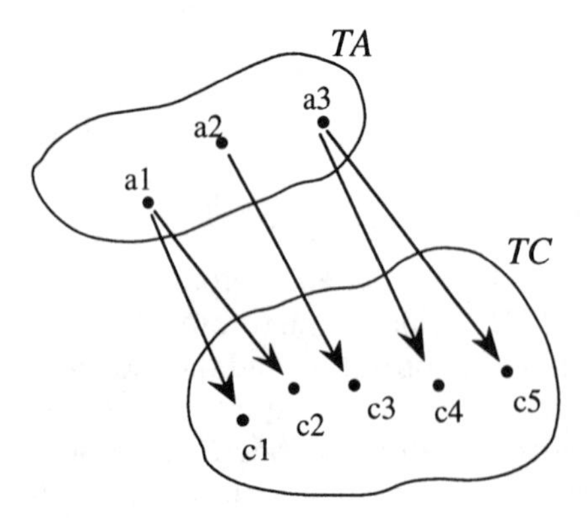

Figure 9.4

A reified specification is correct (with respect to an abstract specification) if it reflects the properties built into the abstract specification.

In VDM, the term used to describe this is that the concrete specification is ***adequate***. The adequacy of a reification is a very important notion, as we shall see.

Consider Figure 9.4. The reification of the abstract type *TA* to the concrete type *TC* will be acceptable if and only if every element in the abstract type *TA* is represented by at least one element in the concrete type *TC*, otherwise the concrete version is too narrow and can represent only some of the values of the abstract type. Concrete operations operate on concrete values to produce new concrete values, and we also require that every such concrete value really does correspond to some abstract value.

How can we express these ideas mathematically? We cannot produce a function from *TA* to *TC* because a function is single valued, and would yield a single concrete value from each value of *TA*. A clue is given in Figure 9.5 which reverses the arrows in Figure 9.4.

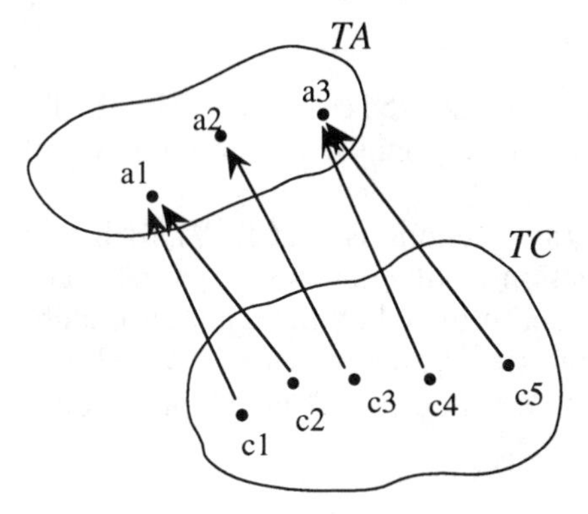

Figure 9.5

The retrieve function

In order for the concrete type to represent the abstract type, it must be possible to say precisely which element of the abstract type is intended to be represented by which particular element of the concrete type. The specifier of the concrete type (perhaps an implementation in code) is required to define a ***retrieve function*** which, given an element of the concrete type, retrieves the corresponding element of the abstract type. The retrieve function must be defined on every element of the concrete type which satisfies the invariant of the concrete type. Also, it must map at least one concrete element onto every single abstract element, or there would be unrepresented abstract elements. Note that by saying it is a *function*, we guarantee that it maps a concrete element to a *single* abstract element, but we allow the possibility that more than one concrete element maps to the same abstract element. It is a ***total function*** in the sense that it can be applied to every single element which satisfies the concrete invariant. As a function it is said to be ***onto*** because every element of the abstract type has some concrete element mapped onto it. There are no abstract elements that cannot be reached by mapping some concrete element.

Exercise 9.7

In Figure 9.5 suppose the elements of the abstract type *TA* are sets of characters and the concrete elements of *TC* are sequences of characters with no duplicate elements. Assume that an element of *TC* maps onto the element of *TA* consisting of the set of characters occurring in the sequence. If the sequences of *TC* contain no repetition, how many elements of *TC* will correspond to the set {'a', 'b', 'c'}?

Solution 9.7

There will be six values. They are:

['a', 'b', 'c']	['b', 'a', 'c']	['c', 'a', 'b']
['b', 'c', 'a']	['c', 'b', 'a']	['a', 'c', 'b']

■

Figure 9.5 shows that an element of *TA* can be represented by either a single element of *TC* or several elements of *TC*. Only *c3* corresponds to *a2* but both *c1* and *c2* correspond to *a1*.

We need a systematic way of naming retrieve functions, and in VDM it is a convention that the name of the retrieve function from a concrete type to an abstract type is written *retr* followed by a hyphen, followed by the name of the abstract type. For example, the function which retrieves an element of *Nbase1* corresponding to an element of *Nbase2* would be called *retr-Nbase1*, and would have the following signature:

$retr\text{-}Nbase1: Nbase2 \to Nbase1$

Exercise 9.8

Define a retrieve function *retr-Nbase1*.

Solution 9.8

An appropriate retrieve function can be defined using *dbvalues*.

$retr\text{-}Nbase1: Nbase2 \to Nbase1$
$retr\text{-}Nbase1(s) \triangleq dbvalues(s)$

Given any member of *Nbase2*, a sequence, the retrieve function delivers the corresponding member of *Nbase1*, a set.

■

Proving adequacy

Consider *Nbase1* and *Nbase2*. *Nbase2* is said to be an adequate representation of *Nbase1* only if every set belonging to *Nbase1* is represented by at least one sequence belonging to *Nbase2*, where 'is represented by' is defined by the retrieve function. In other words, to prove adequacy in this case we must prove that

$$\forall st : Nbase1 \bullet \exists\, sq : Nbase2 \bullet retr\text{-}Nbase1(sq) = st$$

(The names *st* and *sq* are arbitrary but were chosen to remind us that *st* is a set and *sq* is a sequence.)

More generally, if we are trying to prove the adequacy of a concrete type *TC* with respect to an abstract type *TA*, we must show that for every value in the abstract type *TA* there exists a value in the concrete type *TC* that is mapped by the retrieve function to the abstract value. This can be written as:

$$\forall a : TA \bullet$$
$$\quad \exists c : TC \bullet retr\text{-}TA(c) = a$$

This is our first example of a proof obligation for reification. It is a proposition that has to be shown to be true in order for the designer to be assured of the correctness of her concrete specification and ultimately of her program code.

Let us consider *Nbase1* and *Nbase2* and reason informally about this proof obligation. By the properties of sets we know that every set which is an element of *Nbase1* is either the empty set { }, or is the union of two sets—one with a single member and the other containing all of the original set except that member. This suggests that we might reason about sets inductively by building them up, one element at a time.

The condition on adequacy:

$$\forall st : Nbase1 \bullet \exists\, sq : Nbase2 \bullet retr\text{-}Nbase1(sq) = st$$

demands that we prove that for every *set* of natural numbers there is at least one corresponding *sequence* of natural numbers. This is fairly easy to prove inductively. We have to show that for any arbitrary *st* : *Nbase1* we choose, it is true that

$$\exists\, sq : Nbase2 \bullet retr\text{-}Nbase1(sq) = st$$

We start with the empty set as the ***base case*** of the inductive proof. If the set is empty, we could choose *sq* to be [ ] because:

$$\begin{aligned} retr\text{-}Nbase1([\,]) &= dbvalues([\,]) \\ &= \{\,\} \end{aligned}$$

So for this value of *st* at least it is true that

$$\exists\, sq : Nbase2 \bullet retr\text{-}Nbase1(sq) = st$$

Now the ***inductive step***; assume that for each set *stk* whose cardinality is less than or equal to *k* there is an element *sqk* of *Nbase2* such that *retr-Nbase1*(*sqk*) = *stk*. This is called the ***induction hypothesis*** for this particular argument.

Now choose *stk1* to be a typical set in *Nbase1* whose cardinality is $k + 1$. Then *stk1* can be written as the union of a set of cardinality *k* and a set with a single member, say *n*.

i.e. $stk1 = stk \cup \{n\}$ for some natural number n

By the inductive hypothesis we know that for the set *stk* there is a sequence, say *sqk*, such that *stk* = *retr-Nbase1*(*sqk*), i.e. *stk* = *dbvalues*(*sqk*).

Now consider the sequence

$$sqk1 = sqk \frown [n]$$

We shall show that under the retrieve function this sequence represents *stk1*.

$$\begin{aligned} \textit{retr-Nbase1}(\textit{sqk1}) &= \textit{dbvalues}(\textit{sqk} \frown [n]) \\ &= \textit{dbvalues}(\textit{sqk}) \cup \textit{dbvalues}([n]) \\ &= \textit{stk} \cup \{n\} \\ &= \textit{stk1} \end{aligned}$$

There is therefore at least one sequence which maps onto *stk1*, namely *sqk1*.

We have shown that there was a sequence representing the empty set and that if all sets of cardinality up to k have corresponding sequences, then there is also a sequence for any set of cardinality $k + 1$. Therefore, by induction, there is a sequence for representing a set of any cardinality, and we have indeed satisfied the adequacy proof obligation by showing that:

$$\forall st : \textit{Nbase1} \bullet \exists\, sq : \textit{Nbase2} \bullet \textit{retr-Nbase1}(sq) = st$$

Exercise 9.9

Suppose a type *Nat* is defined to be a synonym for the natural numbers $\mathbb{N}_1$. The type *Nat* might be represented in unary notation as a sequence of the character '1', e.g. 4 would be represented by ['1', '1', '1', '1']. Define a data type *Unary* with a suitable invariant, write the retrieve function from *Unary* to *Nat*, and prove that *Unary* is an adequate representation of *Nat*.

Solution 9.9

$\textit{Unary} = \mathsf{char}^*$

$\textit{inv-Unary}\,(u) \triangleq \forall\, i \in \{1, ..., \mathsf{len}\ u\} \bullet u(i) = \text{'1'} \wedge \mathsf{len}\ u \geq 1$

$\textit{retr-Nat}: \textit{Unary} \rightarrow \textit{Nat}$
$\textit{retr-Nat}(un) \triangleq \mathsf{len}\ un$

The proof is by induction. The number 1 is representable by the sequence ['1']. Suppose that all values of *Nat* up to k are representable as *Unary* numbers, and that k is represented by the unary uk; i.e. $k = \textit{retr-Nat}(uk)$. Now consider the unary number $uk \frown [\text{'1'}]$. This retrieves to the natural number $\textit{retr-Nat}(uk \frown [\text{'1'}])$; i.e. $\mathsf{len}(uk \frown [\text{'1'}])$ which is $k + 1$.

Therefore we have shown that 1 is representable, and that if k is representable, then $k + 1$ is. Therefore, by induction, all *Nat* values are representable, and *Unary* is an adequate representation of *Nat*.

■

9.4 Checking the concrete operations

In VDM, the development of a software design consists in choosing ever more concrete representations of the data, and successively respecifying the operations that manipulate the data. We have seen how the concrete type must be related to the abstract type by means of a retrieve function, and we demonstrated the first of the proof obligations — that of adequacy — which have to be satisfied during the reification process. As the representation of the type is made more concrete, the operations on it have to be redefined. Clearly, a concrete operation must in some sense 'do the same thing' as the corresponding abstract operation, although one is specified in terms of the concrete type and the other in terms of the abstract type. Before a concrete operation can be accepted as corresponding correctly with an abstract operation, there are various proof obligations that arise. This sub-section is concerned with what these proof obligations are.

Operations on the concrete type must be at least as generally applicable as the abstract operations and they must also yield correct results. These two requirements are captured in the ***domain rule*** and the ***result rule***.

The domain rule

The domain rule is about the generality of operations. For example, if an abstract operation on sets is specified for all sets of cardinality between 0 and 256, and a putative reification of the operation is defined only for representations of sets having cardinality between 1 and 255, there will be cases when the abstract operation could be applied but the concrete one could not. The concrete operation would therefore not be an acceptable reification of the abstract one.

Figure 9.6 shows this in general. It illustrates an abstract type *TA* and a concrete type *TC*, and the retrieve function from *TC* to *TA*.

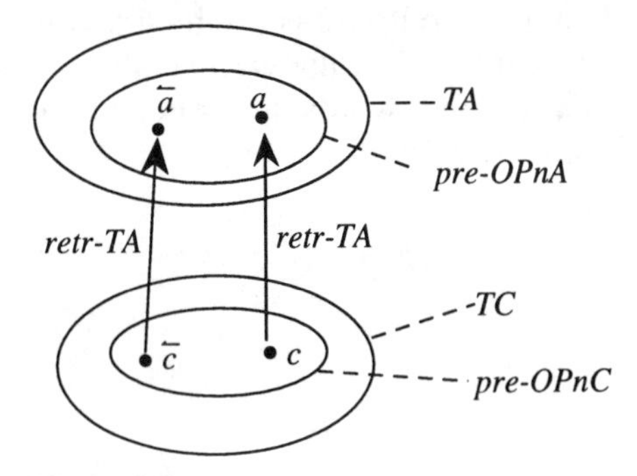

Figure 9.6

We are investigating one particular abstract operation *OPnA* and the corresponding concrete operation *OPnC*. The abstract operation will be defined for just the subset of *TA* given by its pre-condition which we express by the boolean function *pre-OPnA* (as introduced in section 7.3). Similarly, the concrete operation is defined for only the subset of *TC* given by *pre-OPnC*. There must be a relation between these two pre-conditions to guarantee that the concrete operation can cope with at least the values that the abstract operation can handle.

In Figure 9.7 the subset of *TA* containing just the abstract values that satisfy *pre-OPnA* has been indicated, as has the subset of the concrete type satisfying *pre-OPnC*. There are just two abstract values (*a1* and *a2*) satisfying the precondition of the abstract operation. The concrete values *c1* and *c2* which map onto the abstract subset also satisfy the concrete pre-condition. This means that the concrete pre-condition is wide enough to contain all the concrete values that could ever represent abstract values on which *OPnA* might be performed.

Figure 9.7 also shows a concrete value *c3* which satisfies the concrete pre-condition, but which maps to an abstract value which does not satisfy the abstract pre-condition. All this means is that the concrete condition is less restrictive than it could be. The concrete operation is defined for a wider range of input values than is necessary. There is nothing wrong with this: if a program works for conditions outside its specification, that is just a bonus.

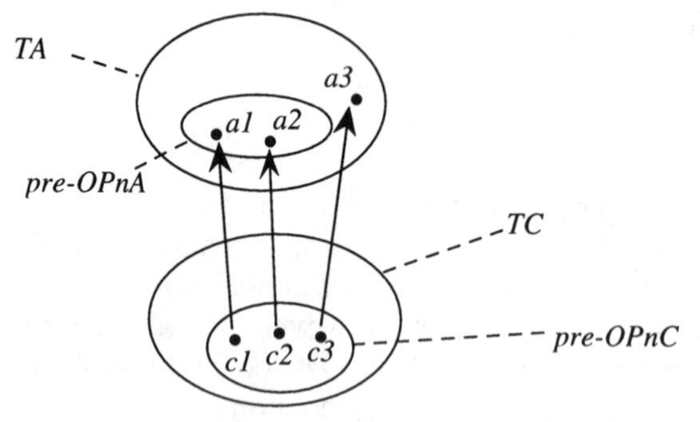

Figure 9.7

In Figure 9.8 a situation is shown in which an abstract value *a2* is within the abstract pre-condition, but a concrete value which maps onto *a2* is not included in the concrete pre-condition. This means that at least for the value *a2*, the abstract operation is defined, but the concrete one is not. In other words, the concrete operation is defined for too small a subset of the concrete type.

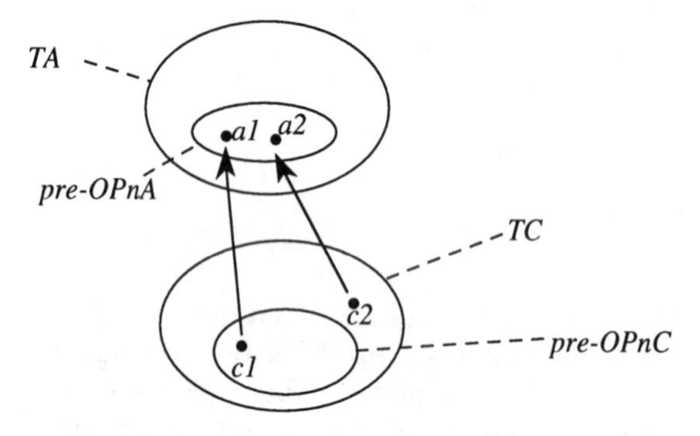

Figure 9.8

For a given *pre-OPnA* we can state formally a constraint on *pre-OPnC* in order for this state of affairs *not* to happen. Assuming no parameters to the operations the domain rule is:

$$\forall c : TC \cdot \text{let } a = retr\text{-}TA(c) \text{ in } pre\text{-}OPnA(a) \Rightarrow pre\text{-}OPnC(c)$$

This says that for every value *c* in the concrete type, if the corresponding value *a* in the abstract type satisfies the pre-condition of *OPnA* then *pre-OPnC* must be true of *c*. This is called the domain rule. It ensures that the domain of *OPnC* is large enough in that it includes at least every concrete element corresponding to an abstract element for which *OPnA* is defined. The domain rule must be shown to be satisfied for every single operation on a data type.

The domain rule for FIND

We shall prove the domain rule for just the operation *FIND*. Here, the abstract operation *OPnA* is *FIND1* and the concrete operation *OPnC* is *FIND2A* . To determine if *FIND2A* satisfies the domain rule we must attempt to prove:

$$\forall c : Nbase2 \bullet \text{let } a = retr\text{-}Nbase1(c) \text{ in } pre\text{-}FIND1(a) \Rightarrow pre\text{-}FIND2A(c)$$

The pre-condition *pre-FIND1(a)* is just the expression true, and *pre-FINDA2A* is also true. The retrieve function *retr-Nbase(c)* is *dbvalues(c)* .

Substituting these expressions gives:

$$\forall c : Nbase2 \bullet \text{let } a = dbvalues(c) \text{ in true} \Rightarrow \text{true}$$

As a does not occur in the expression, this is equivalent to us being required to show that:

$$\forall c : Nbase2 \bullet \text{ true} = \text{true}$$

This does hold, so the domain rule is satisfied by *FIND2A*. In fact, it should be clear that if the pre-conditions of an abstract and a concrete operation are just the expression true, the proof obligation is trivially satisfied. This is because both operations are universally applicable, so there is no question of the concrete operation being invocable under narrower circumstances than the abstract one.

The result rule

A concrete operation not only has to be defined on a sufficiently large subset of the concrete values; it is also required to get the right answer. The concrete action must correspond appropriately to the abstract operation. This is captured in the result rule.

The result rule says the following. A new concrete value produced by a concrete operation must correspond to the new abstract value produced by the abstract operation. Let us assume a concrete operation *OPnC* (with no parameters or result value) with an external variable whose value changes from $\overleftarrow{c}$ to c. Thus, if the condition *post-OPnC*($\overleftarrow{c}$, c) holds, then the corresponding abstract values a and $\overleftarrow{a}$ must be related by *post-OPnA*; i.e. *post-OPnA*($\overleftarrow{a}$, a) must hold. Were this not so, it would mean that the new concrete value c is deemed acceptable by the concrete post-condition, but the corresponding a is not acceptable to the abstract operation. In other words, the concrete operation has produced the wrong value.

Figure 9.9 represents a situation where the result rule does hold. It shows that if one starts with a concrete type $\overleftarrow{c}$, the result of finding the corresponding abstract value $\overleftarrow{a}$ and applying the abstract operation to it should be the same as applying the concrete operation to $\overleftarrow{c}$ and then finding the abstract value corresponding to the result c.

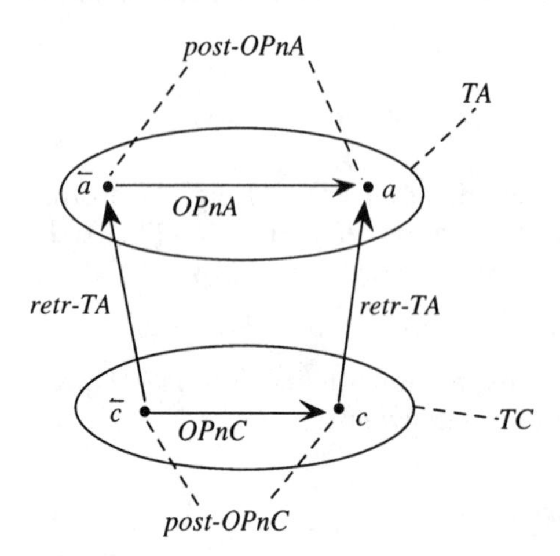

Figure 9.9

Figure 9.10 shows a situation where the rule is violated. The value $\overleftarrow{c}$ corresponds to $\overleftarrow{a}$ but c does not correspond to a; rather, c corresponds to some other abstract value, $a2$. The concrete operation is producing a wrong value. We need to require that whenever a concrete operation is applied, producing a new concrete value which satisfies the concrete post-condition, the abstract post-condition for the corresponding new abstract value must also be satisfied.

Expressed formally, we could say that it must be true that:

$$\forall \overleftarrow{c}, c : TC \bullet \text{let } \overleftarrow{a} = \mathit{retr\text{-}TA}(\overleftarrow{c}),\ a = \mathit{retr\text{-}TA}(c) \text{ in}$$
$$\mathit{post\text{-}OPnC}(\overleftarrow{c}, c) \Rightarrow \mathit{post\text{-}OPnA}(\overleftarrow{a}, a)$$

The implication could be written:

$$\neg\, (\mathit{post\text{-}OPnC}(\overleftarrow{c}, c) \wedge \neg \mathit{post\text{-}OPnA}(\overleftarrow{a}, a))$$

It captures the fact that we cannot have the concrete post-condition accepting the value c as a correct outcome and not have the abstract post-condition accepting the corresponding a.

In fact, this is slightly stronger than is actually required. The concrete operation needs to be implemented only for those cases where the pre-condition of *OPnA* holds. When *pre-OPnA* does not hold, the concrete operation can produce any new value at all without violating the specification. We can therefore reformulate the result rule to restrict its application to just those concrete values that correspond to abstract values satisfying *pre-OPnA*. The final form is:

$$\forall \overleftarrow{c}, c : TC \bullet \text{let } \overleftarrow{a} = \mathit{retr\text{-}TA}(\overleftarrow{c}),\ a = \mathit{retr\text{-}TA}(c) \text{ in}$$
$$\mathit{pre\text{-}OPnA}(\overleftarrow{a}) \wedge \mathit{post\text{-}OPnC}(\overleftarrow{c}, c) \Rightarrow \mathit{post\text{-}OPnA}(\overleftarrow{a}, a)$$

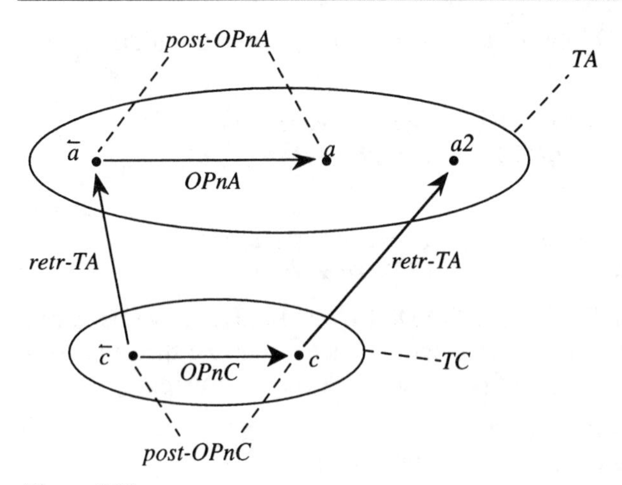

Figure 9.10

Figure 9.11 shows Figure 9.10 amended to represent the extra condition that the requirements of the result rule apply only to those elements satisfying *pre-OPnA*.

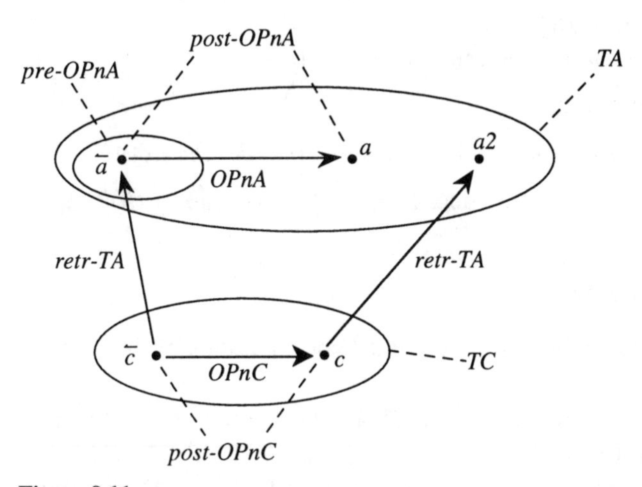

Figure 9.11

The result rule for FIND

To prove the result rule for *FIND* we will show that the concrete operation on *Nbase2*, *FIND2A* (on page 113), properly corresponds to the abstract operation on *Nbase1*, *FIND1* (on page 112). To prove the result rule for *FIND* we must show that

$$\forall \bar{c}, c : Nbase2 \cdot \text{let } \bar{a} = retr\text{-}Nbase1(\bar{c}),\ a = retr\text{-}Nbase1(c) \text{ in}$$
$$pre\text{-}FIND1(\bar{a}) \wedge post\text{-}FIND2(\bar{c}, c) \Rightarrow post\text{-}FIND1(\bar{a}, a)$$

Again, we know that:

$$\forall \bar{c} : Nbase2 \cdot pre\text{-}FIND1(retr\text{-}Nbase1(\bar{c}))$$

is just the constant true, so the proof obligation for the result rule reduces to a requirement to show that:

$$\forall \overleftarrow{c}, c : Nbase2 \bullet \text{let } \overleftarrow{a} = retr\text{-}Nbase1(\overleftarrow{c}),\ a = retr\text{-}Nbase1(c) \text{ in}$$
$$\text{true} \wedge post\text{-}FIND2A(\overleftarrow{c}, c) \Rightarrow post\text{-}FIND1(\overleftarrow{a}, a)$$

or

$$\forall \overleftarrow{c}, c : Nbase2 \bullet \text{let } \overleftarrow{a} = retr\text{-}Nbase1(\overleftarrow{c}),\ a = retr\text{-}Nbase1(c) \text{ in}$$
$$post\text{-}FIND2A(\overleftarrow{c}, c) \Rightarrow post\text{-}FIND1(\overleftarrow{a}, a)$$

The external variable in both *FIND1* and *FIND2A* is read-only, so we need not make the distinction between $\overleftarrow{a}$ and a nor $\overleftarrow{c}$ and c (since $\overleftarrow{a}$ must be the same as a and $\overleftarrow{c}$ must be the same as c). The proof obligation reduces to showing:

$$\forall c : Nbase2 \bullet \text{let } a = retr\text{-}Nbase1(c) \text{ in}$$
$$post\text{-}FIND2A(\overleftarrow{c}, c) \Rightarrow post\text{-}FIND1(\overleftarrow{a}, a)$$

Now the retrieve function *retr-Nbase1* applied to c is $dbvalues(c)$, while the predicate $post\text{-}FIND2A(\overleftarrow{c}, c)$ is $found \Leftrightarrow (n \in dbvalues(c))$ and $post\text{-}FIND1(\overleftarrow{a}, a)$ is $found \Leftrightarrow (n \in a)$. We must therefore show that

$$\forall c : Nbase2 \bullet \text{let } a = dbvalues(c) \text{ in}$$
$$found \Leftrightarrow (n \in dbvalues(c)) \Rightarrow found \Leftrightarrow (n \in a)$$

By replacing a by its definition, this is:

$$\forall c : Nbase2 \bullet found \Leftrightarrow (n \in dbvalues(c)) \Rightarrow found \Leftrightarrow (n \in dbvalues(c))$$

which clearly holds. Thus, the result rule does hold for the operation *FIND2A*.

9.5 Summary of concepts

- A retrieve function relates values of a concrete type to values of an abstract type.
- For a concrete operation to correspond to an abstract operation, it must satisfy the domain and the result rules.
- The domain rule requires that a concrete operation be defined on at least all the concrete values that correspond to the abstract values for which the abstract operation is defined.
- The result rule requires a concrete operation to produce the correct result values by constraining it never to accept as a result any value which the abstract operation would not accept as a result.

10 PROOF OBLIGATIONS OF STACKS AND QUEUES

We now examine various examples of reification and their attendant proof obligations. The intention is not only to show reification in practice, but also to illustrate how it is, in attempting to meet proof obligations, that omissions and invalid assumptions in the reification usually come to light. The examples chosen are the very familiar ones of stacks and queues so that it is easy to concentrate on the details of the proof without being distracted by new data types.

10.1 A stack of characters

We specify a ***stack*** of characters which holds a maximum of m characters. There are five operations:

INIT, which initializes the stack;
POP, which removes the top character of the stack;
PUSH, which places a character on the top of the stack;
IS-EMPTY, which tests whether the stack is empty;
IS-FULL, which tests whether the stack is full.

An abstract stack

The first step is to specify the system to be developed using an abstract data type and an appropriate invariant.

In this case we will call the abstract data type *Stack*. Since one of the important properties of a stack is the order of its elements, unordered types such as sets are probably not an appropriate representation, and we choose to specify it as a sequence type. An invariant is used to capture the constraint that the stack must not exceed some maximum size m. All implementations of real stacks will require such a restriction, even though a mathematically pure stack may be conceived without it.

$Stack = \mathsf{char}^*$

$inv\text{-}Stack(s) \triangleq \mathsf{len}\ s \leq m$

The initialization of the stack consists of setting s to be the empty sequence. We write this as follows.

INIT
ext wr $s : Stack$
pre true
post $s = [\,]$

The operation *PUSH* is shown below. It places the new value c onto the stack. We might choose either end of the sequence to represent the top of the stack. Here the top of the stack is the first element of the sequence.

PUSH(c: char)
ext wr $s : Stack$
pre len $s < m$
post $s = [c] \frown \overleftarrow{s}$

For example, pushing 'x' onto an empty stack results in ['x'], and pushing 'y' onto this results in ['y', 'x'].

Exercise 10.1

Specify the *POP* operation which removes the character at the top of the stack and returns it as the result of the operation.

Solution 10.1

The *POP* operation removes and returns the head of the sequence.

POP( ) r: char
ext wr $s : Stack$
pre $s \neq [\,]$
post $s = \mathsf{tl}\ \overleftarrow{s} \wedge r = \mathsf{hd}\ \overleftarrow{s}$

For example, applying *POP* to the stack ['x', 'y', 'z'] returns 'x' and leaves the stack as ['y', 'z'].

■

The *IS-EMPTY* operation checks to see if the stack is empty. The *IS-FULL* operation checks to see if the stack is full.

Exercise 10.2

Specify the operations *IS-EMPTY* and *IS-FULL*.

Solution 10.2

$IS\text{-}EMPTY()\ r: \mathbb{B}$	$IS\text{-}FULL()\ r: \mathbb{B}$
ext rd $s: Stack$	ext rd $s: Stack$
pre true	pre true
post $r \Leftrightarrow (s = [\,])$	post $r \Leftrightarrow$ (len $s = m$)

■

We have specified a type, *Stack*, and a collection of operations. But are the operations well-defined? Are they consistent with preserving the invariant?

The invariant is concerned only with the stack size not exceeding m, so we must show that none of the operations results in a stack which is too large. Since there is only one operation which increases the number of the characters in the stack (*PUSH*) we have only one operation to check. Clearly, the pre- and post-conditions of *PUSH* demand that the number of characters in the stack be increased only when the pre-condition (len $s < m$) holds for the initial stack s. As the length of the sequence is increased by just one, after the operation we will have len $s \leq m$, and the invariant will not have been violated. Therefore all the operations, *INIT*, *PUSH*, *POP*, *IS-EMPTY* and *IS-FULL*, are consistent with the invariant.

We are now in a position to start the process of data reification.

A reification of Stack

One choice of a concrete state for the finite stack is a fixed length sequence, in which a varying length subsequence is used to hold the actual stack elements. This choice is made with one eye on the final implementation, as most programming languages provide sequences of fixed length, such as fixed-length arrays, but far fewer provide sequences of dynamically varying length. The new concrete state is therefore chosen to be a composite type *StackR*. Names ending in '*R*' or '*C*' are often chosen for the reified or concrete versions of abstract states.

$StackR$ ::
  els: char*
  ctr: $\mathbb{N}$

$$inv\text{-}StackR(sr) \triangleq (\text{len } sr.els = m) \wedge (0 \leq sr.ctr \wedge sr.ctr \leq m)$$

The *els* (elements) field of *StackR* is a sequence which contains the elements currently on the stack. The counter *ctr* serves two functions: first, it is an index into the sequence of characters and points to the 'top' of the stack; second, it holds a count of the number of elements in the stack.

Exercise 10.3

Construct the retrieve function that relates the concrete state *StackR* to the abstract state *Stack*.

Solution 10.3

retr-Stack: *StackR* → *Stack*
retr-Stack(*sr*) △ let *depth* = *sr.ctr* in *reverse*(*sr.els*(1, ..., *depth*))

The particular *Stack* corresponding to a *StackR* called *sr* is the sequence obtained by reversing the first *ctr* elements of the elements *els* in *sr*. We must reverse it because in the abstract state the top of the stack is the first element of the sequence and in the concrete stack it is the element at index *ctr*. We made use of the auxiliary function *reverse* which could be defined by:

reverse: char^* → char^*
reverse(*s*) △
  if *s* = [ ]
  then [ ]
  else *reverse*(tl *s*) ⌢ [hd *s*]

■

Exercise 10.4

If *m* is 4, give two different values of *StackR* that retrieve to the empty stack and two which retrieve to the stack which results from pushing onto an empty stack the numbers 1, 2 and 3.

Solution 10.4

(i) *mk-StackR*([1, 1, 1, 1], 0) and *mk-StackR*([1, 2, 3, 4], 0) retrieve to the empty stack.

(ii) *mk-StackR*([1, 2, 3, 99], 3) and *mk-StackR*([1, 2, 3, 999], 3) both retrieve to the stack [3, 2, 1] which has 3 as its top element.

■

Review Question 10.1

Why is *ctr* not of type $\mathbb{N}_1$? What will *els*(1, ..., *ctr*) evaluate to if *ctr* = 0?

■

Review Question 10.2

Say in your own words what the function *reverse* and the retrieve function *retr-Stack* do.

■

Adequacy of StackR with respect to retr-Stack

Proving adequacy involves showing that to every value of *Stack* there is at least one corresponding value, *sr*, of *StackR*, the correspondence being given by the retrieve function. We must therefore prove:

$\forall s : Stack \bullet \exists\, sr : StackR \bullet s = retr\text{-}Stack(sr)$

We informally demonstrate that the specification *StackR* is adequate with respect to the specification of *Stack* by showing how to represent any arbitrary value of the type *Stack*, a stack of characters, by a value of *StackR*, a fixed-length sequence and a counter.

We shall prove, by induction on the length of the stack, that:

$\forall s : Stack \bullet \exists\, sr : StackR \bullet s = retr\text{-}Stack(sr)$

First consider the empty stack [ ]. Is there a member *sr* of *StackR* such that *retr-Stack(sr)* = [ ]? In fact there are several. Consider the expression:

let *anymseq* : char* be st len *anymseq* = *m* in
mk-StackR(anymseq, 0)

The sequence *anymseq* can be any sequence at all as long as it is of length *m*. This expression certainly retrieves to the value of *Stack* which is [ ], because:

$$\begin{aligned} retr\text{-}Stack(mk\text{-}StackR(anymseq, 0)) &= reverse(anymseq\,(1, ..., 0)) \\ &= reverse([\,]) \\ &= [\,] \end{aligned}$$

The variable *anymseq* can be absolutely *any* sequence of length *m* for *mk-StackR(sm*, 0) to retrieve to the empty stack [ ]. The data values stored in an empty *StackR* do not matter, provided the counter is zero. Thus, by exhibiting a particular value of *sr* we have shown that when *s* is the empty stack, it is certainly true that:

$\exists\, sr : StackR \bullet s = retr\text{-}Stack(sr)$

To prove the inductive step, we assume that for every stack *sk* of length up to *k* there is a corresponding value *srk* of type *StackR*. That is, *sk* = *retr-Stack(srk)*, or in full, *sk* = *reverse(srk.els*(1, ..., *k*)).

Now choose a value of *Stack* of length $k + 1$, say $[c]^\frown sk$. Is there a value of *StackR* corresponding to this? If *t* is any sequence of length $m - (1 + k)$, consider the value:

$mk\text{-}StackR(srk.els(1, ..., k)^\frown [c]^\frown t,\ k + 1)$

We have built up a value of *StackR* which has a counter one greater than that in *srk* and which has the same first *k* values as the original *els* field. What value of *Stack* does this retrieve to? By applying the function *retr-Stack* we get $reverse((srk.els(1, ..., k)^\frown [c]^\frown t)(1, ..., k{+}1))$. By the properties of subsequences this is equivalent to $reverse(srk.els(1, ..., k)^\frown [c])$ and by those of *reverse* it is equivalent to $[c]^\frown reverse(srk.els(1, ..., k))$. Hence, this particular value of *StackR* retrieves to $[c]^\frown sk$.

Thus, if all stacks of length up to *k* have a representation in *StackR*, then so do all stacks of length up to *k*+1. We have already established that stacks of length zero have a representation ([ ]), so, by induction, all stacks of any length have a representation in *StackR*, i.e. :

$\forall s : Stack \bullet \exists sr : StackR \bullet s = retr\text{-}Stack(sr)$

The concrete operations on StackR

First we need to define a concrete version of *INITR* to initialize a concrete or reified stack *sr*. The essential point of this initialization is to set the *ctr* field of the stack to be zero. We do not care what the *els* field contains, as long as the length of the sequence is fixed at *m*; i.e., we will accept any sequence of the type char^*, just as long as it has *m* elements. To specify this arbitrary choice we use an indeterminate form of the let expression:

INITR
ext wr sr: *StackR*
pre true
post let $arbseq : \text{char}^*$ be st len $arbseq = m$ in
$\quad sr = mk\text{-}StackR(arbseq, 0)$

Now we respecify the other stack operations.

PUSHR increases the counter, *ctr*, by one and modifies the sequence representing the stack, *els*, at the position indexed by the counter:

PUSHR(ch: char)
ext wr sr: *StackR*
pre $sr.ctr < m$
post $sr.els = [ch] \frown \overleftarrow{sr}.els \wedge sr.ctr = \overleftarrow{sr}.ctr + 1$

Exercise 10.5

Specify the operations *POPR*, *IS-EMPTYR* and *IS-FULLR*, the concrete operations corresponding to the abstract operations on *Stack* (without the μ operator).

Solution 10.5

The *POPR* operation decreases the counter by one and returns the character that was on the top of the stack.

POPR( ) r: char
ext wr sr: *StackR*
pre $sr.ctr \neq 0$
post let $oldctr = \overleftarrow{sr}.ctr$ in
$\quad sr = \mu(\overleftarrow{sr}, ctr \mapsto oldctr - 1) \wedge r = \overleftarrow{sr}.els\,(oldctr)$

The *IS-EMPTYR* operation just needs to check if the counter is zero. The precondition is true, and so we omit it. The *IS-FULLR* operation checks to see if the counter value is equal to the maximum capacity of the stack:

IS-EMPTYR( ) r: $\mathbb{B}$
ext rd s: *StackR*
post $r \Leftrightarrow (s.ctr = 0)$

IS-FULLR( ) r: $\mathbb{B}$
ext rd s: *StackR*
post $r \Leftrightarrow (s.ctr = m)$

■

The next step is to demonstrate that the initialized concrete state is correct. This means that we need to show that:

$retr\text{-}Stack(mk\text{-}StackR(s, 0)) = [\,]$

where $s : \mathsf{char}^*$ and $\mathsf{len}\ s = m$.

We have

$$\begin{aligned} retr\text{-}Stack(mk\text{-}StackR(s, 0)) &= reverse(s(1, \ldots, 0)) \\ &= reverse([\,]) \\ &= [\,] \end{aligned}$$

And this is indeed the initialized state in the abstract state *Stack*.

Checking the concrete operations on StackR

Finally, to show that the concrete operations on *StackR* mirror the properties of the corresponding operations on *Stack*, we take just one example, *POP* and the reified operation *POPR*. We want to show that *POPR* satisfies the domain and result rules with respect to *POP* and *retr-Stack*. However, to demonstrate how incorrect development can be discovered we will deliberately replace μ in the post-condition of *POPR* by an incorrect simplification. The specifications for *POP* and *POPR* with the μ replaced are:

POP( ) *r*: char	*POPR*( ) *r*: char
ext wr *s*: *Stack*	ext wr *sr*: *StackR*
pre $s \neq [\,]$	pre $sr.ctr \neq 0$
post $s = \mathsf{tl}\ \overleftarrow{s} \wedge r = \mathsf{hd}\ \overleftarrow{s}$	post let $oldctr = \overleftarrow{sr}.ctr$ in
	$sr.ctr = oldctr - 1 \wedge r = \overleftarrow{sr}.els\ (oldctr)$

The general domain rule is:

$$\forall c : TC \bullet \mathsf{let}\ a = retr\text{-}TA(c)\ \mathsf{in}\ pre\text{-}OPnA(a) \Rightarrow pre\text{-}OPnC(c)$$

Substituting *sr* for *c* and *StackR* for *TC*, etc., we must therefore satisfy:

$$\forall sr : StackR \bullet \mathsf{let}\ a = retr\text{-}Stack(sr)\ \mathsf{in}\ pre\text{-}POP(a) \Rightarrow pre\text{-}POPR(sr)$$

We can now make substitutions using the definitions of the retrieve function and the pre-conditions of *POPR* and *POP*. This gives us the proposition:

$$\begin{aligned} &\forall sr : StackR \bullet \mathsf{let}\ a = (\mathsf{let}\ depth = sr.ctr\ \mathsf{in}\ reverse(sr.els(1,.., depth)))\ \mathsf{in} \\ &\qquad a \neq [\,] \Rightarrow a.ctr \neq 0 \end{aligned}$$

Substituting using the definitions of *depth* and *a*, we need to show that:

$$\begin{aligned} &\forall sr : StackR \bullet \\ &\qquad (reverse(sr.els(1, \ldots, ctr)) \neq [\,] \Rightarrow (ctr \neq 0)) \end{aligned}$$

The boolean expression $reverse(sr.els(1, \ldots, ctr)) \neq [\,]$ is the same as $sr.els(1, \ldots, ctr) \neq [\,]$, since all *reverse* does is to reverse a sequence.

However, $els(1, \ldots, ctr) \neq [\,]$ is the same as $(ctr \geq 1)$, since for an indexed subsequence to be non-empty, the final index must be at least as big as the starting index. From arithmetic, the condition $(ctr \geq 1)$ implies $(ctr \neq 0)$.

The result rule for POPR

To prove the result rule we need to demonstrate that:

$$\forall \overleftarrow{sr}, sr : StackR \bullet$$
$$\quad \text{let } \overleftarrow{a} = retr\text{-}Stack(\overleftarrow{a}),\ a = retr\text{-}Stack(a) \text{ in}$$
$$\quad pre\text{-}POP(\overleftarrow{a}) \wedge post\text{-}POPR(\overleftarrow{a}, a) \Rightarrow post\text{-}POP(\overleftarrow{a}, a)$$

If we substitute for *pre-POP*, *post-POPR* and *post-POP* we obtain:

$$\forall \overleftarrow{sr}, sr : StackR \bullet$$
$$\quad \text{let } \overleftarrow{a} = retr\text{-}Stack(\overleftarrow{a}),\ a = \text{retr-}Stack(a) \text{ in}$$
$$\quad \overleftarrow{a} \neq [\,] \wedge sr.ctr = \overleftarrow{sr}.ctr - 1 \wedge r = \overleftarrow{sr}.els(\overleftarrow{sr}.ctr) \Rightarrow a = \mathsf{tl}\,\overleftarrow{a} \wedge r = \mathsf{hd}\,\overleftarrow{a}$$

Now using the definition of *retr-Stack* to substitute the definitions of $\overleftarrow{a}$ and a gives:

$$\forall \overleftarrow{sr}, sr : StackR \bullet$$
$$\quad \text{let } \overleftarrow{a} = reverse(\overleftarrow{sr}.els(1, ..., \overleftarrow{sr}.ctr)),\ a = reverse(sr.els(1, \ldots, sr.ctr)) \text{ in}$$
$$\quad \overleftarrow{a} \neq [\,] \wedge sr.ctr = \overleftarrow{sr}.ctr - 1 \wedge r = \overleftarrow{sr}.els(\overleftarrow{sr}.ctr)) \Rightarrow a = \mathsf{tl}\,\overleftarrow{a} \wedge r = \mathsf{hd}\,\overleftarrow{a}$$

We prove an implication by assuming the left-hand side, and attempting to derive the right-hand side. Substituting in the right-hand side both the definitions of a and $\overleftarrow{a}$ and the assumptions on the left-hand side, we can express the right-hand side solely in terms of concrete variables:

$$reverse(sr.els(1, ..., sr.ctr)) = \mathsf{tl}\,(reverse(\overleftarrow{sr}.els(1, ..., \overleftarrow{sr}.ctr))) \wedge$$
$$r = \mathsf{hd}\,(reverse(\overleftarrow{sr}.els(1, ..., \overleftarrow{sr}.ctr))$$

Replacing unhooked variables by hooked ones reduces it to:

$$reverse(sr.els(1, ..., \overleftarrow{sr}.ctr - 1)) = \mathsf{tl}\,(reverse(\overleftarrow{sr}.els(1, ..., \overleftarrow{sr}.ctr))) \wedge$$
$$r = \overleftarrow{sr}.els(\overleftarrow{sr}.ctr))$$

Under the assumption that the left-hand side of the implication is true, the second clause follows. The first looks as though it follows from the definitions of *reverse* and tl, though in fact it does not. The reason is that it depends on $sr.els(1, ..., sr.ctr)$ being the same as $\overleftarrow{sr}.els(1, ..., \overleftarrow{sr}.ctr)$. This is the condition that popping one element from the stack leaves the others unchanged. This was never asserted as part of the post-condition of *POPR*. Failure to prove the result rule has revealed an omission in the specification of an operation.

Omissions of vital details are extremely common when writing specifications of all kinds, whether formal or informal. They are normally difficult to find, and are often overlooked until late in the software development when their correction can be very expensive. Imposing formal proof obligations on the developer ensures that undocumented assumptions are exposed. If they are valid, they can then be added to the pre-conditions. If not, the post-conditions will need tightening to make them true.

Exercise 10.6

Rewrite the post-condition of *POPR* without μ to make explicit the fact that all the unpopped elements in the stack are unchanged.

Solution 10.6

post $sr.ctr = \overleftarrow{sr}.ctr - 1 \wedge r = \overleftarrow{sr}.els(\overleftarrow{sr}.ctr) \wedge$
let $newdepth = sr.ctr$ in
$sr.els(1, ..., newdepth) = \overleftarrow{sr}.els(1, ..., newdepth)$

■

With this revised version of *POPR*, the proof which failed above will now go through. Similar, though simpler, arguments establish that the domain and result rules hold for *PUSHR*, *IS-EMPTYR* and *IS-FULLR* with respect to their corresponding operations, when given the retrieve function *retr-Stack*.

10.2 A circular buffer

A ***queue*** is a sequence of elements, constrained so that elements are removed in the order in which they are inserted. Whereas a stack is 'first-in, last-out', a queue is 'first-in, first-out'. If no limit is placed on the number of items in the queue, the space needed to implement it will be unbounded. If the number of items is guaranteed not to exceed some maximum, say *m*, it is possible to implement a queue in a finite amount of space. One well-known technique for implementing a finite queue is that of a ***circular buffer***. This consists of a sequence of values, which are thought of as being arranged in a circle, so that the last element appears to be followed by the first. When an element is removed by a consumer, the space becomes available for re-use in subsequent insertions by a producer.

This section first defines a bounded queue (one with a set maximum number of elements, *m*), and then develops a refinement of it. The refinement, though apparently plausible, is found to be deficient when a proof of the domain rule is attempted, and a second, more satisfactory, refinement is developed.

An abstract Queue

A finite queue is simply a sequence which never exceeds a certain size. If we assume *Info* to be the type of data to be placed in the buffer, a first attempt at specifying an appropriate data type might be:

$Queue = Info^*$

$inv\text{-}Queue(q) \triangleq \text{len } q \leq m$

This is simply the specification of a sequence of *Info* items with a maximum length of *m*.

Exercise 10.7

Specify an *INIT* operation for the *Queue* data type which initializes it to a suitable state.

Solution 10.7

INIT
ext wr q: *Queue*
post $q = [\,]$

■

Four operations are to be specified: *ENQUEUE*, *DEQUEUE*, *IS-EMPTY* and *IS-FULL*. *ENQUEUE* appends an element to the end of the sequence, and *DEQUEUE* removes one from the front:

ENQUEUE(*e*: *Info*)
ext rd q: *Queue*
pre len $q < m$
post $q = \overleftarrow{q} \frown [e]$

DEQUEUE( ) *r*: *Info*
ext rd q: *Queue*
pre len $q > 0$
post $r = \text{hd}\, \overleftarrow{q} \wedge q = \text{tl}\, \overleftarrow{q}$

Compare these with *PUSH* and *POP* of the previous section. The last element to be *PUSH*-ed is the first to be *POP*-ed. The first element *ENQUEUE*-d is the first to be *DEQUEUE*-d. A stack is a last-in, first-out structure. A queue is a first-in, first-out structure.

Exercise 10.8

Specify *IS-EMPTY* and *IS-FULL*.

Solution 10.8

IS-EMPTY( ) *r*: $\mathbb{B}$
ext rd q: *Queue*
post $r \Leftrightarrow (q = [\,])$

IS-FULL( ) *r*: $\mathbb{B}$
ext rd q: *Queue*
post $r \Leftrightarrow (\text{len}\, q = m)$

■

These operations, *IS-EMPTY* and *IS-FULL*, can be used by both producers and consumers to check whether the queue is empty or full before reading data from the buffer or depositing data in the buffer.

Once we are satisfied with the operations on the abstract state we turn our attention to the concrete state.

A reification of Queue and its retrieve function

A first attempt at a concrete type might be:

Queue1 ::
  buf: $Info^*$
  next: $\{1, \ldots, m\}$
  free: $\{1, \ldots, m\}$

$inv\text{-}Queue1(q) \triangleq \text{len}\, q.buf = m$

Here we have chosen a fixed-length buffer to hold the elements, together with pointers, *next* and *free*, to the next item to read from the buffer, and the next free location that can be written to. As in the case of a stack, a fixed length sequence is chosen because it is nearer to the structures provided in most programming languages than is a variable length sequence.

Once we have defined a concrete state the next step is to devise the retrieve function: *retr-Queue* which is shown below (and explained afterwards):

retr-Queue: *Queue1* → *Queue*
retr-Queue(*q*) $\triangleq$
  if *q.next* < *q.free*
  then *q.buf*(*q.next*, …, *q.free* – 1)
  else (*q.buf* ⁀ *q.buf*)(*q.next*, ..., *m* + *q.free* – 1)

What does this mean? The retrieve function is to return an abstract *Queue*—a sequence of all the unread items in the queue. If the free pointer is further up the buffer than the read pointer, *next*, the unread items are just the elements in the buffer at indices *next*, ..., *free*–1. If the *free* pointer is equal to or below the *next* pointer it means that the queue items 'wrap around' past the end of the buffer and are in two different subsequences in the buffer. The first subsequence is at *next*, ..., *m* and the other at 1, ..., *free*–1. One way of viewing them is to consider two copies of the buffer concatenated. This will make the two subsequences adjacent to each other, so that they can be combined by a single indexing operation—hence the expression *q.buf* ⁀ *q.buf*.

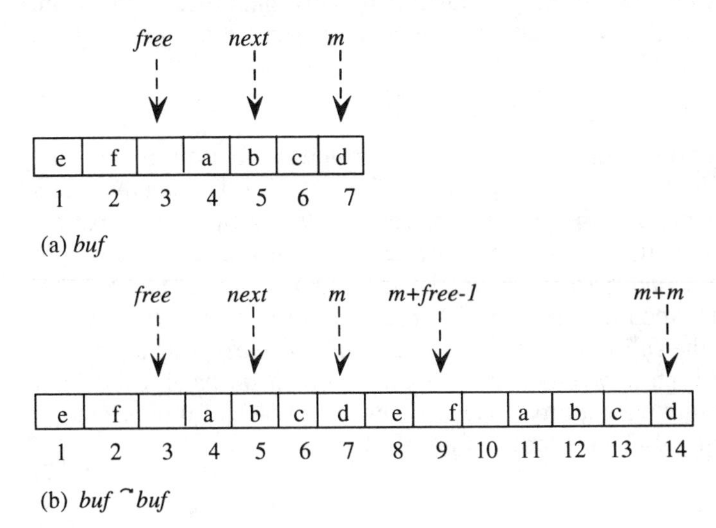

Figure 10.1

Figure 10.1 demonstrates this. Figure 10.1(a) shows the sequence *buf* which models a queue of maximum length 7 from which we wish to read ['b', ..., 'f']. The element 'a' lies outside the area of the buffer bounded by *next* and *free*–1 (remembering wrap-around). Therefore 'a' is data that is no longer in the logical queue, although still present in the physical buffer, having been previously read from the queue but not yet overwritten. Figure 10.1(b) depicts $q.buf \frown q.buf$ from which the required subsequence is easily specified because all its elements are now adjacent. (In the diagram, the '$q.$' prefixes are omitted for brevity.)

Review Question 10.3

Specify *retr-Queue* differently, retrieving the two subsequences of *buf* explicitly. ■

Exercise 10.9

Consider whether this representation is adequate by seeing whether an 'empty' buffer is representable in the concrete type.

Solution 10.9

Consideration of a concrete buffer of type *QueueR* suggests that to correspond to the empty buffer in the abstract type *Queue* the *next* pointer should have the same value as the *free* pointer. Therefore an example of an empty queue would be:

$$mk\text{-}Queue1([\text{'a'}, \text{'b'}, ..., \text{'z'}], 3, 3)$$

The values 'a', 'b', etc. are just values which have been 'left behind' in the buffer, i.e., values in the buffer which have been processed by a consumer process but have not been overwritten by a producer process. The value 3 is just an arbitrary example value less than m. (All that matters is that the read and write pointers be the same; another value could have been chosen.) Since $next = free$, the retrieve function applied to this value gives:

$$([\text{'a'}, \text{'b'}, ..., \text{'z'}] \frown [\text{'a'}, \text{'b'}, ..., \text{'z'}])(3, \ldots, m + 3 - 1)$$

Now the length of any non-empty subsequence is (top-index – bottom-index + 1), so the above expression is a sequence with $(m + 3 - 1) - 3 + 1$ elements, i.e. a sequence with m elements. But this ought to represent a *full* buffer in the abstract type. What this means is that there is an abstract value in *Queue*—the empty buffer—which has no counterpart in *Queue1*! Furthermore, there is no way that we can differentiate between an empty buffer and a full buffer since they would both be equivalent to the full buffer in the abstract state. Clearly, our attempt at producing a concrete type is wrong. The reification given on page 138 is not adequate despite its initial plausibility. Inadequacies in a choice of representation are often revealed during such an attempted proof.

■

A second reification of Queue

As an alternative to *Queue1*, we could count the number of accesses to the buffer by the consumer and the producer; if at any time they are the same the buffer is empty. If they differ by m the buffer is full.

Here is a formal specification of this solution:

$QueueR$ ::
  buf: $Info^*$
  $writes$: $\mathbb{N}$
  $reads$: $\mathbb{N}$

$inv\text{-}QueueR\ (q) \triangleq$
  $(\text{len } q.buf = m) \wedge (0 \leq (q.writes - q.reads)) \wedge ((q.writes - q.reads) \leq m))$

The invariant records the requirement that the buffer size is fixed. More importantly, it records that the number of reads can never exceed the number of writes, and that the amount of unread data must never overflow the buffer.

The second retrieve function

The second version of the retrieve function again allows for wraparound by indexing a double copy of the buffer. During the first filling of the buffer, the unread items would be at indexes (*reads* + 1, ..., *writes*). When more than *m* reads or writes have been performed, the positions within the buffer must be computed using the mod function to allow for wrap-around:

$retr\text{-}Queue$: $QueueR \rightarrow Queue$
$retr\text{-}Queue(q) \triangleq$
  let $bufbuf = (q.buf \frown q.buf)$ in
  let $startpos = (q.reads \text{ mod } m) + 1$ in
  let $endpos = (q.writes - 1) \text{ mod } m + 1$ in
  $bufbuf\,(startpos, ..., endpos)$

Exercise 10.10

Define *INITR* which initializes the queue to an empty state.

Solution 10.10

INITR
ext wr q: $QueueR$
pre true
post $\text{len } q.buf = 0 \wedge q.reads = 0 \wedge q.writes = 0$

The initial values in the buffer do not matter, but it must be of length *m* to satisfy the invariant.

■

Adequacy of QueueR with respect to retr-Queue

The next step that we have to carry out is the proof of adequacy of *QueueR* with respect to *Queue* and *retr-Queue*. We must show that:

$\forall q : Queue \bullet \exists qr : QueueR \bullet retr\text{-}Queue(qr) = q$

Exercise 10.11

Prove *QueueR* to be adequate with respect to *Queue* and the new version of *retr-Queue*.

Solution 10.11

We show that to each member *aq* of the type *Queue* of abstract queues, there is at least one corresponding member of *QueueR*. There will in fact be many corresponding members of *QueueR*, but to show there is at least one we just need to exhibit one of them and show that the retrieve function maps it to the correct member of *Queue*. The particular member of *QueueR* we shall choose is the one which results from inserting in order all the values from the abstract queue, into an empty instance of *QueueR*. This will result in the elements being at the start of the buffer, the number of reads being zero and the number of writes just len *aq*.

Because the buffer is constrained to be a sequence of length *m*, it must be padded out with arbitrary values to this length. For any abstract queue *aq* which is a member of *Queue*, we know that len $aq \le m$. Suppose *filler* is any arbitrary member of $Info^*$ such that len *aq* + len *filler* = *m*, i.e.:

$$\text{let } filler : Info^* \text{ be st len } aq + \text{len } filler = m$$

The concrete value *mk-QueueR*(*aq* ⁀ *filler*, len *aq*, 0) represents a value of *QueueR* with the component *buf* equal to *aq* ⁀ *filler*, *writes* equal to len *aq* and *reads* equal to zero. This corresponds to the abstract value *aq* because

$$\begin{aligned}
& retr\text{-}Queue(mk\text{-}QueueR(aq \frown filler, \text{len}(aq), 0)) \\
&= \text{let } bufbuf = (aq \frown filler) \frown (aq \frown filler) \text{ in} \\
&\quad \text{let } startpos = (0 \text{ mod } m) + 1 \text{ in} \\
&\quad \text{let } endpos = (\text{len } aq - 1) \text{ mod } m + 1 \text{ in} \\
&\quad bufbuf(startpos, ..., endpos) \\
&= \text{let } bufbuf = (aq \frown filler) \frown (aq \frown filler) \text{ in } bufbuf(1, ..., \text{len } aq) \\
&= aq
\end{aligned}$$

■

The concrete operations on QueueR

We now need to examine the concrete operations on *QueueR*.

Exercise 10.12

Specify the operations *ENQUEUER* and *DEQUEUER*, which respectively places items of type *Info* into the buffer and removes them. You will need to use the mathematical modulo operator, mod.

Solution 10.12

$$\begin{aligned}
& ENQUEUER(e: Info) \\
& \text{ext} \quad \text{wr } q: QueueR \\
& \text{pre} \quad q.writes - q.reads < m \\
& \text{post} \quad q.writes = \overleftarrow{q}.writes + 1 \wedge q.reads = \overleftarrow{q}.reads \wedge \\
& \qquad q.buf = \overleftarrow{q}.buf \dagger \{\overleftarrow{q}.writes \text{ mod } m + 1 \mapsto e\}
\end{aligned}$$

The number of writes has increased by one and the buffer is modified in the appropriate position.

$DEQUEUER(\,)\ r\colon Info$
ext wr $q\colon QueueR$
pre $q.writes > q.reads$
post $q.reads = \overleftarrow{q}.reads + 1 \wedge q.writes = \overleftarrow{q}.writes \ \wedge r = \overleftarrow{q}.buf(\overleftarrow{q}.reads \text{ mod } m + 1)$

The number of reads is increased by one and the next piece of information to be processed is read from the appropriate place in the buffer.

■

The two operations, *IS-EMPTY* and *IS-FULL*, check whether the concrete buffer is empty or full; if it is empty then the number of reads is equal to the number of writes and if it is full they differ by the size of the buffer.

Review Question 10.4
The invariant includes the clause $0 \leq (q.writes - q.reads) \wedge (q.writes - q.reads) \leq m$. If this had been omitted from the invariant, but you were told that it was made true initially by the initialization, could you deduce that it was an invariant?

■

Review Question 10.5
Specify *IS-EMPTYR* and *IS-FULLR*.

■

Checking the concrete operations on QueueR

We must demonstrate that the operations preserve the data invariant and also that the concrete operations satisfy the domain and result rules. As an example, we show that *ENQUEUER* satisfies the result rule.

For the *ENQUEUER* operation it is necessary to show

$$\begin{array}{l} \forall \overleftarrow{c}, c : QueueR \bullet \\ \quad \text{let } \overleftarrow{a} = retr\text{-}Queue(\overleftarrow{c}), a = retr\text{-}Queue(c) \text{ in} \\ \quad pre\text{-}ENQUEUE(\overleftarrow{a}) \wedge post\text{-}ENQUEUER(\overleftarrow{c}, c) \Rightarrow post\text{-}ENQUEUE(\overleftarrow{a}, a) \end{array}$$

Substituting for the pre- and post-condition functions and the retrieve function, proving the result rule demands that we prove:

$$\begin{array}{l} \forall \overleftarrow{c}, c : QueueR \bullet \\ \quad \text{let } \overleftarrow{a} = retr\text{-}Queue(\overleftarrow{c}), a = retr\text{-}Queue(c) \text{ in} \\ \quad \text{len } \overleftarrow{a} < m \ \wedge \\ \quad c.writes = \overleftarrow{c}.writes + 1 \wedge \\ \quad c.buf = \overleftarrow{c}.buf \dagger \{\overleftarrow{c}.writes \text{ mod } m + 1 \mapsto e\} \Rightarrow \ a = \overleftarrow{a} \frown [e] \end{array}$$

For the conclusion to be true, a would have to agree with $\overleftarrow{a}$ in all but the last element, and the last element of a would have to be e.

The definitions of $\overleftarrow{a}$ and a, from the retrieve function, are:

$$\overleftarrow{a} = (\overleftarrow{c}.buf \frown \overleftarrow{c}.buf)\ (1 + (\overleftarrow{c}.reads + 1) \text{ mod } m, \ldots, 1 + (m + \overleftarrow{c}.writes) \text{ mod } m)$$

$$a = (c.buf \frown c.buf)\ (1+(c.reads+1) \text{ mod } m, ..., 1+(m+c.writes) \text{ mod } m)$$

Because $c.writes = \overleftarrow{c}.writes+1$ and *reads* is not changed, all but the last elements of a and $\overleftarrow{a}$ are the same. The last element of a is at index $(c.writes \text{ mod } m)+1$, and from the left-hand side and the properties of the sequence modification operator, †, (see page 37) we know that this element is equal to e. Therefore, by assuming the left-hand side of the implication we can deduce the right-hand side, and so we have shown the implication is valid.

10.3 Summary of concepts

- A proposed refinement imposes proof obligations. The refined type must be shown to satisfy the domain rule, to demonstrate that it can represent all values of the abstract type, and each operation must be shown to satisfy the result rule, to demonstrate that it computes the correct result.
- Attempting to satisfy these proof obligations very often ends in failure, revealing unjustified assumptions and incorrectly specified refined operations.
- The enormous benefits which come from attempting to satisfy the proof obligations are lost if formal methods are used only as concise descriptive notations.

11 CORRECTNESS STATEMENTS AND PROOF RULES

So far in this book we have seen how VDM can be used to specify the required behaviour of programs. We saw how such a specification can be successively refined, both in terms of the data types manipulated and the operations performed on them. This refinement can be repeated until the data types are close to those that are familiar to us in various programming languages. The specifications will grow ever more detailed but will never actually produce an executable program; specifications are restricted to describing *what* state changes should be brought about, whereas implementation requires us to decide *how* particular sequences of statements will actually change states. At some stage lines of code have to be written in a programming language in an attempt to produce program code that does indeed satisfy the specification.

One way to make use of VDM in software development is to confine it to the task of specifying programs. A specification would eventually be handed to a programmer, who would then make use of traditional approaches of design and testing to implement the program. When the program was finished, it would be hoped that it did indeed satisfy the specification, and testing might tend to confirm this hope, but there would be no practical formal way of demonstrating correctness. If a formal definition exists of the programming language used to implement the program, a formal approach is possible, though usually impractical for sizeable programs. Much of the use of formal methods in industry is currently confined to *specification* rather than *development*. Thus, for most companies, there is a gulf between having a specification and having a program, and this gulf is bridged by non-formal methods. What is required is a method where proof and program design and implementation proceed hand-in-hand.

We illustrate this idea by extending the formal treatment down to the level of the statements in a programming language. Note that most of the new formal notation in this and subsequent chapters is not VDM-SL.

11.1 Specifying programming statements

Each statement of a language can be thought of as being an implementation of a particular, very detailed specification. Consider, for example, the Pascal statement:

```
x := y * y
```

This could be thought of as one possible implementation of the trivial operation specified as follows:

SET-X-TO-Y-SQUARED
ext wr x: $\mathbb{Z}$,
rd y : $\mathbb{Z}$
pre true
post $x = y \times y$

Programming languages provide a number of such basic operations, such as assignment, together with ways of combining them, such as sequences (between **begin** and **end**) and loops. The programmer's task is to combine operations to produce program code which implements a larger, more complex specification. Thus, if we are to extend the VDM approach to the level of program statements, each statement must have a rigorous definition of what it does, in the form of which pre-condition is necessary for a statement to achieve a valid post-condition.

Besides their simple, unstructured statements, programming languages also provide various ways of combining statements into larger groups. These include sequencing, conditional statements (such as **if** statements) and loop statements (such as **while** statements). For each method of combining statements, we shall need to develop a proof rule which shows how the meaning of the whole relates to the meanings of the constituent statements. Ideally, these rules would be provided as part of the reference manual of a language and they would be the way in which the meaning of each construct was explained, instead of the paragraphs of English which are generally used. This has not been done for the subset of Pascal which we shall be using as the target language in this part, so we shall have to develop the proof rules ourselves.

Once the basic mechanism of proof rules is provided, it is theoretically possible to take an existing program and attempt to prove that it meets its specification. However, such proofs very rapidly become dauntingly large, error-prone and unmanageable. If instead, while the program is being developed, the structure of its eventual proof is borne in mind, programming choices will be made in the light of the available proof rules, and the proof can be constructed at the same time as the program itself.

This chapter develops proof rules for a number of programming constructs available in Pascal-like languages, and presents some simple examples of their use in building programs. It attempts to present proofs in such a way that they should be compelling, but not in so much detail that you are swamped by uninteresting steps. The aim here is to be rigorous rather than totally formal.

This chapter is about how to proceed from specification to program code, and how by constructing the code systematically one can have confidence that the resulting software is correct. To achieve this we need two tools—one notational and one methodological. The former is an extension to the VDM specification language used to express the relationship between a specification and the fragment of code which implements it. The latter is a system of proof rules which enables us to construct correct implementations.

Implementing operations

We have seen plenty of examples of the use of VDM to specify operations. We now want to extend the syntax of the VDM specification language to permit such specifications to include the code which implements them. This is done so that actual programs can be built up by allowing code in a programming language to be inserted between the pre and post clauses, once it has been proved to satisfy those clauses. Consider the following (rather odd) operation which multiplies x by 5, and subtracts 1 from y.

MULTX-DECY
ext wr x: $\mathbb{Z}$ wr y: $\mathbb{Z}$
pre $x < 100 \wedge y > 20$

```
x := x * 5;
y := y - 1
```

post $x = 5 \times \overleftarrow{x} \wedge y = \overleftarrow{y} - 1$

The way to read this extended 'specification' is first to read the VDM which states *what* the operation means (i.e. what software function it specifies) and then to study the program fragment between the pre and post clauses—the details of *how* the operation is to be provided. Care must be taken to distinguish between the mathematical representation of the meaning of the operation and the less tractable program notation; we emphasize the difference between them by using a typewriter font for the code, Pascal in this case.

Note that the identifiers which appear in the program fragment denote program variables (components of a program state) which implement the components of the abstract (VDM) state. Usually this means that the Pascal identifiers match the state identifiers in the external variables clause of the operation. Thus, we shall refer to the program x and the abstract x as if they are the same entity; they are *not* the same but distinguishing them further would overcomplicate the text.

Exercise 11.1

Include some Pascal code in the following operation which initializes the *number* and *rate* parts of an abstract state.

INIT-NUMS
ext wr *number*: $\mathbb{N}$ wr *rate*: $\mathbb{R}$
pre true
post $number = 0 \wedge rate = 1.0$

Solution 11.1

INIT-NUMS
ext wr *number*: $\mathbb{N}$
wr *rate*: $\mathbb{R}$
pre true

```
number := 0;
rate := 1.0
```

post $number = 0 \wedge rate = 1.0$

■

11.2 Correctness statements

The extension suggested in Section 11.1 has the advantage that the specification is easily available while one is reading the code, and may be a good way of presenting the finished code for a particular project. However, it proves a little cumbersome when we want to talk about the structure of proof rules in general: we shall need to present several program fragments together and printing them underneath each other makes it difficult to see structural patterns. An alternative notation is therefore used, in which the pre- and post-conditions, and the statements that implement them, are laid out horizontally instead of vertically. The example used in the previous section would be expressed:

$$\{x < 100 \wedge y > 20\}\ \texttt{x := 5 * x; y := y - 1}\ \{x = 5 \times \overleftarrow{x} \wedge y = \overleftarrow{y} - 1\}$$

Here the pre-condition has been placed in curly brackets to the left of the statements, and the post-condition to the right. This combination of a piece of program with pre- and post-conditions we shall call a ***correctness statement***. It can be thought of as asserting that in any circumstances in which the pre-condition holds, executing the fragment program will bring about a situation in which the post-condition holds. It makes no claim about what will happen if the program is executed in a state where the pre-condition does not hold.

Correctness statements can clearly be either ***valid*** or ***invalid***. They are valid if the program fragment really does make the post-condition true whenever it is executed from a state where the pre-condition is true. They are invalid if this is just wishful thinking, and the post-condition cannot be guaranteed.

Some examples of valid correctness statements with English commentaries are as follows:

$$\{x \geq 0\}\ \texttt{x := x + 1}\ \{x > 0\}$$

If x is greater than or equal to 0, then, when 1 is added to it, the result must be greater than 0:

$$\{x > 10\}\ \texttt{x := x + 1}\ \{x = \overleftarrow{x} + 1 \wedge x > 11\}$$

If x is greater than 10, then, when 1 is added to it, the result must be one greater than its previous value, and greater than 11.

Exercise 11.2

Say why the following correctness statement is valid:

$\{x+y=100\}$ `x := x + 1; y := y - 1` $\{x+y=100\}$

Solution 11.2

If the sum of x and y is 100 then adding 1 to one variable and subtracting 1 from the other cannot have any effect on their sum, which is still 100. Hence the correctness statement is valid.

■

An example of an invalid correctness statement is:

$\{r=n!\}$ `r := r` **`div`** `n;  n := n - 1` $\{r=n!\}$

If $n = 0$ and $r = 1$, the post-condition cannot be guaranteed to hold after executing the assignments, so the correctness statement is invalid.

Review Question 11.1

Which of the following correctness statements is valid? If invalid, say why.

(i) $\{x>0\}$ `y := x * x` $\{y>0\}$

(ii) $\{x<0\}$ `y := x * x` $\{y<0\}$

■

Note that the braces (the curly brackets) used in correctness statements have nothing to do with VDM sets. They simply separate the conditions from the statements. They are much like the comments in Pascal, in that they contain information *about* the program source code rather than code itself.

Because correctness statements may be invalid, if we are to reach true conclusions when reasoning about programs, it is necessary to start with some correctness statements which are known to be valid, and from them use proof rules to deduce other valid correctness statements. Ideally, an initial set of valid correctness statements would be provided by the designers of a programming language. These would define precisely what the meaning of each construct is. Unfortunately, older programming languages usually have the meaning of their constructs defined in English rather than formally, so we will have to spend time establishing the initial set of correctness statements defining the meaning of Pascal statements before we can use them in reasoning about programs.

The rest of the chapter is concerned with correctness statements in two different ways. Firstly, it is concerned with the correctness statements for Pascal statements—ranging from the simple assignment statement to the more complex ones such as compound and conditional statements. Secondly, it is concerned with the development of proof rules which show how correctness statements for the more complex constructs can be derived from the correctness statements of their components.

Exercise 11.3

What is the meaning of a correctness statement where the pre-condition is just a boolean constant:

(i) {true} `x := x + 13` $\{x = \overleftarrow{x} + 13\}$

(ii) {false} `x := 27` $\{x = 1\}$

Solution 11.3

(i) A correctness statement asserts that in all states where the pre-condition evaluates to true, executing the program statement will yield a state in which the post-condition is true. If the pre-condition is the constant true, this condition holds for any state, so the correctness statement asserts that executing the program statement in any system state whatsoever will make the post-condition true. For example:

{true}`x := x + 13` $\{x = \overleftarrow{x} + 13\}$

means that this particular assignment statement is defined to be a meaningful operation in all possible system states, and that it always brings about the given post-condition.

(ii) The constant false evaluates to true in no possible states at all. The correctness statement therefore asserts that in the states where false evaluates to true, executing the body will make the post-condition true. There are no such states, so the correctness statement therefore tells us nothing. For example:

{false} `x := 27` $\{x = 1\}$

is a valid (though not very useful) correctness statement asserting that in all system states satisfying {false}—i.e. in no states at all—the statement `x := 27` makes the post-condition true.

■

General form of correctness statements

The general form of a correctness statement is:

$\{P\}$ `S` $\{R\}$

`S` is one or more statements in a programming language, P stands for the pre-condition and R for the relation that is the post-condition. The conditions are both boolean expressions; they are exactly the same as the pre- and post-conditions we have met in earlier chapters. They will relate the values of variables which are either passed as parameters to an operation, or are declared in the ext part of an operation specification, or are the results of an operation.

P will involve just the values of variables before the execution of the operation `S`. In general R involves reference to the values of the state both before and after the operation of `S`, and will therefore need to use both hooked and unhooked variables.

The relation of the two is illustrated in Figure 11.1. We often use names beginning with a σ (the Greek letter sigma) to refer to the value of a system state (i.e. the value composed of the values of all the variables constituting the state). Thus Figure 11.1 shows the statement *S* operating on a state's value σ_0 to produce the state's value σ_1. The pre-condition *P* of *S* is evaluated on just σ_0 whereas the post-condition *R* is evaluated on both σ_0 and σ_1. *P* is thus a boolean function of one state value, whereas *R* is a boolean function of two values; therefore *R* expresses a relationship between the values of that state before and after execution. This relationship is required whenever *S* is executed on a state which satisfies *P*. If a state does not satisfy *P*, we can say nothing about the final state—it is undefined.

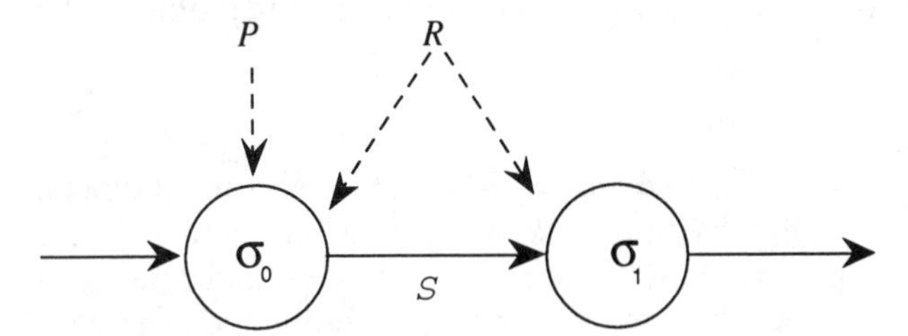

Figure 11.1

Conditions expressed as functions of the state

Consider an operation which involves two variables: the pre-condition for such an operation will be an expression with at most two different variables. Another operation involving three variables will have a pre-condition involving up to three variables. Though this varying number of variables causes no problems when discussing any particular specification, when we wish to make general remarks about all specifications it is convenient if all pre-conditions can be in the same format.

Although a particular VDM operation will typically operate on only a few of the total number of variables defined in the system (i.e. on a few components of the state), it is often convenient to think of it as operating on them all. Thus, in a system with three variables, *x*, *y* and *z*, an operation to change the value of *x* will in VDM make no reference to *y* or *z*. We shall, however, think of such an operation as operating on the entire set of variables, the state, even though it may leave *y* and *z* unaltered. It is convenient to behave as though there was a composite data type defined which contained all the separate system variables as components. For example, in a system with three variables we could imagine grouping them into a composite type called *System-state*:

System-state ::
$x : \mathbb{N}$
$y : \mathbb{R}$
$z : \mathbb{N}$

Every operation can now be viewed as operating on a single variable of type *System-state*, rather than on a number of separate variables. The convention makes easier general discussions about all operations, even when they have varying numbers of external variables. The values of each separate variable can then be accessed by using the field selectors (such as x, y or z) on the state variable σ.

Instead of expressing a pre-condition simply as a boolean expression of a few variables, we will think of it as a boolean function, which takes a whole state as its parameter and yields true or false. (For simplicity, we will ignore input parameters.) This will make it easier to discuss the evaluation of conditions in different states.

An example of a boolean function P as a pre-condition of an operation on the system state might be:

$$P(\sigma) \triangleq \sigma.x = \sigma.y + 10$$

This evaluates to true in any system state where $x=y+10$ and to false in all others.

Whereas the pre-condition in a correctness statement is a function of just a single state value (i.e. the state value before the statement is executed) a post-condition R in general involves both the values of the state before and after execution. (It is because it expresses a *relation* between two values that we choose the letter R.) The relationship might be that the value of x in state σ_1 is greater than the value of x in state value σ_0. We shall therefore need to be able to refer separately to values of x in the two different values of the system state.

Thus we could write the above example as:

$$R(\sigma_0, \sigma_1) \triangleq \sigma_0.x < \sigma_1.x$$

This captures the fact that between these two particular values of the state x has increased.

Review Question 11.2

For the following correctness statement, express the pre- and post-conditions as functions of a single state value:

$$\{x < y\}\ x := x + y\ \{x < 2 \times \overleftarrow{x}\}$$

■

When we define a relation R between two values of the state, σ_0 and σ_1, it is important to realize that these state value names are simply the names of parameters to the relation R. They could be replaced by any other names. We know that the following definitions of f are equivalent:

$$f(x) \triangleq x + 15$$

$$f(y) \triangleq y + 15$$

We can read these as 'for any value (x or y), f(of the value) is the value plus 15'.

Similarly, the definition:

$$R(\sigma_0, \sigma_1) \triangleq \sigma_0.x < \sigma_1.x \wedge \sigma_0.y > \sigma_1.y$$

could as well have been written:

$$R(\sigma_A, \sigma_B) \triangleq \sigma_A.x < \sigma_B.x \wedge \sigma_A.y > \sigma_B.y$$

What matters is the relation being defined, not the names of the particular parameters. In defining a relation, names like σ_A are arbitrary.

Exercise 11.4

Suppose that for any state values σ_A and σ_B the post-condition relations $R1$ and $R2$ are defined by:

$$R1(\sigma_A, \sigma_B) \triangleq \sigma_A.x < \sigma_B.x \wedge \sigma_A.y > \sigma_B.y$$

$$R2(\sigma_A, \sigma_B) \triangleq \sigma_A.x = \sigma_B.x + 13$$

Suppose you are told that $R1$ holds between particular state values σ_8 and σ_9, and $R2$ holds between σ_9 and σ_{10}, what can be said about the relation between σ_8 and σ_{10}?

Solution 11.4

The point of the question is to avoid getting confused between formal and actual parameters: here σ_8, σ_9 and σ_{10} are real particular state values and σ_A and σ_B are just arbitrary names for formal parameters used in definitions.

We know that $R1$ holds between particular states σ_8 and σ_9, and $R2$ holds between σ_9 and σ_{10}. Substituting in the definitions of $R1$ and $R2$ we know that:

$$R1(\sigma_8, \sigma_9) \text{ is } \sigma_8.x < \sigma_9.x \wedge \sigma_8.y > \sigma_9.y$$

$$R2(\sigma_9, \sigma_{10}) \text{ is } \sigma_9.x = \sigma_{10}.x + 13$$

Combining these gives:

$$\sigma_8.x < \sigma_9.x \wedge \sigma_8.y > \sigma_9.y \wedge (\sigma_9.x = \sigma_{10}.x + 13)$$

By substituting for $\sigma_9.x$ we can eliminate some of the references to values of variables in σ_9. Of what is left, the only relationship we can assert directly between σ_8 and σ_{10} not involving any variables in state σ_9 is :

$$\sigma_8.x < \sigma_{10}.x + 13$$

■

The ability to combine relationships expressed between different values of the state will be needed when we come to consider sequences of program statements. For each separate statement we will know a relationship between its input and output values, and we will need to express a relationship between the input and output values of the whole sequence of statements.

The role of pre- and post-conditions in correctness statements

Note that there can be more than one valid correctness statement involving any particular piece of program. For example, all of the following, which involve `x := 23`, are valid.

$\{x > 0\}$ `x := 23` $\{is\text{-}prime(x)\}$

$\{x > 10\}$ `x := 23` $\{is\text{-}odd(x)\}$

$\{\mathsf{true}\}$ `x := 23` $\{x = 23\}$

In reasoning about a particular program involving this assignment statement, any one of these may be relevant. Besides their use in reasoning about existing code fragments, another use of correctness statements is in defining the meaning of Pascal statements such as `x := 23`. Clearly the definition of Pascal could not specify every possible valid correctness statement for each construct, so it must give the most precise formulation possible that captures the essence of its meaning. The statement

```
x := 23
```

can be used when it is required to force x to be positive, or greater than 15, or greater than 10, or exactly 23. If the Pascal programming manual told us only that it made x positive, we could not use it in the other cases, whereas if we are told that it makes x equal to 23, we can deduce that it also makes x positive. Thus, when using correctness statements to define a language construct, the post-condition should be expressed as strongly as possible: it aims to capture everything that can be guaranteed to be true after the execution of that construct.

Consider now how the pre-condition is used when specifying the meaning of the Pascal statement:

```
y := 1/x
```

This statement will successfully bring about a post-condition of $x \times y = 1$ when $\overleftarrow{x} > 10$ before execution.[1] It will also do it provided $\overleftarrow{x} > 3$, and indeed for any non-zero x. Thus there are many possible pre-conditions which successfully guarantee the post-condition. For the statement to be as widely useful as possible, we want to know what are the minimum conditions that have to be observed before it can be used. That is, we need to know the *weakest* pre-condition that guarantees that executing the statement will bring about the post-condition. In this case, if we are told that the statement works whenever $\overleftarrow{x} \neq 0$, we can deduce that it also works when $\overleftarrow{x} > 3$. If we had merely been told that it worked for $\overleftarrow{x} > 3$, we would have no knowledge of its behaviour for values of 2, 1, –1, –2 and so on.

Thus, when correctness statements are used to give the meaning of the constructs of a programming language, the pre-condition is made as weak as possible, and the post-condition as strong as possible. However, when we are given a

---

[1] Unfortunately the limited precision of floating point arithmetic, which is usually used for implementing real numbers such as `x` and `y` means that `x`× `1/x` is not usually exactly equal to 1. We ignore this problem.

specification of an operation and are looking for program statements to implement it, it is very unlikely that the operation's conditions will exactly match the defined conditions of any existing statement of the language. We might have a requirement to make x odd, but all the statements we have definitions for merely make x equal to 1 or 2 or 3 and so on. We must therefore develop a logical mechanism which we can use to deduce, from the defining conditions of statements specified in language manuals, what other conditions will also hold. For example, we might want to deduce that any statement that set x to 3 thereby also made x odd and thus satisfied the specified requirement.

More generally, we must be able to combine operations into larger components (e.g. program units or procedures), and we must be able to make suitable deductions relating the conditions of the larger operations to those specifying the component operations.

11.3 Proof rules

A proof takes a number of valid correctness statements and produces a new valid correctness statement. Proofs are laid out with a number of ***premises***, separated by commas, above a line, and the conclusion below the line. For example, an alleged proof might be expressed as in Figure 11.2. This shows the two premises or assumptions above the line, and the conclusion below the line.

$$\frac{\{ x \geq 0 \}\ \texttt{x := x + 1}\ \{ x \neq 0 \},\ \{ x \neq 0 \}\ \texttt{y := 1/x}\ \{ x \times y = 1 \}}{\{ x \geq 0 \}\ \texttt{x := x + 1; y := 1/x}\ \{ x \times y = 1 \}}$$

Figure 11.2

This alleged proof aims to show that given the first two correctness statements, each about a single Pascal statement, it is permissible to deduce the lower correctness statement about the piece of Pascal made by joining the pair by a semicolon representing sequential execution. But is this a valid deduction?

A ***proof rule*** is a rule which says which deductions of this form are in fact valid deductions. Whether or not this is a valid proof will depend on the Pascal definition of sequencing as expressed using the semicolon. In another language the semicolon might have been defined to have the meaning that in `S1; S2`, one of the two statements was randomly picked and executed and the other ignored; under this definition our alleged proof would clearly not be valid. If a semicolon means that the statements are executed in turn, then our proof probably is valid. Thus it is the proof rule for the semicolon that precisely defines its meaning.

We therefore need to have a number of proof rules to tell us when it is valid to infer a new correctness statement from a number of others. Some proof rules are needed to justify various rearrangements of logical expressions that we will wish to make in the pre- and post-conditions. The more interesting proof rules are concerned with how we can validly deduce correctness statements about large pieces of program from correctness statements about the component smaller pieces.

A programming language consists of certain simple, unstructured statement types, together with various means of combining them into larger pieces of program. In Pascal, the simple statements provided include assignment, read, and write statements. The methods of combination include sequencing (semicolon), selection (i.e. **`case`** and **`if-then-else`** statements), and loops (e.g. **`repeat`** and **`while`** statements). The meaning of any of these statements is specified by giving correctness statements for them. The meaning of a combination is given by a proof rule which says how the pre- and post-conditions of the combination is related to the pre- and post-conditions of the constituent statements.

Before we can construct proofs about real Pascal programs, we must have available both correctness statements for each statement type in Pascal, and valid proof rules for each way the language provides for combining statements. Ideally, this should be provided by the language designer as part of the language definition. We now give the correctness statements and combination proof rules for some Pascal statements.

The rule of consequence

Our first proof rule is fairly simple. It is concerned not with combinations of Pascal statements but with rearranging the pre- and post-conditions of a single statement. It allows us to make a pre-condition more restrictive and a post-condition less restrictive. The rule is:

$$\frac{PP \Rightarrow P,\ \{P\}\ S\ \{R\},\ R \Rightarrow RR}{\{PP\}\ S\ \{RR\}}$$

This says that, given a correctness statement $\{P\}\ S\ \{R\}$ for some S, if we can find a condition PP that implies P, and if from R we can infer a condition RR, then we can also deduce the valid correctness statement:

$$\{PP\}\ S\ \{RR\}$$

For example, consider a statement S about which we know:

$$\{x > 5\}\ S\ \{y > 25\}$$

We can certainly find a PP such that $PP \Rightarrow P$; for example, PP might be $x > 10$ because $x > 10 \Rightarrow x > 5$. Similarly, we can find an RR which we can infer from R, such as $y > 15$, because $y > 25 \Rightarrow y > 15$.

The rule of consequence tells us that it *is* therefore valid to deduce:

$$\{x > 10\}\ S\ \{y > 15\}$$

Exercise 11.5

A program fragment called $SQRT$ sets y to the square root of x under certain conditions. Given the correctness statement $\{x \geq 0\}\ SQRT\ \{y^2 = x\}$, which of the following is true by virtue of the rule of consequence?

(i) $\{x > 0\}\ SQRT\ \{y^2 = x\}$

(ii) $\{x \geq 0\}\ SQRT\ \{y^4 = x^2\}$

(iii) $\{x > 100\}\ SQRT\ \{y > 10\}$

(iv) $\{x \neq 0\}\ SQRT\ \{y^2 = x\}$

Solution 11.5

(i) True. $\{x > 0\}$ implies $\{x \geq 0\}$

(ii) True. $\{x > 0\} \Rightarrow \{x \geq 0\}$ and $\{y^2 = x\} \Rightarrow \{y^4 = x^2\}$

(iii) False. It is valid, but cannot be demonstrated by this rule alone, as the post-condition $\{y^2 = x\}$ by itself does not imply $\{y > 10\}$. To show $y > 10$ also needs the pre-condition to still be true after the operation if the deduction is to go through. The next section covers deductions involving the pre-condition.

(iv) False. Clearly if $x = -1$ it must be false. The reason the deduction fails is that $\{x \neq 0\}$ does not imply $\{x \geq 0\}$.

■

In the rule of consequence, *PP* is more restrictive than *P*, in that it is true of fewer possible states of the system than *P*. It is sometimes described as being 'strengthened' to *PP*, and this can lead to confusion as we sometimes think of a strong statement as being a very general one, whereas here we mean that it has become more specific and less general. Similarly, *R* is described as being 'weakened' to *RR*. *RR* is true not only of all states where *R* is true, but also of other general states. The states where *R* is true form a subset of the states where *RR* is true.

An alternative way of looking at the same rule is to observe that if logically $PP \Rightarrow P$, then given a state in which *PP* holds, one does not have to execute any Pascal code to make *P* true. If, for consistency, one wants to execute a Pascal statement, the null statement will do. This is expressed as:

$$\{PP\}\ \{P\}$$

where the space between the two conditions can be taken to represent a null statement. Thus we could restate the rule of consequence as a rule for combining three statements, two of which are null.

$$\frac{\{PP\}\ \{P\},\ \{P\}\ S\ \{R\},\ \{R\}\ \{RR\}}{\{PP\}\ S\ \{RR\}}$$

Inherit-the-pre-condition rule

When manipulating pre- and post-conditions to fit a desired specification it is often important to note explicitly that if a condition *P* is true before executing a statement, *P* must be expressed in terms of the values of variables *before* execution. Even after execution, that same condition on the variables before execution must still be true. Thus, for instance, if we want to be able to justify the move from:

$$\{x > 0\}\ S\ \{y = \overleftarrow{x}^2\}$$

to:

$$\{x > 0\}\ S\ \{y = \overleftarrow{x}^2 \wedge \overleftarrow{x} > 0\}$$

we can express this by saying that in a post-condition it is permissible to inherit the pre-condition. As in VDM specifications, there is a slight possibility of confusion here, because the pre-condition is expressed using unhooked names to refer to the old values of variables, whereas the post-condition refers to both old and new values, but uses hooked names to refer to the old values. In cases where we want to inherit a pre-condition and copy it across to form part of the post-condition, it is vital that in the post-condition, the unhooked name x is not used ambiguously to refer to both old and new values. Therefore, when the pre-condition is copied over into the post-condition, hooks must be added.

A simple application of the rule allows the deduction from:

$$\{x>0\}\ S\ \{y=\overleftarrow{x}^2\}$$

to:

$$\{x>0\}\ S\ \{y=\overleftarrow{x}^2 \wedge \overleftarrow{x}>0\}$$

An example where care in adding a hook is vital is the following. Given:

$$\{x<5\}\ x := x + 3\ \{x>\overleftarrow{x}\}$$

we inherit the pre-condition, correctly giving:

$$\{x<5\}\ x := x + 3\ \{x>\overleftarrow{x} \wedge \overleftarrow{x}<5\}$$

If we had omitted to add the hooks when copying the pre-condition, we would end up with an alleged post-condition of $\{x > \overleftarrow{x} \wedge x < 5\}$ which is clearly not the case if x happens to be 4 initially.

If we have a general pre-condition P, the version of P produced by adding hooks to all the variables is represented by $\overleftarrow{P}$. The rule about inheriting pre-conditions can therefore be expressed as:

$$\frac{\{P\}\ S\ \{R\}}{\{P\}\ S\ \{R \wedge \overleftarrow{P}\}}$$

Review Question 11.3

Which of the following alleged proofs are valid according to the inherit-the-pre-condition rule?

(i) $$\frac{\{x>1\}\ S\ \{y>1\}}{\{x>1\}\ S\ \{\overleftarrow{x}>1 \wedge y>1\}}$$

(ii) $$\frac{\{x>2\}\ S\ \{x<0\}}{\{x>2\}\ S\ \{\overleftarrow{x}<0 \wedge x>2\}}$$

(iii) $$\frac{\{x>2\}\ S\ \{x<0\}}{\{x>2\}\ S\ \{x<0 \wedge x>2\}}$$

■

11.4 Correctness statement for assignments

The assignment of a value to a variable is probably the most common operation in Pascal programs. An assignment causes the variable to which it refers to contain the assigned value. Assignment statements therefore have very simple correctness statements, like the following:

{true} `x := 27` $\{x = 27\}$

An assignment statement in Pascal consists of a variable name, followed by the symbol `:=` followed by an expression. This arrangement of symbols can be stated formally by the following syntax rule:

assignment statement ::= *variable* := *expression*

The italic words are names of syntactic classes and the symbol ::= can be read as 'is defined to be'. The rule therefore says:

> an assignment statement is defined to be anything which designates a variable, followed by :=, followed by anything designating an expression.

If we ignore the possibility of the expression having an undefined value, the correctness statement for assignment can be generalized thus:

{true} *variable* := *expression* {*variable* = *expression*}

This single correctness statement really represents an infinite number of different correctness statements, one for each possible variable and expression in the language.

Note that the expression is computed using the values before the assignment statement, so they should all be hooked. Statements like `x := x + 1` are common in Pascal programs; we rather take for granted that the `x` on the right-hand side is the value in the variable *before* the statement. Thus, if *variable* occurs within *expression* it is vital to note this difference as in:

{true} `x := 2 * x + 3 * y` $\{x = 2 \times \overleftarrow{x} + 3 \times \overleftarrow{y}\}$

We will use correctness statements for language constructs such as assignment in two distinct ways. We will use them 'forwards' in order to justify a post-condition, given a pre-condition and the assignment. We can also use them 'backwards' as a way of choosing which assignment statement to include in a program, given a post-condition which it is desired to bring about.

Thus we might be trying to implement an operation whose specification is:

ALTER-X-AND-Y
ext wr x: $\mathbb{Z}$ rd y: $\mathbb{Z}$
pre $x > 10$
post $x = 2 \times \overleftarrow{x} + 3 \times \overleftarrow{y}$

With luck we might recognize that the post-condition is one we have seen before, in the correctness statement above. If we could show that the pre-condition of the operation ($x > 10$) implied the pre-condition of the Pascal statement (true), it would mean that the operation was required to work in just a subset of the cases where the assignment does indeed bring about the required post-condition. We could use this Pascal statement to implement the operation.

In fact it is possible to show that $x > 10 \Rightarrow$ true, so by the rule of consequence we can deduce that

$$\{x > 10\}\ \texttt{x := 2 * x + 3 * y}\ \{x = 2 \times \overleftarrow{x} + 3 \times \overleftarrow{y}\}$$

The Pascal statement `x := 2 * x + 3 * y` does therefore correctly implement the desired operation. We discovered this by recognizing the post-condition of an existing statement, using its correctness statement *backwards* to determine its pre-condition, and then showing that in the cases required by the specification the pre-condition was indeed satisfied.

In contrast, when we, as software developers, come to present a proof of our implementation to the client we will use the correctness statement the other way, arguing *forwards*. We will say that from the specification of the operation we are guaranteed that the pre-condition $x > 10$ is true. Therefore, we can deduce that the pre-condition of the Pascal statement is true. By the definition of the Pascal statement we therefore know its post-condition to be true, and as this is the same as the post-condition of the operation, we know that its specification is satisfied.

Therefore, when reading proofs, bear in mind that though logically they are to be read forwards, when building proofs, and building programs that are to be proved, we always start at the conclusion and try to assemble the steps that will take us back to the premises.

Review Question 11.4

What do we mean by using correctness statements 'forwards' and 'backwards'?

■

Pre-conditions of assignment statements

When arguing forwards, the pre-condition on an assignment statement is usually just the constant true. One might say that the pre-condition of `y := 1/x` is not true, owing to the possibility of division by zero. It is clear that restrictions must be imposed when an expression involving operations such as division is to be evaluated. (As this is a general problem which affects not just expressions used in assignment statements but all expressions, such as those in array indexes, and the actual parameters of a procedure, it is not clear whether it is better to build the restriction into each type of statement that uses expressions, or capture it once in the definition of expression evaluation. The issue is beyond the scope of the current discussion; when necessary we will constrain the whole assignment statement.)

We have seen that the post-condition of an assignment statement like `x := 27` is $\{x = 27\}$, while the pre-condition is usually just {true}. This enables us to argue backwards when constructing programs, thus: if we want to bring about a condition that $x = 27$, we can use the assignment statement (`x := 27`), with a trivial pre-condition. Suppose, however, we try to implement an operation whose post-condition is:

$$\{x = 27 \wedge x + y < 50\}$$

It is not clear if we can still use the assignment statement `x := 27`, and if so, under what pre-conditions. It clearly will not be of use if, for example, we have the pre-condition $\{y = 100\}$. We therefore need a way of taking a complex post-condition and passing it 'backwards' through an assignment statement to discover a suitable pre-condition which, if true, will ensure that the assignment statement does guarantee the post-condition.

In the current case, $\{x + y < 50\}$ is to be true after the assignment statement. Because the assignment statement guarantees that $\{x = 27\}$, the post-condition is equivalent to $\{27 + y < 50\}$ or $\{y < 23\}$. The variable y is not changed by the assignment, so any condition on y must also hold in the pre-condition. In other words, we have deduced that:

$$\{y<23\}\ \texttt{x := 27}\ \{x=27 \wedge x+y<50\}$$

We could now set about seeing whether in the desired program fragment it really is the case that $\{y < 23\}$. If so, we have generated provable code to establish the post-condition.

When we come to present the proof that the program fragment does indeed establish the post-condition, we will start with the fact that $\{y < 23\}$ and argue by the rule of consequence, thus:

$$\frac{\{y<23\} \Rightarrow \{\text{true}\},\ \{\text{true}\}\ \texttt{x := 27}\ \{x=27\}}{\{y<23\}\ \texttt{x := 27}\ \{x=27\}}$$

Then, by inheriting the pre-condition we get:

$$\frac{\{y<23\}\ \texttt{x := 27}\ \{x=27\}}{\{y<23\}\ \texttt{x := 27}\ \{x=27 \wedge \overleftarrow{y}<23\}}$$

Because y is not changed by the assignment, we know that $y = \overleftarrow{y}$ and so the post-condition is $\{x = 27 \wedge y < 23\}$. We can show arithmetically that:

$$x=27 \wedge y<23 \Rightarrow x+y<50$$

So by the rule of consequence, we can weaken the post-condition, concluding:

$$\{y<23\}\ \texttt{x := 27}\ \{x+y<50\}$$

We have made use of knowledge about assignment statements in two different ways. We have used it as a design rule, to suggest what code might be used to bring about some desired post-condition. Then we have used it, starting with a pre-condition and some code, to deduce the post-condition of that code.

When used as a design rule, we started with a post-condition and noticed that it was of the form $\{x = \textit{expression} \wedge R\}$. This suggested that an assignment statement might be used to establish the post-condition. We are therefore aiming to construct a correctness statement of the form:

$$\{???\}\ \texttt{x := }\ \textit{expression}\ \{x = \textit{expression} \wedge R\}$$

The problem is to know under what conditions $\{???\}$ this will be valid. The assignment will establish the condition $\{x = \textit{expression}\}$—one part of the post-condition. For the whole post-condition to be true after the assignment, in the pre-condition a modified R must be true, where every occurrence of x has been replaced by *expression*. This is called 'pushing the post-condition back through the assignment statement'. In the above case we wanted to establish the post-condition $\{x = 27 \wedge x + y < 50\}$. We concluded that this could be done by an assignment statement `x := 27` under the pre-conditions '$x + y < 50$ with x replaced by 27', i.e. $27 + y < 50$ or $y < 23$.

The pre-condition that we get by pushing back the post-condition is the weakest possible pre-condition that guarantees the post-condition. There are of course an indefinite number of correctness statements about any given assignment statement. For example, we have just established that:

$$\{ y < 23 \}\ \texttt{x := 27}\ \{ x = 27 \wedge x + y < 50\}$$

It is also true that:

$$\{ y < 10 \}\ \texttt{x := 27}\ \{ x = 27 \wedge x + y < 50\}$$

Indeed, it will be true for any pre-condition that logically implies the weakest pre-condition. We can use this observation to check the validity of assertions about assignment statements. If the given pre-condition of the assignment statement logically implies its weakest pre-condition, it is valid.

Review Question 11.5

Answer the following questions concerning the cost of board and lodging:

(i) If the condition $\{board + lodging < 100\}$ is to be true after the assignment `lodging := 43`, what must the pre-condition of the assignment be?

(ii) If the same condition is to be true after doubling the cost of board and adding a supplement of £10 to the cost of lodging, what is the pre-condition?

(iii) If the post-condition $\{3x + 4y > 110 \wedge x > 30\}$ is to be true after the statement `x := x + y` what is the weakest pre-condition that must be true before the assignment?

■

11.5 Proof rule for sequential composition

In procedural languages like Pascal, the simplest way of combining statements together to make larger ones is by performing them in order; this is known as sequencing. Pascal uses a semicolon to represent this idea, so that

```
S1;S2
```

means that `S1` must be performed first, and then `S2`. If we are to prove anything about programs of this structure, we must have a proof rule relating the pre- and post-conditions of the sequence `S1;S2` to the separate conditions of `S1` and `S2`. Once we have such a rule, we can use it to prove that pieces of existing program containing sequences of statements are correct, given the correctness statements of their components. We will also have a tool for decomposing a complex specification into two simpler ones which, if implemented separately and then executed in sequence, would satisfy the original specification.

Unfortunately, although sequencing is one of the simplest programming ideas, its proof rule is more complicated than those of more complex constructs like conditional statements. The reason is that in discussing sequencing of two statements, we must reason about three different states—the state before executing the sequence, that state afterwards, and the state when just the first of the two statements has been executed.

Clearly, we can perform the statement sequence `S1;S2` only if we can first perform the statement `S1`. Therefore, the pre-condition for `S1;S2` is exactly the pre-condition of `S1`. We can also only perform `S1;S2` if the pre-condition for `S2` holds after executing `S1`. Thus, whatever else `S1` establishes in its post-condition, it must at the very least include the pre-condition for `S2`. In other words, if `S2` satisfies:

$$\{P2\}\ \mathtt{S2}\ \{R2\}$$

the post-condition of `S1` must be of the form $\{R1 \wedge P2\}$, where *R1* represents that part of the post-condition of `S1` which is 'surplus' to the needs of `S2`.

We therefore need a proof rule of the form:

$$\frac{\{P1\}\ \mathtt{S1}\ \{R1 \wedge P2\},\ \{P2\}\ \mathtt{S2}\ \{R2\}}{\{P1\}\ \mathtt{S1;S2}\ \{R12\}}$$

R12[1] is the post-condition for the whole sequence. We need to express the relation *R12* in terms of *R1* and *R2*. The *P*s and *R*s could, in general, refer to all the variables in the system, but for the moment consider the simpler case where a single variable, say *x*, is changed by both `S1` and `S2`. `S1` might be the implementation of an operation like *DOUBLEX* which doubles the value of the variable *x*, and `S2` the implementation of an operation like *SQUAREX* which squares *x*. We are trying to capture the effect of the two-stage sequence *DOUBLEX*;*SQUAREX*. Let us call the initial state σ_A and the final state σ_B. There will be an intermediate state after the execution of *DOUBLEX* and before that of *SQUAREX*. Call this σ_t. The value of *x* before the combined operation is $\sigma_A.x$, and afterwards $\sigma_B.x$. In the intermediate state the value of *x* is $\sigma_t.x$.

For the *DOUBLEX* operation, *R1* holds between the before and after states. Here, we are calling the before and after states σ_A and σ_t so we have:

$$R1(\sigma_A,\ \sigma_t) \triangleq (\sigma_t.x = 2 \times \sigma_A.x)$$

Similarly for the second operation, *SQUAREX*:

$$R2(\sigma_t,\ \sigma_B) \triangleq (\sigma_B.x = \sigma_t.x^2)$$

R12 will relate $\sigma_B.x$ and $\sigma_A.x$ in some way, whereas *R1* relates $\sigma_A.x$ and $\sigma_t.x$ and *R2* relates $\sigma_t.x$ and $\sigma_B.x$.

---

[1] *R12* should be read as 'R-one-two', not 'R-twelve'.

The relation we are trying to define, *R12*, will be true of exactly two states σ_A, σ_B when there is a two-step computational path via an intermediate state which we can call σ_t, such that *R1* holds over the first step between σ_A and σ_t and *R2* holds over the second between σ_t and σ_B. This is represented in Figure 11.3.

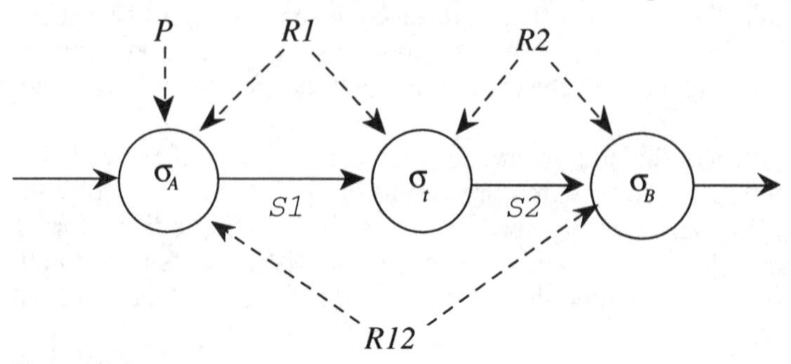

Figure 11.3

In other words we can define:

$$R12(\sigma_A, \sigma_B) \triangleq \exists \sigma_t \cdot R1(\sigma_A, \sigma_t) \wedge R2(\sigma_t, \sigma_B)$$

As *R1* is the operation *DOUBLEX* and *R2* is *SQUAREX* this gives:

$$R12(\sigma_A, \sigma_B) \triangleq \exists \sigma_t \cdot \sigma_t . x = 2 \times \sigma_A . x \wedge \sigma_B . x = \sigma_t . x^2$$

At first glance this looks to be of an impossible form to evaluate, because of the existential qualifier. How, given any particular states, such as σ_5, σ_6, for example containing particular values of $\sigma_5 . x$ and $\sigma_6 . x$, could we ever evaluate something containing an existential quantifier (i.e. $\exists$)? To determine the truth of a formula starting with an existential quantifier would apparently require examining every possible value to see if it satisfied the requirements. However, on simplifying the expression, the problem disappears. We can first eliminate $\sigma_t . x$ giving:

$$R12(\sigma_A, \sigma_B) \triangleq \exists \sigma_t \cdot \sigma_B . x = (2 \times \sigma_A . x)^2$$

As no reference to any variables in the state σ_t occurs in the expression, all reference to it can be dropped, yielding:

$$R12(\sigma_A, \sigma_B) \triangleq \sigma_B . x = (2 \times \sigma_A . x)^2$$

Given any two states, this boolean function can be evaluated to yield a boolean result which indicates whether the second state can be reached by executing *DOUBLEX* ; *SQUAREX* when in the first state. Indeed, this is exactly the intuitive meaning of executing the two operations in sequence.

In order to save always having to introduce new names like *R12*, we need a notation for relations like *R12* which hold between two states when these are linked through an intermediate state by other relations with names like *R1* and *R2*. We shall use the notation *R1* | *R2*[1] for this purpose. We define *R1* | *R2* thus:

---

[1]If you have studied general mathematical relations, you may recognize this as simply another notation for the join of two relations.

$$(R1 \mid R2)(\sigma_A, \sigma_B) \triangleq \exists \sigma_t \bullet R1\,(\sigma_A, \sigma_t) \wedge R2(\sigma_t, \sigma_B)$$

A slight disadvantage of our notation is that it is often necessary to enclose the $R1 \mid R2$ in brackets (as above) to make clear that it is the whole of $R1 \mid R2$ that applies to the following arguments.

Review Question 11.6

Given the following definitions of $R1$ and $R2$, what is the relation $R1 \mid R2$?

(i) $R1(\sigma_A, \sigma_B) \triangleq \sigma_A . x^2 = \sigma_B . x$
$R2(\sigma_A, \sigma_B) \triangleq 2 \times \sigma_A . x = \sigma_B . x$

(ii) $R1(\sigma_A, \sigma_B) \triangleq \sigma_A . x < \sigma_B . x$
$R2(\sigma_A, \sigma_B) \triangleq \sigma_A . x < \sigma_B . x$

(iii) $R1(\sigma_A, \sigma_B) \triangleq \sigma_B . x = -\sigma_A . x$
$R2(\sigma_A, \sigma_B) \triangleq \sigma_B . x = \sqrt{\sigma_A . x}$

■

The purpose of all the above symbol manipulation is to provide a notation for composing two simple relations into a compound condition, and for breaking a compound condition into two simple ones, which might be implemented separately by a two-step sequential program.

We are now in a position to state the proof rule for sequencing.

$$\frac{\{P1\}\ S1\ \{P2 \wedge R1\},\ \{P2\}\ S2\ \{R2\}}{\{P1\}\ S1;S2\ \{R1 \mid R2\}}$$

In Pascal, compound statements may be formed by enclosing sequences within **begin** and **end**. Where necessary we shall assume that `S1;S2` is identical in meaning to:

```
begin S1;S2 end
```

Formally, this could be introduced either by a separate proof rule, or by considering such details merely as a matter of syntax, and having proofs operate only on 'abstract syntax' where superficial details of languages, such as **begin**s and **end**s, had been removed.

Review Question 11.7

What can you deduce about the post-condition of the program fragment

```
y := x + 1;
z := y * y
```

given:

$\{\text{true}\}$ `y := x + 1` $\{\text{true} \wedge y = \overleftarrow{x} + 1\}$, $\{\text{true}\}$ `z := y * y` $\{z = \overleftarrow{y}^2\}$

■

The proof rule for sequencing is straightforward to apply forwards, though the post-condition of `S1` may need a little rearranging to make it into the form $P2 \wedge R1$. It is less obvious how it would be used backwards when designing a program. The difficulty apparently lies in the existential quantifier within

R1 | *R2*. When an operation is first specified, the post-condition expresses what must be true after execution, but this is never of the form:

$$\exists \sigma_t \ldots$$

However, there is nothing to stop us adding superfluous quantifiers to the post-condition as specified. This is where the creative side of design is well shown.

Suppose you are to implement a specification whose post-condition is $\{x = 4 \times \overleftarrow{x}^2\}$. As an inspired guess you might think that there might be a two-step solution. This will involve discussing three different states, so it will be better to express the post-condition in subscript notation as

$$R(\sigma_A, \sigma_B) \triangleq \sigma_B . x = 4 \times \sigma_A . x^2$$

You can now rewrite this post-condition by adding an apparently redundant quantifier:

$$R(\sigma_A, \sigma_B) \triangleq \exists \sigma_t \bullet \sigma_B . x = 4 \times \sigma_A . x^2$$

Now you might try to rearrange the expression to involve values in the intermediate state σ_t which can be computed from σ_A by one simple step, and from which the new σ_B can be computed by another. Such an intermediate state may or may not involve introducing an extra variable. It is usually less confusing to consider programs which assign to new variables rather than update old ones, so search for a two-step solution where an intermediate value is assigned to a variable w.

In this case two different possible reformulations in terms of an intermediate temporary variable w are as follows:

$$R(\sigma_A, \sigma_B) \triangleq \exists \sigma_t \bullet \sigma_t . w = \sigma_A . x^2 \wedge \sigma_B . x = 4 \times \sigma_t . w$$

$$R(\sigma_A, \sigma_B) \triangleq \exists \sigma_t \bullet \sigma_t . w = 2 \times \sigma_A . x \wedge \sigma_B . x = \sigma_t . w^2$$

If the first of these is to lead to a possible implementation, we must be able to find operations `S1` and `S2` with post-conditions *R1* and *R2* such that

$$R1(\sigma_A, \sigma_B) \triangleq \sigma_t . w = \sigma_A . x^2 \quad \text{and}$$

$$R2(\sigma_A, \sigma_B) \triangleq \sigma_B . x = 4 \times \sigma_t . w$$

We have thus moved the search for a programming solution backwards to the search for two simpler program fragments, and on the way we have prepared ourselves for an eventual proof of the final program in the form:

$$\frac{\{\text{true}\}\ S1\ \{\text{true} \wedge w = \overleftarrow{x}^2\} \quad , \quad \{\text{true}\}\ S2\ \{x = 4 \times \overleftarrow{w}\}}{\{\text{true}\}\ S1; S2\ \{x = 4 \times \overleftarrow{x}^2\}}$$

Exercise 11.6

Rearrange the following specification in such a way that it could be implemented by a two-step program involving the operations of cubing and taking the square root—represented below by the program fragment name `X-TO-3-OVER-2`.

$$\{x > 0\}\ \texttt{X-TO-3-OVER-2}\ \{z = \overleftarrow{x}^{3/2}\}$$

Solution 11.6

We are looking for a program fragment $S1$; $S2$ which would map any state value σ_A into σ_B and bring about the post-condition:

$$\sigma_B . z = \sigma_A . x^{3/2}$$

One possible rearrangement of this condition is as follows:

$$\exists \sigma_t \bullet \sigma_t . w = \sqrt{\sigma_A . x} \wedge \sigma_B . z = \sigma_t . w^3$$

This would suggest searching for sub-program fragments, which we call *SQRT* and *CUBE*, satisfying:

$$\{\text{true}\}\ SQRT\ \{w = \sqrt{\overleftarrow{x}}\}$$

$$\{\text{true}\}\ CUBE\ \{z = \overleftarrow{w}^3\}$$

In fact we know from arithmetic that the pre-condition on $SQRT$ must be stronger than this, of the form

$$\{x \geq 0\}\ SQRT\ \{w = \sqrt{\overleftarrow{x}}\}$$

We have as yet no means of knowing if operations to these specifications are implementable, but if they are, they could be sequenced to give a program, whose proof is as follows:

$$\frac{\{x \geq 0\}\ SQRT\ \{w = \sqrt{\overleftarrow{x}}\},\ \{\text{true}\}\ CUBE\ \{z = \overleftarrow{w}^3\}}{\{x \geq 0\}\ SQRT\ ;\ CUBE\ \{z = \overleftarrow{x}^{3/2}\}}$$

■

We have now established the proof rule for sequences. It needed a rather lengthy digression to introduce the notation *R1*|*R2* because this rule alone needs a way of discussing the composition of two relations. The other rules are both more interesting, in that they treat more complex types of statement, and simpler, in that they have no need of the notation for composition.

11.6 Proof rule for conditional statements

The proof rule for sequencing is, if tedious, relatively straightforward, because there is only one execution path to consider so every invocation of the sequence involves the execution of the same statements. Correctness statements for conditional statements are rather more complex, as a different branch (the **then** or the **else**) is executed, depending on the condition. In order to make a true deduction about the post-condition of the whole conditional statement, without knowing which branch is to be taken on any particular execution, we must search for some property that is guaranteed by both branches of the conditional.

Our intention is to produce a correctness statement of the form:

$\{P\}$ **if** B **then** T **else** E $\{R\}$

B is a boolean expression, and T and E are Pascal statements. We wish to know how the pre- and post-conditions of T and E relate to P and R for the whole conditional.

The conditional statement will never be executed unless its pre-condition P is true. If it is, B is then evaluated, and only if B is true will T be executed. Therefore, whenever T is executed we know that both P and B will be true, i.e. $\{P \wedge B\}$. Similarly, E is executed only when B is false, so its minimum pre-condition is $\{P \wedge \neg B\}$.

The post-condition R of the whole conditional expresses a relationship that always holds between the old state and the new one after the conditional has been executed, whichever route was taken internally. It must therefore be a relationship that is established by both T and E separately. Put the other way round, if some relationship R is established separately by both T and E, it will be established whichever route through the conditional is taken, and so it is a post-condition of the whole conditional. This leads to the proof rule for conditional statements:

$$\frac{\{P \wedge B\}\ T\ \{R\},\ \{P \wedge \neg B\}\ E\ \{R\}}{\{P\}\ \textbf{if}\ B\ \textbf{then}\ T\ \textbf{else}\ E\{R\}}$$

As with all proof rules, this can be used forwards (for proving existing code) or backwards (for developing code). To use it forwards, we might want to take an arbitrary $S1$ and $S2$ and deduce something about the statement **if** B **then** $S1$ **else** $S2$. The rule tells us that we must first rearrange the pre-conditions of $S1$ and $S2$ to be of the forms $\{P \wedge B\}$ and $\{P \wedge \neg B\}$ for some value of B. We must also arrange the post-conditions to be the same R, probably by using the rule of consequence. If we can do all this, then we can validly deduce the correctness statement:

$$\{P\}\ \textbf{if}\ B\ \textbf{then}\ T\ \textbf{else}\ E\ \{R\}$$

For example, suppose we have the program fragment

```
if x ≥ 0 then y := x else y := -x
```

and that we wish to prove an 8-bit micro-computer implementation of Pascal, where integers are constrained to be in the range –128..127. We shall show that the above fragment is indeed a correct implementation of an operation which has the post-condition $\{y = \text{abs } x\}$.

Consider `y := x`. We can easily justify:

$\{0 \le x \le 127\}$ `y := x` $\{y = \text{abs } x\}$ and
$\{-128 \le x < 0\}$ `y := -x` $\{y = \text{abs } x\}$

To invoke the proof rule we must rearrange these conditions into the forms $\{P \wedge B\}$ and $\{P \wedge \neg B\}$. One choice is:

$\{-128 \le x \le 127 \wedge x \ge 0\}$ `y := x` $\{y = \text{abs } x\}$ and
$\{-128 \le x \le 127 \wedge \neg(x \ge 0)\}$ `y := -x` $\{y = \text{abs } x\}$

Thus P is $\{-128 \le x \le 127\}$, B is $\{x \ge 0\}$, and R is $\{y = \text{abs } x\}$.

The proof rule therefore allows us to deduce:

$\{-128 \le x < 127\}$ **if** $x \ge 0$ **then** $y := x$ **else** $y := -x$ $\{y = \text{abs } x\}$

In the above example we used the proof rule for conditionals to argue forwards from the correctness statements of the **then** and **else** clauses to a correctness statement for the conditional statement as a whole. Consider now how we might use the rule to guide us in a search for a program decomposition.

Suppose we are to implement a program fragment specified thus:

$\{\text{true}\}$ $MAXIJ$ $\{(i \ge j \wedge max = i) \vee (\neg(i \ge j) \wedge max = j)\}$

Here R is $\{(i \ge j \wedge max = i) \vee (\neg(i \ge j) \wedge max = j)\}$. We might have a hunch that a conditional statement would be useful. If so, we need to find two statements, T and E, with pre-conditions that can be expressed in terms of some P and B such that:

$\{P \wedge B\}$ T $\{R\}$
$\{P \wedge \neg B\}$ E $\{R\}$

The obvious candidate for B is the condition $i \ge j$. The hunt has reduced to looking for P, S and T such that:

$\{P \wedge i \ge j\}$ T $\{(i \ge j \wedge max = i) \vee (\neg(i \ge j) \wedge max = j)\}$

$\{P \wedge \neg(i \ge j)\}$ E $\{(i \ge j \wedge max = i) \vee (\neg(i \ge j) \wedge max = j)\}$

The statement T must make its post-condition true. The post-condition is a logical alternation, and because from the pre-condition $i \ge j$ it cannot make the second alternate true, so it must make the first one true. By inheritance of pre-condition, it knows that already $i \ge j$, so the only change required by T is to make $max = i$. As we know from the post-condition of assignment statements, this is easily achieved by the statement `max := i`. As the condition P is never used, we can take it to be the weakest possible pre-condition—the constant true. Similar arguments apply for E, giving us as valid correctness statements:

$\{\text{true} \wedge i \ge j\}$ `max := i` $\{(i \ge j \wedge max = i) \vee (\neg(i \ge j) \wedge max = j)\}$

$\{\text{true} \wedge \neg(i \ge j)\}$ `max := j` $\{(i \ge j \wedge max = i) \vee (\neg(i \ge j) \wedge max = j)\}$

From this we will be able to prove that:

$\{\text{true}\}$ **if** $i \ge j$ **then** $max := i$ **else** $max := j$
$\{(i \ge j \wedge max = i) \vee (\neg(i \ge j) \wedge max = j)\}$

Thus by bearing in mind how our final implementation might be proved, we have been guided in the construction of a program which is clearly provable.

Exercise 11.7

The following is a different program for computing the maximum of i and j. It uses the name `skip` for the null statement instead of the usual Pascal space in order to make null statements visible. Outline how the correctness statement might be proved correct:

$\{\text{true}\}\ max\ :=\ i;\ \textbf{if}\ i < j\ \textbf{then}\ max\ :=\ j\ \textbf{else}\ \text{skip}$
$$\{(i<j \wedge max=j) \vee (i \geq j \wedge max=i)\}$$

Solution 11.7

After the first assignment has been executed, we can guarantee, by the proof rule for assignment statements, that the post-condition $\{max = i\}$ will be true. We must now consider the conditional statement. Any proof involving a conditional with post-condition R and statements T and E involves discovering conditions P and B such that:

$$\{P \wedge B\}\ T\ \{R\}$$
$$\{P \wedge \neg B\}\ E\ \{R\}$$

Here we have:

B: $i<j$
P: $max = i$

We must therefore justify:

$$\{max=i \wedge i<j\} \quad max\ :=\ j \quad \{(i<j \wedge max=j) \vee (i \geq j \wedge max=i)\}$$

$$\{max=i \wedge \neg(i<j)\} \quad skip \quad \{(i<j \wedge max=j) \vee (i \geq j \wedge max=i)\}$$

These follow from the rules for inheriting pre-conditions, and assignment, thus proving:

$\{max=i\}\ \textbf{if}\ i < j\ \textbf{then}\ max\ :=\ j\ \textbf{else}\ skip$
$$\{(i<j \wedge max=j) \vee (i \geq j \wedge max=i)\}$$

From the rule for assignment we can show

$$\{\text{true}\}\ max\ :=\ i\ \{max=i\}$$

This and the correctness statement for the conditional can be combined by the sequencing rule to complete the proof.

■

Review Question 11.8

Use the proof rule for conditionals to suggest an implementation of the following fragment from a calendar program.

$$\{1 \leq today \leq 365\}\ FIND\text{-}TOMORROW\ \{tomorrow = \overleftarrow{today} \bmod 365\ +1\}$$

■

11.7 Summary of concepts

- Correctness statements assert that executing a certain piece of program in a state satisfying the pre-condition will bring about a state which is related to the initial state by the given post-condition. A correctness statement can be valid or invalid. Valid correctness statements can be used to define each simple statement type in a language. They specify the meaning of the statement by treating it as a program fragment which has a certain specific effect on the system state. Here the only *simple* statement type we have considered is the assignment statement.

- Proof rules enable us to argue from one or more valid correctness statements to another. We need a proof rule for each different way that a programming language provides for constructing complex statements out of simple ones. We have looked at proof rules for sequential execution and for conditional statements, as well as two rules which merely rearrange the conditions in a correctness statement—the rule for inheriting pre-conditions and the rule of consequence. The proof rule for sequences required us to develop a notation for expressing the relationship between states before and after a statement.
- Proof rules can be used in two ways. They can be used in the forward direction to justify a correctness statement with respect to the correctness statements of its components. They can also be used backwards to suggest a possible way of breaking down a complex post-condition into simpler conditions which can be implemented separately and then combined using the programming constructs and proof rules for combining statements. (That is, the rules can be turned upside down for the purposes of refinement.)

12 PROGRAMS WITH LOOPS

We come now to the most interesting of the proof rules—that for the looping construct. A simple conditional statement has only two possible execution routes through it and therefore two possible actions which must be related to the post-condition. In contrast, a general looping construct has an indefinite number of possible actions between the start and end of its execution. Therefore the post-condition, which must relate its final state to its initial state, must cater for this situation. We shall find that the general case is rather intractable. However, in the special case where the loop has been developed by first considering an invariant, the proof rule takes a fairly simple form.

12.1 General loops

It is helpful first to observe that a program loop can be 'unwound' to give a conditional statement followed by a loop. Consider the looping construct:

```
while B do S
```

It is equivalent to the program:

```
if B
then
  begin
    S;
    while B do S
  end
else
  skip
```

Here we again use `skip` to represent the null statement, although in Pascal it is represented simply by empty space. This will make it easier to see where a null statement has been placed. Having unwrapped the `while` loop once, we could do it again. By repeatedly doing this, it is easy to see that a `while` loop is 'just' a very long, deeply nested sequence of conditional statements. The only problem is that we cannot predict in advance how many conditional statements we should write. If we unwind a loop to 100 conditionals, then any data that requires the loop to be executed 101 times will cause the program to execute incorrectly. We will not find this approach a useful or practical transformation, but it does let us see that the execution of the loop is equivalent to one of:

```
skip            or
S               or
S; S            or
S; S ; S        or
S; S ; S ; S
```
and so on.

Which of these sequences the loop is equivalent to will not be predictable before a program executes. One consequence of this unwrapping is that we can see immediately that not every statement, with arbitrary pre- and post-conditions, can meaningfully be inserted into a `while` loop. When we considered the semicolon sequencing construct, we realized that, for `S1; S2` to be sensible, the post-condition of the first statement, `S1`, must imply the pre-condition of the second statement, `S2`. A loop can be thought of as an indefinite number of semicolon sequencings, where for each semicolon the statement before the semicolon is the same as the one just after it. We can therefore see by considering the loop as an extended sequence that the post-condition of the loop body, `S`, must imply the pre-condition of `S`. If it does not, on the second time round the loop, the pre-condition of `S` cannot be guaranteed to be true, although the body `S` is about to be executed. The effect of executing `S` without guaranteeing its pre-condition is undefined, so the whole loop would be undefined.

Consider the statement:

$\{x > 0\}$ `x := -sqrt(x)` $\{x < 0\}$

The post-condition does not imply the pre-condition, so there will be immediate problems if it is inserted in a loop such as:

```
while abs(x) > 0.1 do x := -sqrt(x)
```

On the start of the second iteration, the post-condition of `S` will hold, so $\{x < 0\}$, but this is incompatible with the pre-condition of `S` that $\{x > 0\}$. We will therefore execute the body of the loop under circumstances where its pre-condition does not hold. The result of the whole loop will therefore be undefined.

Review Question 12.1

Which of the following correctness statements would make it reasonable to form a loop with the corresponding `S` as the loop body?

(i) $\{x > 1\}$ `S` $\{x > 10\}$ (ii) $\{x > 10\}$ `S` $\{x > 1\}$

(iii) $\{x + y = 10\}$ `S` $\{x + y = 10\}$ (iv) $\{2 + 2 = 5\}$ `S` $\{2 + 2 = 5\}$

■

A looping program is equivalent to a sequential program of indeterminate length. Each iteration will have some effect on the system state, so that the total effect of the program depends on the number of iterations. Reasoning about such programs is rather difficult, so it is often easier to consider, not what each iteration does, but what it does *not* do. By concentrating on some aspect of the system state which is left unchanged by a single iteration, we can make deductions about what will be left unchanged by the repeated execution of the loop.

12.2 Loop invariants

We shall approach loops by considering properties of the system state that are not affected by execution of the loop body. A boolean property of the system state which does not change its value however often the loop is executed is called a ***loop invariant***. For instance, the property $\{x = 2^n\}$ is invariant under the statements `n := n + 1; x := 2 * x.` If it is true before the execution of the double assignment, it will be true afterwards. The truth of an invariant condition of a statement is unaffected by executing the statement. If it is true before execution, it will remain so after one execution of the statement and hence even after repeated executions.

When designing a program it is usually helpful to identify the loop invariant as the first step. Having decided on a loop invariant P, we then look for a statement S that preserves P. That is, we aim to produce a valid correctness statement of the form:

$$\{P\}\ S\ \{P\}$$

For example, consider:

$$\{x + y = 27\}\ x := x + 1;\ y := y - 1\ \{x + y = 27\}$$

Here the invariant condition P is $\{x + y = 27\}$. In general, S is usually chosen to do more than just preserve P. (After all, even the null statement preserves all its pre-conditions!) It will also establish something else. For example, in this case S, besides maintaining P, also establishes the post-condition $\{x > \overleftarrow{x}\}$ although this particular correctness statement does not assert this.

Note that in general a pre-condition is a property of a single value of the state—the value of the state before execution of S—and a post-condition is in general a relation between the old value of the state and the new value. An example of a post-condition of this general form for the above double assignment is:

$$\{x + y = 27 \wedge x > \overleftarrow{x}\}$$

This is a property of two states. However, if we are looking for a property P that holds both in the old and new states, it cannot be a relation between two different states because before execution there is only one state to discuss. In other words, when looking for an invariant property, the property must be a property of a single state. There are in general numerous different invariant properties for any particular program construct. Two alternatives to the above are as follows.

$\{x+y>0\}$ `x := x + 1; y := y - 1` $\{x+y>0\}$

$\{x>0\}$ `x := x + 1; y := y - 1` $\{x>0\}$

Exercise 12.1

Each of the following questions consists of a statement S and a condition P. Determine whether P is an invariant of S. One way is to assume it holds after the execution of S, and see if this implies that it must therefore also hold before execution. This can be done by pushing P back through the assignment statements.

(i) S: `x := x + 1; y := y - 2`
P: $2 \times x + y = 10$

(ii) S: `i := i div 2; j := j * 2`
P: $i \times j = 64$

Solution 12.1

(i) Yes. Pushing the condition back through the second assignment gives $2 \times x + (y - 2) = 10$. Pushed through the first assignment it becomes $2 \times (x + 1) + (y - 2) = 10$ which simplifies to the original condition.

(ii) Yes.

■

Review Question 12.2

Each of the following questions consists of a statement S and a condition P. Determine whether P is an invariant of S.

(i) S: `i := i div 2; j := j * 2`
P: $even(i) \wedge i \times j = k$

(ii) S: `n := n + 1; sn := sn + n * n`
P: $sn = \sum_{i=1}^{n} i^2$

■

Once we have an invariant P of a statement S we can consider the meaning of the construct:

```
while B do S
```

What pre-condition for the whole loop will ensure that the pre-condition of S is met? When the loop starts executing nothing is done to change the system state before the first execution of S. Therefore a sufficient pre-condition on the loop is simply that P, the pre-condition of S, holds before the loop is started. We can thus see that the proof rule for a loop built out of a statement and its invariant might be of the form:

$$\frac{\{P\}\ S\ \{P\}}{\{P\}\ \textbf{while}\ B\ \textbf{do}\ S\ \{??\}}$$

We must now determine what the post-condition is which was left as $\{??\}$. If the loop body is executed zero times, B must have initially evaluated to false, and the post-condition will be $\neg B$. In fact, as we know that P will still hold, this condition can be strengthened to $P \wedge \neg B$. If the body does get executed, we know that however many times we execute S, P is still preserved, so P is part of the post-condition. If the loop ever terminates, B must be false, so the post-condition is again $P \wedge \neg B$. We have no way of knowing if the loop will ever terminate, but should it do so, we can be sure of $P \wedge \neg B$. Observe that S is executed only when B is true, so we can actually restrict the pre-condition of S to include B, thus $\{P \wedge B\}$. Moreover, S does not need to be defined when B is false. We can combine the two previous results to give the proof rule for while statements.

$$\frac{\{P \wedge B\}\ S\ \{P\}}{\{P\}\ \textbf{while}\ B\ \textbf{do}\ S\{P \wedge \neg B\}}$$

This proof rule is represented in Figure 12.1:

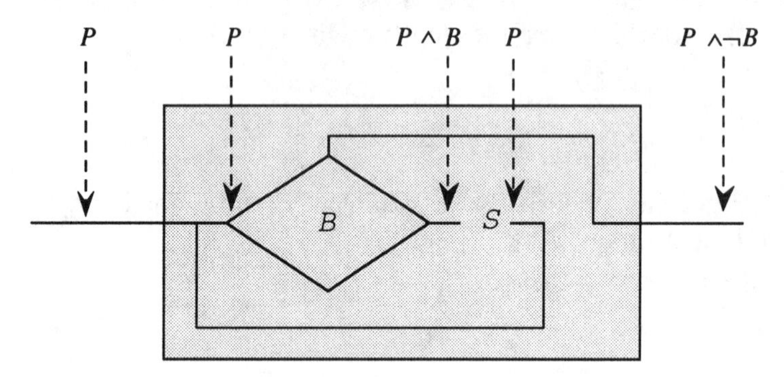

Figure 12.1

We shall now consider how we might embed in a loop the statements `x := x + 1; y := y - 2`. In Exercise 12.1 we established:

$$\{2 \times x + y = 10\}\ \texttt{x := x + 1; y := y - 2}\ \{2 \times x + y = 10\}$$

This is of the form $\{P\}\ S\ \{P\}$. By the rule of consequence, by conjoining $y > 0$, we can deduce a more restricted correctness statement:

$$\{2 \times x + y = 10\ \wedge\ y > 0\}\ \texttt{x := x + 1; y := y - 2}\ \{2 \times x + y = 10\}$$

This is of the form:

$$\{P \wedge B\}\ S\ \{P\}$$

If we embed S in a loop of the form:

while B **do** S

the proof rule for loops allows us to conclude:

$$\{P\}\ \textbf{while}\ B\ \textbf{do}\ S\ \{P \wedge \neg B\}$$

Thus the proof rule for this particular loop (when you substitute for P, B and S) becomes:

$$\frac{\{2\times x+y=10 \wedge y>0\}\ x := x + 1;\ y := y - 2\ \{2\times x + y = 10\}}{\{2\times x + y = 10\}\ \textbf{while}\ y > 0\ \textbf{do begin}\ x := x + 1;\ y := y - 2\ \textbf{end}\ \{2\times x + y = 10 \wedge \neg y>0\}}$$

Re-arranging the post-condition of the loop gives $\{x \geq 5\}$. Thus whatever the initial values of x and y, we can deduce that after the loop has executed x is at least 5. We have a proof rule powerful enough to reason about loops—provided we can find an invariant of the loop body.

This proof rule applies only to loops that terminate. This is because we assumed that the loop terminated in order to establish that B was false after the execution of the loop. However, the rule by itself is no help in determining if a given program does actually terminate and, therefore, using it we can give only a proof of ***conditional correctness***. A program is said to be conditionally correct if we have established only that it is correct whenever it terminates. A full proof of ***total correctness*** must also prove that it does in fact terminate. We shall return to this later.

12.3 Using loop invariants to construct programs

The proof rule for loops can be used to prove the conditional correctness of arbitrary programs involving loops, provided we can find an invariant of the loop body. However our main concern is not with proving existing programs, but with providing guidelines for constructing new programs which will be easy to prove.

We shall consider creating a program to compute the sum of the squares of the integers 1,…, 10, as expressed by the formula for *sn*:

$$sn = \sum_{i=1}^{10} i^2$$

More formally, we want to build a program *SUMSQ* which satisfies

$$\{\text{true}\}\ SUMSQ\ \{sn = \sum_{i=1}^{10} i^2)\}$$

One way is to start by varying the upper bound of the summation, and by considering the general expression $\{sn = \sum_{i=1}^{n} i^2\}$. Suppose for some value of n we had set the variable *sn* appropriately so that this expression was true. If n were to be increased by 1, how must *sn* be changed to maintain the relationship that *sn* is the sum of the first n squares? The range 1,…,n has been extended by 1, so we must clearly add to *sn* the value of the new square, which is n^2.

In other words, if we execute both the statements:

```
n := n + 1; sn := sn + n *n
```

the relation $\{sn = \sum_{i=1}^{n} i^2\}$ will still be true.

That is, we have a valid correctness statement in

$\{sn = \sum_{i=1}^{n} i^2\}$ `n := n + 1; sn := sn + n * n` $\{sn = \sum_{i=1}^{n} i^2\}$

The condition is an invariant of the sequence of two assignments.

Review Question 12.3

Is the condition $\{sn = \sum_{i=1}^{n} i^2\}$ an invariant of the following program fragments?

(i) `sn := sn + n * n;    n := n + 1`

(ii) `sn := sn - n * n;    n := n - 1`

(iii) `sn := sn - (n+1) * (n+1) ;    n := n + 1`

■

Let us call P the invariant $sn = \sum_{i=1}^{n} i^2$. We would have solved the problem of computing the sum of the first ten squares if P were initially true for some value of n, and then if we could change n to make $\{n = 10\}$ without upsetting P. That is, we are trying to establish the post-condition for *SUMSQ* of:

$$\{sn = \sum_{i=1}^{n} i^2 \wedge n = 10\}$$

If B were to be defined as $\{n \neq 10\}$, the desired post-condition of the whole program is the same as wanting to establish $P \wedge \neg B$. In the review question we saw that the condition P is an invariant of the statements:

```
sn := sn + n * n; n := n + 1 .
```

By the proof rule for loops, we know that if we can establish $\{P \wedge B\}$ S $\{P\}$, we can deduce:

$\{P\}$ **while** B **do** $S\{P \wedge \neg B\}$

Substituting our definitions of P, S and B, we have

$\{sn = \sum_{i=1}^{n} i^2\}$ **while** $n \neq 10$ **do** `sn := sn + n * n; n := n + 1` $\{sn = \sum_{i=1}^{n} i^2 \wedge \neg n \neq 10\}$

This is almost what we need to meet the original specification, except that there is no reason to believe P will be true before the loop unless we make it so. How can we establish P for some state? We must initialize n and sn to values that we know will make P true. One possibility is:

```
n := 1; sn := 1
```

Review Question 12.4

How else might P be established?

■

Let us call this initialization code *INIT*. *INIT* has the required P as its post-condition. As it consists only of assignment statements, its pre-condition is just {true}, so we do not have to prove that the pre-conditions for *INIT* are met for it to be validly invoked. We have therefore succeeded in establishing that the program

INIT; **while** *B* **do** *S*

satisfies our specification, as:

- *INIT* establishes P;
- the loop maintains it whilst eventually making B false;
- the required post-condition of the whole program is equivalent to $P \wedge \neg B$.

Writing out the program in full we have:

```
n := 1;   sn := 1;
while n <>10 do
begin
  n := n + 1;
  sn := sn + n * n
end
```

12.4 Finding loop invariants

In the previous example, we produced a candidate S and its invariant out of the blue. It was clearly a good choice, but how is one to be guided in finding such choices? Beginners often find such proofs relatively easy to understand, but totally baffling when they are expected to create them. Though there is no algorithm that can capture the art of program design, there are various guidelines which can reduce the mystery. To illustrate the most important of them, let us consider the same problem and derive a different program.

The requirement is again to find *sn* such that $sn = \sum_{i=1}^{10} i^2$.

In other words, we want to find a piece of program with this as its post-condition, and something trivially true as its pre-condition. One fruitful guideline is to replace a constant by a variable in the target condition and add a clause restricting the variable to the original constant value. This seems an implausible line of attack as it seems to make a concrete problem more general and therefore more intractable, but the idea is that we will produce the variable expression that will be computed at each pass through the loop. In the expression for *sn* there are two constants, 1 and 10. The suggestion is that one of these be replaced by a variable. Replacing 10 by a variable leads to the program we have already seen, so try replacing 1 by a variable, say n. Our required post-condition is now:

$$sn = \sum_{i=n}^{10} i^2 \wedge n = 1.$$

This is a conjunction, and we know from the proof rule for loops that conjunctions of the form $P \wedge \neg B$ are often easy to establish. Can we manipulate our required post-condition into this form? With two conjuncts there are clearly two choices, as each in turn could be taken as P and the other $\neg B$. However we know that whichever is chosen as P must be easily established by some *INIT*, and it must be possible to find an S that keeps P invariant. This usually makes the choice obvious. Here we take P as $sn = \sum_{i=n}^{10} i^2$ and B as $n \neq 1$. The other choice is not open to us as, if we used $sn = \sum_{i=n}^{10} i^2$ for B, we would not have an easily computable expression to control the loop.

Our target post-condition is $P \wedge \neg B$. We know that if we can find some `S` which has P as an invariant, and if we can establish P as being initially true by some code `INIT`, our desired program is therefore:

```
INIT; while B do S
```

What are the candidates for `S`, which maintain invariant the relation $sn = \sum_{i=n}^{10} i^2$? There are always numerous statements which maintain any invariant P. Here are some:

- `skip`
- `sn := sn - n * n;    n := n + 1` this shortens series to $(n + 1)^2 ... 10^2$
- `n := n - 1; sn := sn + n * n` this lengthens series to $(n - 1)^2 ... 10^2$

Clearly `skip` maintains P, just as it maintains everything else! The reason that it is an unhelpful choice is that it does not change anything at all—it makes no progress towards a solution.

The second line would mean that if, for example, we already knew the value of $\sum_{i=4}^{10} i^2$, we would then be able to compute $\sum_{i=5}^{10} i^2$. This is indeed true, but unhelpful, as the second identity is further away than the first from the target of $n = 1$. Moving in this direction involves throwing away knowledge rather than extending it. Thus in choosing `S` we need to have some notion of progress towards a solution.

A good choice is the third line, which means that if we know the sum starting at a particular n, we can compute the sum starting at $n - 1$. This clearly has the required sense of direction, as our final aim is to compute the sum starting at 1. In addition, by decreasing n sufficiently we will eventually get to $n = 1$, which is not only part of the target condition, but also the condition for terminating the loop. Knowing that we cannot continue a loop for ever is a vital part of proving a program correct.

We have so far chosen:

B: `n` $\neq$ `1`

S: `n := n - 1; sn := sn + n * n`

P: $sn = \sum_{i=n}^{10} i^2$

Though we have not yet defined `INIT`, we know that the shape of the final program will be:

```
INIT;
while n <> 1 do
begin
  n := n - 1;    sn := sn + n * n
end
```

All that remains is to implement *INIT* to establish a state in which the condition P holds before entry to the loop. Because $10^2 = 100$, we know that $\sum_{i=10}^{10} i^2 = 100$, and we can establish one program state in which P does hold by `n := 10; sn := 100`.

Review Question 12.5

Suggest a different way of establishing a state in which P holds.

■

Our whole program is now:

```
n := 10;    sn := 100;
while n <> 1 do
begin
  n := n - 1;    sn := sn + n * n
end
```

Exercise 12.2

Design a program whose post-condition is $\{r = 3^{10}\}$.

Solution 12.2

The requirement is to find some result $r = 3^{10}$. Start by replacing one of the constants by a variable. We could try $r = i^{10} \wedge i = 3$. This does not look fruitful because, if we vary i, there is no easily computed relation between i^{10} and $(i + 1)^{10}$. Therefore, replace the 10 by a variable, say k, giving the following post-condition:

$$r = 3^k \wedge k = 10$$

This is of the form $P \wedge \neg B$ if we take:

P: $r = 3^k$
B: $k \neq 10$

This suggests a looping program of the form:

```
INIT; while B do S
```

This depends on being able to find a statement *S* that has P as an invariant. We also require in some informal way that *S* should progress towards a solution. Candidates for *S* include:

- `k := k - 1; r := r div 3`
- `k := k + 1; r := 3 * r`

The first of these would, for example, help us find 3^9 if we already knew 3^{10}. It would be suitable if we already knew one particular high power of three and needed to compute lower powers. This is not our problem: we cannot assume this knowledge, though we can assume that we know some very low power of three, such as 3^0 or 3^1. The second candidate will be helpful in deriving a higher power from a lower power, so we choose this as S.

Our program is therefore:

```
INIT;
while k <> 10 do
begin
  k := k + 1;    r := 3 * r
end
```

Provided P holds in the initial state, the state on termination will satisfy our desired post-condition. To guarantee that P does hold before the loop starts, we need an initialization section establishing $r = 3^k$.

Candidates include:

- `k := 0; r := 1`
- `k := 1; r := 3`
- `k := 2; r := 9`

All of these have the pre-condition {true}, and the correctness statement for the final program could be as follows.

{true} `k := 1; r := 3;`
while `k <> 10` **do begin** `k := k + 1; r := 3 * r` **end** $\{r = 3^k \wedge k = 10\}$

■

12.5 Termination

We have seen a possible proof rule for `while` loops, and how it can be used to guide the creation of programs. By assuming that $\neg B$ is true after a loop, our proof rule implicitly assumes that the loop will terminate. If it does not, we can conclude nothing. However, we have as yet no way of persuading ourselves that our loops do terminate. This is because we have concentrated on the invariant of the loop—that is, on what the loop does *not* do. We saw that in order to avoid choosing a loop body which either did nothing at all, like `skip`, or which went off in the wrong direction towards more and more complex problems instead of simpler and simpler ones, we needed to appeal to some sense of whether a statement S got us any closer to the target condition. We need to look at the *variant* part of the loop, and consider what *does* get changed.

Even to talk about a 'sense of direction' will require that we use relations between two states, rather than just a predicate applying to the single new state. For example, if we want a variable i to decrease for each execution of S, we cannot express this by looking just at its latest value. We need a relation between its value before and after the operation.

If the new state is to be in some sense 'nearer' the target state than the old state, we will need some measure of the 'distance' still left to go, and whether or not this is decreasing. In Section 12.4 we produced the following program for establishing $sn = \sum_{i=1}^{10} i^2$

```
n := 10;   sn := 100;
while n <> 1 do
begin
  n := n - 1;   sn := sn + n * n
end
```

We realized that if we could compute $sn = \sum_{i=n}^{10} i^2$ for some value of n bigger than one, then decreasing n while preserving the relationship would decrease the distance still to go. One suitable function to measure the distance remaining would be $n-1$. It is easy to see that our particular statement S does decrease the distance function every time round the loop, because it decreases n. Because the distance function is integer valued, it cannot decrease indefinitely and still remain greater than zero, so it must eventually reach the value zero. By the meaning of **while**, the loop continues as long as condition B is true, but condition B ($n <> 1$) implies that the distance is non-zero. The distance function must eventually reach zero, so therefore the loop condition must eventually become false and the loop terminate within a finite amount of time.

To formalize this sort of intuitive reasoning, when considering any loop of the form **while** B **do** S, we search for an integer function of the system state, called the ***bound function***, such that:

- $P \wedge B \Rightarrow \textit{bound function} > 0$
- S always decreases the bound function.

If such a function can be found, we can conclude that while inside the loop the bound is greater than zero, and also that while repeatedly executing S the bound is decreasing. Taken together, these two statements are incompatible with the loop continuing for ever, so it must halt at some time. Note that the bound function must be an integer function. It might be possible to find a real function which decreased indefinitely but always remained greater than zero, thus failing to prove termination.

Consider the program above which we claimed established $r = 3^{10}$.

```
{true}  k := 1; r := 3;
        while k <> 10 do begin k := k + 1; r := 3 * r  end {r = 3^k ∧ k = 10}
```

We proved this *conditionally* correct, but made no attempt to prove that it terminated. Here P is $\{r = 3^k\}$ and the condition B is $\{k \neq 10\}$. We therefore want to find a bound function such that:

- $r = 3^k \wedge k \neq 10 \Rightarrow \textit{bound function} > 0$
- The bound function is decreased by executing `k := k + 1; r := 3 * r`

Consider the function $10 - k$. This is certainly decreased by the body of the loop, but can we show:

$$r = 3^k \wedge \ k \neq 10 \Rightarrow \ (10 - k) > 0?$$

Certainly this does not follow in general, as the value $k = 11$ demonstrates. However, in this program we know that k is increased from values less than 10, and that the loop continues while $1 \leq k \leq 10$. It also follows that:

$$1 \leq k \leq 10 \wedge \ k \neq 10 \Rightarrow (10 - k) > 0$$

This suggests that if, instead of using the expression $r = 3^k$ as P, we had used $r = 3^k \wedge 1 \leq k \leq 10$, the original *conditionally* correct program could have been proved *totally* correct. We could now rework the derivation of the program by expressing the required post-condition, not as $\{r = 3^k \wedge \neg (k \neq 10)\}$, but as:

$$\{r = 3^k \wedge \ (1 \leq k \leq 10) \wedge \neg (k \neq 10)\}$$

Now we must prove that S maintains the new invariant $(r = 3^k) \wedge (1 \leq k \leq 10)$. Clearly, this cannot be true in general, as eventually $k > 10$ which violates the second clause. However the invariant does not have to be maintained under every conceivable set of circumstances. We have to prove only that it is maintained while inside the loop; we must only prove $\{P \wedge B\}$ S $\{P\}$ rather than the more general $\{P\}$ S $\{P\}$.

Here we must show that:

$$\{(r = 3^k \wedge \ 1 \leq k \leq 10) \wedge \neg (k \neq 10)\} \ S \ \{r = 3^k \wedge 1 \leq k \leq 10\}$$

where S is the statement `k := k + 1; r := 3 * r`.

The post-condition is a conjunct of two clauses, and we showed earlier that S did maintain the first clause, $r = 3^k$. We therefore only need to show that it also maintains the second clause, i.e. that $\{1 \leq k \leq 10 \wedge \neg (k \neq 10)\}$ S $\{1 \leq k \leq 10\}$. As the second assignment in S modifies only the variable r, leaving k unchanged, we need consider only the first assignment, `k := k + 1`.

We must show that:

$$\{1 \leq k \leq 10 \wedge \neg (k \neq 10)\} \ k := k + 1 \ \{1 \leq k \leq 10\}$$

This is equivalent to trying to establish:

$$\{1 \leq k < 9\} \ k := k + 1 \ \{1 \leq k \leq 10\}$$

which is easily done.

Review Question 12.6

How would you show that the last correctness statement is valid?

■

We have now shown that our program does terminate and is therefore not just conditionally but totally correct.

Bound functions can usually be found by a trivial manipulation of the looping condition. Constructing a proof of termination of a conditionally correct program often involves adding to the invariant some clause describing the range of a variable in order to make into a valid implication $P \wedge B \Rightarrow$ *bound* > 0. We must also show that the new P is established by the initialization. In our example this follows because it is possible to derive:

$$\{\text{true}\}\ k := 1\ \{1 \le k \le 10\}$$

Exercise 12.3

In Section 12.4 we showed the conditional correctness of the following program to compute $sn = \sum_{i=1}^{10} i^2$.

```
n := 10;    sn := 100;
while n <> 1 do
begin
  n := n - 1;    sn := sn + n * n
end
```

Prove that this program terminates.

Solution 12.3

We need a bound function to measure the distance still to go in the computation. A simple one might be the function n.

We must prove that:

- the bound is decreased by the body of the loop

- $P \wedge B \Rightarrow n > 0$
  i.e. $sn = \sum_{i=n}^{10} i^2 \wedge (n \ne 1) \Rightarrow n > 0$

The bound is certainly decreased by the body of the loop. However the desired implication does not go through. The substitution of $n = 0$ is a counter-example to the implication $(n \ne 1) \Rightarrow n > 0$.

But we know from our understanding of programming that in this program n can never be 0. Why not, and how can this intuitive understanding be captured?

In the program n steadily decreases, approaching 1 from above; it also never goes outside the range $1, \ldots, 10$. This suggests that we should extend the loop invariant P by adding a clause $\{1 \le n \le 10\}$. This would make the implication we have to show into the following:

$$sn = \sum_{i=n}^{10} i^2 \wedge (n \ne 1) \wedge (1 \le n \le 10) \Rightarrow n > 0$$

From $(n \ne 1) \wedge (1 \le n \le 10)$ we can deduce that $(2 \le n \le 10)$, and hence that $n > 0$. The implication is therefore valid and termination is proved, but the earlier proof of conditional correctness must be reworked to show that the new P is indeed a loop invariant of S, and that it is established by the initialization code. This experience of finding it necessary to include in the loop invariant a clause about the range of the loop variable is very common. It is interesting to note that the bound function chosen in this case never actually reaches zero as the loop stops when $n = 1$. The loop has actually stopped one iteration before that at which we proved it must stop. This does not matter as all we wanted was a proof that it would stop sometime. There is always more than one possible choice of bound function. Here $(n - 1)$ or $(2 \times n)$ would have been just as good.

■

12.6 Annotating programs with loops

All the loops we have seen so far have involved much the same sequence of activities. We needed to:

- express the target post-condition in the form $P \wedge \neg B$;
- find a statement `S` with invariant P;
- produce code to establish P before the loop: we call this `INIT`;
- discover a bound function which decreases with each execution of `S` and which is such that $P \wedge B \Rightarrow bound > 0$; alternatively discover a bound function which decreases with each execution of `S` and a modification of P, P', which is such that $P' \wedge B \Rightarrow bound > 0$;

Having done all this, we have a proof that the desired post-condition is indeed established by the program:

```
INIT;
while B do S
```

Having convinced ourselves of the correctness of our program, it is foolish not to document our reasoning so that others can be similarly convinced. Rather than long-windedly spelling out the proof of the whole program each time, it is enough to identify the invariant of the loop and the bound function. With this information, it is fairly easy for a reader to check that the required properties do indeed follow.

The invariant and bound function should be identified in comments at suitable places. The following shows a suggested style of presentation of the final code in the case of a program to establish $r = 3^{10}$:

```
{true}

k := 1;    r := 3;
{invariant r = 3^k ∧ 1 ≤ k ≤ 10}
{bound 10 – k}
while k <>10 do
begin
  k := k + 1;    r = 3 * r
end

{r = 3^k ∧ (1 ≤ k ≤ 10) ∧ k = 10}
```

This avoids having to spell out tedious details such as the invariant of a loop body is an invariant of the whole loop, or that on termination the condition in the `while` loop is false.

12.7 Another view of termination

We have by now established sufficient mechanisms to prove conditional correctness of programs with loops using the proof rules, and to prove the termination of those programs by considering bound functions. This is adequate, but slightly unsatisfactory, for the following reasons.

In addition to the proof rules for loops, we had to introduce a completely new mechanism for proving termination. It does not fit cleanly with the previous discussion of post-conditions and relations. The bound function is a function of a single state, but we express, in English, a requirement that it should be decreased by the body of the loop. That is, we require that evaluating the bound function in a sequence of states yields a sequence of decreasing integers. This could be better expressed by directly specifying a relationship that must exist between two successive states.

We have also depended on finding a function expressing the bound function as an integer. In many problem domains not concerned with numbers this may be inconvenient. It is often neater to map states into sequences of strings, or sequences of other data structures, instead of using integers. What we require of the bound function is more general than any property of integers: it needs to be some function which maps successive values of a system state onto members of some ordered sequence of values which has the property that there is in some sense a 'minimum'. We can deduce from this property that there cannot be an infinite number of different values of a state, and that the loop must halt.

It is possible to prove termination simply by considering the nature of the relation used to express the post-condition, without the extra stage of inventing a bound function. Termination can be proved if the post-condition R can be shown to have a mathematical property called 'well-foundedness' which is connected with whether it is meaningful to form the relation $(R \mid R \mid R \mid R...)$ with indefinitely many repetitions. The advantage of this approach is that it is then possible to have a single proof rule for loops which shows total correctness by demonstrating both that the final state is correct and that termination occurs. However, a separate proof of termination, as used here, is perfectly adequate, if less elegant.

12.8 Summary of concepts

- If P is an invariant of the statement S, after executing the statement **while** B **do** S, the condition P is still true but B is false, providing that the loop really does terminate.

- Looping programs may be constructed by expressing a desired post-condition in the form $P \wedge \neg B$, and then searching for statements that have P as an invariant.
- Termination of a looping program can be proved by finding a bound function which is decreased by the body of the loop, but which is greater than zero while the loop is executing.

13 DATA TYPES: FROM VDM TO PASCAL

All the examples we have seen so far have manipulated only scalar variables; i.e. variables which have no substructure. The reason for this is that unstructured scalar variables in VDM are always easily represented in target languages like Pascal. Indeed we have implicitly assumed that most of the desirable properties of VDM scalars were automatically inherited by Pascal scalars and the operations on them. We felt no need to justify the assumption that a VDM scalar x could be represented by a Pascal scalar variable called x, and that expressions like $x + 1$ meant the same in both notations. Most of these assumptions are justified, but it is important to realize that there is a level of implementation design decision here that we have skipped over. We examine this type of design decision in this chapter by looking at how VDM and Pascal correspond.

13.1 Identifiers and numbers

An example of an assumption we have made implicitly is that permitted identifiers in VDM can be mapped into identical identifiers in Pascal, though in fact we know that Pascal has many restrictions on the choice of identifiers.

More importantly, we assumed that operations like < and + operating on Pascal integers had all the properties of their mathematical counterparts, although in an actual implementation of the language this will not be so. For instance, mathematically it is always true that $n < n + 1$. In contrast, when using a Pascal implementation which implements integers in 16 bits, 32767 + 1 evaluates to –32768, because of integer overflow: 32767 is the largest integer which can be represented, and adding 1 results in the smallest, and so it is *not* always true that $n < n + 1$. Differences between mathematical real numbers and their computer equivalents are even more marked.

Strictly, we should use a VDM specification of every single Pascal operation (e.g. +, **mod**, etc.). This would make clear under exactly which pre-conditions the

Pascal operation produces which results. Pascal integer addition would then be defined only for integers in a certain range, and operations on real numbers only for certain combinations of arguments.

Suppose we try to construct and prove a program from a specification of an operation which manipulates members of $\mathbb{Z}$. That is, there are no restrictions on the range of values on which the operation is defined. An attempt to prove a program satisfying such a general specification will fail because the correctness statements for all Pascal constructs will contain pre-conditions which restrict the range of values to within implementation-defined limits. (For example, in many implementations of Pascal, integers are restricted to the range –32768, ..., 32767.) This failure to construct a correct proof forces us to revise the original (unimplementable) specification by constraining it sufficiently to be able to complete the proof. In practice, we would trim down the original specification by restricting the range of applicability of all conditions to the level where the differences between mathematical integers and Pascal integers could be ignored.

This is not just a problem for integers; we may need to constrain specifications involving other types. For some Pascal types this is easy: for integers we can express the constraint that variables lie within some range by declaring them as a subrange type of the form:

```
var i, j : -512..511;
```

If the constraint involves more complicated numerical properties, this can be almost impossible to capture: for example, when specifying under what conditions the finite precision of the Pascal statement $\mathring{a}$ really does produce the post-condition $\{x \times z = y\}$. To add complicated pre- and post-conditions to every single operation would lead to an enormous increase in complexity, and in practice one is likely to ignore the whole question, perhaps just adding a general caveat in English about not invoking the operations on extreme values!

Ideally, a specification should not need to include such low-level details as ranges of numbers on some particular target machine. However, if the target language data types are more restrictive than their mathematical counterparts, it is inevitable.

13.2 VDM and Pascal data structures

Even if VDM scalar variables can be assumed to be representable simply by Pascal ones, this is certainly not the case for the data structures. VDM provides a very rich and powerful set of data structuring facilities, including composite objects, sets, maps and sequences. Pascal provides only records, arrays, files and a very restricted form of set. Pascal sets are usually too limited to be used to represent VDM sets, and Pascal files, though they *are* sequential, are usually inappropriate to represent VDM sequences because they do not support the full range of operations on sequences. More complicated abstract types such as stacks, trees and graphs must be built out of these basic ones. For example, we might represent a set using an array or a sequence as a linked list of records. In the case of an array as a set, we would have to develop Pascal operations on the array corresponding to each set operation used in a specification, and prove that each program fragment implementing an operation on the array implied the corresponding VDM operation on the set. Notice the implication goes from the concrete to the abstract. The abstract cannot imply the concrete as the concrete representation involves many details not even mentioned in the abstract representation.

Records

Both Pascal and VDM provide composite objects consisting of a grouping of more basic components. If there are a fixed number of the basic components, a Pascal record type is a direct analogue of the VDM composite object type.

Here, for instance, is a VDM declaration of a composite object type:

Recordtype ::
 key: *Keytype*
 info: *Infotype*

The direct equivalent in Pascal is:

```
type Recordtype =  record
                     key: Keytype;
                     info: Infotype
                   end;
```

`Keytype` and `Infotype` will be the Pascal implementations of the VDM *Keytype* and *Infotype*. In VDM, components of objects can be referred to by using selectors of the form *rec1.key*, which is identical to the Pascal notation.

More of a problem is the creation of composite objects. VDM allows constructs such as:

let *rec1* = *mk-Recordtype*(*kval*, *dval*) in ...

The *mk* function constructor constructs a new item of type *Recordtype*, out of the components values *kval* and *dval*. In Pascal, records can be created either by declaring them, or by using the standard procedure `new`, but in both cases the fields of the record are not initialized. To make them have specific values, assignment statements must be used, one for each field, as in the following:

```
new (rec1 ) ;
rec1.key := kval ;
rec1.info := dval ;
```

Thus, to bring about a simple condition expressed by VDM in terms of a make function, we will have to execute a whole sequence of Pascal statements. The essence of the problem is that VDM allows expressions to deliver values which are records, created by make functions. Standard Pascal never allows expressions to deliver record values, so usually when implementing make functions, each field of the record must be manipulated separately. The only exception to this is when the whole of one record is being copied to another record variable: then we are allowed to write statements such as:

```
recx := recy;
```

A consequence of having to set the fields of a Pascal record one by one using a sequence of statements is that if there is a relationship between different fields that is meant to be held invariant, it may temporarily become untrue in the middle of the Pascal sequence, even though the sequence as a whole may restore it. We must therefore realize that our implementations of VDM operations must be considered to be indivisible actions. We cannot expect all invariants to hold in the middle of an implementation of an operation.

For example, the invariant on all values of type *Recordtype* might be that the *key* field is twice the *info* field. Pascal could update the fields of a record `rec1` by:

```
rec1.key := 10;
rec1.info := 20;
```

However, between the two assignment statements, the invariant of the record type is temporarily untrue. It is the sequence as a whole that preserves the invariant.

Arrays

Pascal has relatively few ways of forming data structures: arrays are one of the most widely used. VDM, in contrast, has a very rich variety of data structures, such as sets, sequences and maps, although none of them correspond precisely to Pascal arrays. This means that very many specifications which are naturally expressed in VDM cannot be transformed easily into Pascal. If the specification uses sets, maps or sequences in their full generality, translation to Pascal will be very difficult; however some special cases can be easily translated. A consequence is that even during specification it is important to be aware of which VDM structures are likely to cause difficulties during later stages of software production.

A VDM structure that looks as though it might translate conveniently into a Pascal array is the map, and more especially, the special form of map called a sequence. (Essentially a sequence is a map from $\mathbb{N}_1$ to the sequence's component type—hence the sequence modification operator.) A VDM map may be from any type to any other type and is dynamic in length; i.e. the number of maplets in a value of a map type can vary. For example, if a map is used to model a personnel file by mapping staff numbers to salaries, the length of the map will vary with the number of employees. In contrast, Pascal arrays are fixed in length and have restrictions on the index type. The varying length of the personnel file is expressed in VDM as a varying length sequence. It is not so easy to capture the idea with a Pascal array, which must be of fixed length, although a common programming technique is to use an array of a size big enough to cope with the largest possible set of data, and then associate with the array a counter indicating how much of the array is in use at any one time. This technique simulates arrays of dynamic length, at the cost of some wasted space.

A VDM model of a personnel file might just as likely be a map from names to salaries. Since Pascal arrays can be indexed only by scalars such as integers, string valued subscripts are not allowed, and the map could not simply be represented as an array.

However, if a VDM map were not a general map but specifically a map of integers to something, the integers might be represented in Pascal by integer indexes. Because array indexes must form a sequence with no gaps, this will work only if the integers in the mapping form an adjacent sequence. We can directly implement a map whose domain is the set $\{500, \ldots, 699\}$ (using the Pascal type `array[500..699]`) but not a map whose domain is an arbitrary set of integers like $\{3, 55, 999\}$.

We can thus conclude that in the particular case of VDM maps of integers where the integers form a sequence, the map can be represented as a fixed length Pascal array with integer indexes and an associated variable indicating the current length in use.

For example, a type *T* in VDM might be defined by:

$$T = \{501, ..., 699\} \xrightarrow{m} Thing$$

An instance of *T* could be defined by ext *t1*: *T*. The variable *t1* at any moment will map some or all of 501, ..., 699 to various instances of *Thing*. Because in this case we can guarantee that the map never contains more than 199 maplets, we can represent it in Pascal using an array, as in:

```
type T = array [500..699] of Pthing;

var  a: T;
     aSize: 0..199;
```

`Pthing` is the Pascal equivalent of the VDM type *Thing*. At any time, `aSize` is intended to have the value of the VDM expression card *a*, which is the number of different elements in the map. Whereas a maplet can be completely removed from a map, an array element always exists and continues to contain some value. We therefore need to make the Pascal type `Pthing` contain a representation of a deleted *Thing*. `Pthing` therefore contains one more value than *Thing*.

Array operations

It is not enough to show that a VDM map can be represented as a data structure in Pascal. We must also be able to represent the operations on the map as operations on the Pascal data structures, and this proves to be more difficult.

In VDM, we can declare a map as having a specific value by writing down the value as a set of maplets. We can create new maps by using map expressions which build new maps out of old ones, merging two maps or restricting the range of a map. For example:

$$m1 = \{1 \mapsto 2, 2 \mapsto 4, 3 \mapsto 7\}$$

$m2 = m1 \dagger \{1 \mapsto 9, 4 \mapsto 15\}$

$m3 = \{1, 2\} \lhd m1$

In all these examples, the right-hand side of the equality is a map expression, which enables us to define the new map completely. Such map expressions can be built up into bigger map expressions, for example:

$(\{1, 2\} \lhd m1) \dagger \{1 \mapsto 9, 3 \mapsto 15\} \dagger m2$

There is nothing equivalent to this for arrays in Pascal; even array constants are not allowed. Thus, in a Pascal program you cannot write down a value for the contents of an array, although other languages do allow constructs to update a whole array at once, such as `a := (1, 3, 5, 26, 27)`. Instead, in Pascal one must write:

```
a[1] := 1;
a[2] := 3;
a[3] := 5;
a[4] := 26;
a[5] := 27;
```

Equally, there is nothing like an array expression in Pascal. One cannot write

```
a1 := a2 + inverse(a3)
```

Any manipulation of the array must be done one element at a time. This general lack of array expressions means that there is a large gulf between what will be written in VDM and any Pascal implementation.

Exercise 13.1

Write the statement which would initialize the implementation of the following map:

$m1 = \{1 \mapsto 2, 2 \mapsto 4, 3 \mapsto 7\}$

Solution 13.1

In Pascal we shall need multiple statements, as follows:

```
m1[1] := 2; m1[2] := 4; m1[3] := 7;
```

■

VDM usually creates new maps using an expression for the whole of the new map. For example:

$mm = \overleftarrow{mm} \dagger \{2 \mapsto 4\}$

Here the right-hand side represents the whole of the new map. In contrast, in Pascal we cannot create a new value for the whole array, but must instead update a single element of an existing array, as in the following:

```
a[2] := 4
```

If we are to use this as an implementation of the VDM fragment, we must show that it has the same properties. Ideally, we would consult a Pascal manual for a precise specification of what assignment to an array element does, and show that this implies the defining properties of the map operation †.

The operation † is actually defined as a merge of two maps, for example:

$$\begin{aligned} & ma \dagger mb \triangleq \\ & \quad \{d \mapsto (\text{if } d \in \text{dom } mb \text{ then } mb(d) \text{ else } ma(d)) \mid \\ & \quad\; d \in (\text{dom } ma \cup \text{dom } mb)\} \end{aligned}$$

The essence of this is that the result contains maplets for all elements mapped by either *ma* or *mb*. If an element is mapped by just one of *ma* and *mb*, that maplet is in the result. If it is mapped by both *ma* and *mb*, the *mb* mapping is included in the result.

In the case that *mb* contains a single maplet, it could be defined as:

$$ma \dagger \{i \mapsto x\} \triangleq \{d \mapsto (\text{if } d = i \text{ then } x \text{ else } ma(d)) \mid d \in (\text{dom } ma \cup \{i\})\}$$

Assignment of a value to a component of an array (e.g. `A[i] := x`) is usually defined only informally in most Pascal manuals, but it must satisfy the properties given in the (not quite VDM-SL) specification below.

ASSIGN-X-TO-A-I(*x*: *Array-component*, *i*: *Index-type*)
ext wr *a*: $Array\text{-}component^*$ -- *a is a sequence representing a Pascal array*
pre $1 \le i \wedge i \le \text{len } a$
post $a[i] = x \wedge (\forall j : Index\text{-}type \cdot j \ne i \Rightarrow a[j] = \overleftarrow{a}[j])$

This captures the essential fact that only one element of the array is updated by the assignment and that all others remain unaltered.

In the particular case of maps from integers which correspond to the array indexes, these formulations in terms of maps and arrays are equivalent. Here, we shall be concerned only with maps of the integers starting at 1, and arrays indexed from 1 upwards.

Review Question 13.1
According to the above definition of array assignment, which elements of an array are left unaltered by an array assignment when the index is out of range?

■

VDM types and Pascal variables

There are two situations in which the use of types and variables becomes awkward and for which the relationship between VDM notation and Pascal is not obvious. The first is where we would rather express a data invariant in terms of variables, rather than types. The second is where a VDM type is used for only a single variable (typically a system state).

VDM provides mechanisms for expressing data invariants, but these are defined on VDM types, and not on variables. Suppose the integer variables *x* and *y* are always required to sum to 100. We cannot express this directly in VDM-SL, because the constraint is not a property of the data types of x and y, integers, but of this particular pair of variables. In VDM we would therefore need to define a type of composite object consisting of a pair of integers, express the invariant as an invariant of this composite object type, and then declare one particular composite object to play the part of the original x and y, for example:

Pair-adding-to-100 ::
  x: $\mathbb{N}$
  y: $\mathbb{N}$

$inv\text{-}Pair\text{-}adding\text{-}to\text{-}100(p) \triangleq p.x + p.y = 100$

Then, in any operation which might have involved x and y the following external clause would be used:

ext wr *xypair*: *Pair-adding-to-100*

In places where x and y might have been used, we would need to use *xypair.x* and *xypair.y*.

Though slightly cumbersome, this is reasonable if there are many such pairs in a system. If there is just one such pair, it becomes awkward. In Pascal, we often do not introduce a type definition when there is just a single variable declared of that type. If this is the case, then, when the type is a composite object, we shall declare variables directly with the names of the fields, rather than declaring a single object of the composite type and using the fields as selectors. Thus, if the VDM specification contains a (fairly concrete) type definition such as:

Dbase ::
  dbarray: *Array1000*
  size: {0..1000}

and then declares a single variable of this type called *db*, we may in program code directly declare variables called `dbarray` and `size`, thus:

```
type
  Array1000 = ...;
var
  dbarray: Array1000;
  size: integer;
```

Review Question 13.2

If a specification involves two variables, *db1* and *db2*, of type *Dbase*, write the Pascal declarations to implement the specification.

■

13.3 Implementing a database

Previously (in Chapter 9) we have developed a number of simple database specifications. Here we shall carry one through to Pascal code; it is called *Dbase4*, as if it is the third reification of an abstract type. (Thus the name of the type and its associated operations have the suffix 4.) The data model and the intilization operation to be implemented are given below. The model represents a database as a set of key–value items, where each key is unique. Although a set is unordered, this set is represented as a mapping from unique integers to the items. This representation has been chosen with a view to eventual implementation in terms of Pascal arrays, when the integers will become the subscripts of the array.

$ArrayIndexType = \{1,...,1000\}$

$Array1000 = ArrayIndexType \xrightarrow{m} Item$

Dbase4 ::
  dbarray: *Array1000*
  size: $\mathbb{N}$

$inv\text{-}Dbase4(db4) \triangleq$
  $db4.size = 0 \lor 0 < db4.size \land$
    $db4.size \leq 1000 \land uniquekeys(db4.dbarray, db4.size)$

$Keytype = \mathbb{N}_1$
Item ::
  key: *Keytype*
  data: *Datatype*

$uniquekeys: Array1000 \times \mathbb{N} \to \mathbb{B}$
$uniquekeys(a, n) \triangleq$
  $\forall i, j : \mathbb{N} \cdot (i \leq n \land j \leq n \land a(i).key = a(j).key \Rightarrow i = j)$

INITIALIZE4
ext wr *db4*: *Dbase4*
pre true
post $db4.size = 0 \land db4.dbarray = \{\mapsto\}$

The size of the set is maintained explicitly in the component *size*. In a specification this is strictly redundant, as *size* is always equal to the cardinality of the map, i.e. card *dbarray*. It has been included because in the Pascal implementation the (variable sized) map is represented by a fixed sized array, together with a variable recording how much of the array is in use.

We will need operations to insert an item, delete one , and find one—*INSERT4*, *DELETE4* and *FIND4*. Because the operations *FIND4* and *DELETE4* both need to establish where an item is located in the database, an operation *LOCATE4* will also be defined to do the searching, i.e. to locate an index of a given key. The post-condition of this operation can then be quoted in other operations to save repeating large expressions. The condition *post-LOCATE4*(*k*, *db*, *r*) is just the condition that the index *r* is the location of the database *db* where key *k* occurs. *INSERT4* and *LOCATE4* are given below.

> *INSERT4*(*k*: *Keytype*, *d*: *Datatype*)
> ext wr *db4*: *Dbase4*
> pre $db4.size < 1000 \wedge \neg \exists i \in \{1 ,...., db4.size\} \bullet db4.dbarray(i).key = k$
> post $db4.size = \overleftarrow{db4}.size + 1 \wedge$
> $\quad db4.dbarray = \overleftarrow{db4}.dbarray \dagger \{db4.size \mapsto mk\text{-}Item(k, d)\}$
>
> *LOCATE4*(*k*: *Keytype*) *r*: $\mathbb{N}$
> ext rd *db4*: *Dbase4*
> pre $\exists i \in \mathrm{dom}(db4.dbarray) \bullet db4.dbarray(i).key = k \wedge i \leq db4.size$
> post $db4.dbarray(r).key = k$

Figure 13.2

The insertion operation, *INSERT4*, works by creating a new item for the given key and value, and then adding a maplet which maps the integer $\overleftarrow{db}.size + 1$ onto the new item. The locate operation, *LOCATE4*, simply determines what integer maps onto an item with the desired key.

Review Question 13.3
What is the signature of *post-LOCATE4*?

■

Exercise 13.2

Specify *FIND4* and *DELETE4* (you may find the corresponding operations in 9.2 helpful).

Solution 13.2

> *FIND4*(*k*: *Keytype*) *info*: *Datatype*
> ext rd *db4*: *Dbase4*
> pre $\exists i \in \mathrm{dom}(db4.dbarray) \bullet db4.dbarray(i).key = k \wedge i \leq db4.size$
> post $\exists i \in \mathrm{dom}(db4.dbarray) \bullet$
> $\quad (post\text{-}LOCATE4(k, db4, i) \wedge db4.dbarray(i).data = info)$
>
> *DELETE4*(*k*: *Keytype*)
> ext wr *db4*: *Dbase4*
> pre $\exists i \in \mathrm{dom}(dbarray) \bullet (db4.dbarray(i).key = k \wedge i \leq db4.size)$
> post $\exists i \in \mathrm{dom}(dbarray) \bullet$
> $\quad$ let $oldsize = \overleftarrow{db4}.size$ in
> $\quad (post\text{-}LOCATE4(k, db4, i) \wedge db4.size = oldsize - 1 \wedge$
> $\quad db4.dbarray = \overleftarrow{db4}.dbarray \dagger \{i \mapsto \overleftarrow{db4}.dbarray(oldsize)\})$

DELETE is slightly more subtle than the other operations. It is specified in such a way that in Pascal it will mean that the unwanted item is overwritten by the item at the end of the database (thus deleting it), and the size of the database is decreased by one, thus making the original version of the now duplicated item inaccessible. In VDM this is done by remapping the identifying integer of the unwanted item to the item mapped to by the highest identifying integer.

Review Question 13.4
Explain *post-LOCATE4*. Is anything missing?

■

One type declared here is *Array1000*. Remember that this is only a type declaration. No variables have yet been declared. As the type *Array1000* has all the properties of a Pascal array type, we can declare a Pascal version of it as:

```
type
  ArrayIndexType = 1..1000;
  Array1000 = array [ArrayIndexType] of Item;
```

The next part of the database specification declares a type called *Dbase4* as a composite object type. It expresses the fact that any variable of this type will contain a field called *dbarray* and one called *size*. The constraints on such variables are expressed by the invariant *inv-Dbase4*, which says that for any variable *db* of type *Dbase4*, the *size* field will always satisfy $0 \leq db.size \leq 1000$, and the field *dbarray* will satisfy the predicate *uniquekeys* (*db.dbarray*, *db.size*). This captures the fact that within the first *size* elements all keys are unique. The unused part of the array can contain anything at all.

In our actual program there will be only one variable of type *Dbase4*. Rather than declare it as a record type and always need to extract fields, we will declare Pascal variables with names corresponding directly to the fields.

```
var
  dbarray: Array1000;
  size: 0..1000;
```

The database array consists of elements of the composite type *Item*. Because record types in Pascal are so similar to composite types in VDM, the composite type is easily transformed to a Pascal record type definition.

```
type Item = record
              key: Keytype;
              data: Datatype;
            end;
```

For any particular database, suitable definitions of `Keytype` and `Datatype` will need to be provided.

Consider now the invariant on *Dbase4*. It is in two parts: the first insists that the *size* field of anything of this type stays within bounds. In our implementation, this corresponds to a restriction on the variable called `size`. The second part of the invariant expresses the integrity constraint that all keys in the database are unique. We shall have to establish that these conditions hold for our implementation. They clearly do not hold for all possible arrays of records, so we cannot establish them by considering Pascal data types. We shall have to establish them by showing that they are made true by the initialization operation, and that all other operations maintain them unchanged.

Review Question 13.5
How does the auxiliary function *uniquekeys*(a, k) express the constraint that the first k elements of array a contain no duplicate keys? Suggest an alternative formulation.

■

Review Question 13.6
In *Dbase4*, what limits the number of items that can be inserted in the database?

■

All the operations defined on *Dbase4* manipulate external variables, which in Pascal simply become global variables.

Consider the specification of the initialize operation. The post-condition to be established is that the *size* field of the database is set to zero. This is trivially done by setting the corresponding global variable.

```
size := 0;
```

This also establishes the invariant *inv-Dbase4*, in that $0 \leq 0 \leq 1000$, and (using the *uniquekeys* function) for all $i \leq 0$, it is vacuously true that the keys in the range 1, ..., 0 are unique.

Implementing INSERT4

The specification requires that size be increased and that a new element be inserted at the position given by *size*. Appropriate code is:

```
size := size + 1;
dbarray[size].key := k;
dbarray[size].data := d;
```

This certainly establishes $size = \overleftarrow{size} + 1$. It also establishes the condition on the new map *dbarray*, through the properties of array element assignment and the Pascal equivalent of *mk*-functions. It is not yet clear if it maintains the invariant *inv-Dbase4*.

Review Question 13.7
Does the code which has been suggested as an implementation of this operation maintain the data type invariant *inv-Dbase4*?

■

Implementing LOCATE4

The purpose of this operation is to set the variable r to an array index which maps to the value of the given key.; i.e. to determine r for the key k. We might guess that a loop is involved in the search. To develop a looping program, we must express the required post-condition in the form $P \wedge \neg B$, and then discover a statement S that has P as an invariant. A technique for developing invariants is to replace a constant by a variable. If we assume *mk-Dbase4(dbarray, size) = db4*, then he post-condition of *LOCATE4* is:

$$dbarray(r).\,key = k$$

We can inherit the pre-condition that $r \leq size$ giving:

$$dbarray(r).\,key = k \;\wedge\; r \leq size$$

where r is some fixed integer, though we do not know which one. It is guaranteed to exist by the pre-condition. We also know from the uniqueness condition that all other components, and in particular all components with smaller indexes, do not contain the key. If we decide to concentrate on the part of the array below the component containing k, we can add this fact to give the following post-condition to implement:

$$\forall j \in \{1, ..., r-1\} \bullet dbarray(j).\,key \neq k \;\wedge\; r \leq size \;\wedge\; dbarray(r).\,key = k$$

Our strategy will be to vary r from 1 upwards using a loop. We want to rearrange the post-condition into the form $P \wedge \neg B$. If this is possible, and having chosen to maintain P as an invariant, we will then construct a loop of the form **while** B **do** S.

Here we can take

P: $\forall j \in \{1, ..., r-1\} \bullet dbarray(j).\,key \neq k \;\wedge\; r \leq size$
B: $dbarray(r).\,key \neq k$

In searching for a statement S that maintains P as an invariant, we wish also to make some progress. Intuitively, this means extending the range of location indices $1, \ldots, r-1$ in which the key is known not to lie. The statement `r := r + 1` extends the range, but does it maintain the invariant? Clearly, it does not always maintain it, as eventually the statement will move `r` beyond the index where the key is actually stored and it will no longer be true that all component values less than `r` do not contain the key. However, we do not need to show that P is unconditionally an invariant of S. The proof rule for loops requires only that P is an invariant while the loop continues to be executed. That is, P satisfies:

$$\{P \wedge B\}\; S\; \{P\}$$

Review Question 13.8

Show that the statement `r := r + 1` does satisfy:

$$\{P \wedge B\}\; S\; \{P\}$$

■

To establish P initially, we must find some r such that k is not in the items located at the indices $1, \ldots, r-1$. A trivial solution is:

```
r := 1
```

The condition B expressed in Pascal syntax is:

```
dbarray[r].key <> k
```

Thus, the complete implementation of *LOCATE4* is:

```
r := 1;
while dbarray[r].key <> k do r := r + 1;
```

If this loop ever terminates, it will have established the desired post-condition. To prove that it does terminate, we need to find a bound function such that S decreases the bound function and $P \wedge B \Rightarrow bound > 0$.

The bound function $(size - r)$ has the desired property. The statement S increases r, and as *size* is fixed, S must decrease the bound function. To prove loop termination, we must show that $P \wedge B$ implies it is strictly positive.

Taken together, $P \wedge B$ express the fact that the key is not at the locations indexed by $1, \ldots, r$. Suppose it were the case that $r = size$. Then the key would not be present anywhere in the array, which contradicts the pre-condition of *LOCATE4*. Therefore we know $r \neq size$. In conjunction with the clause of P that $r \leq size$, we can deduce that $r < size$. But if $r < size$, the bound function $(size - r)$ is strictly positive. That is, we have shown $P \wedge B \Rightarrow bound > 0$.

This, together with the fact that S decreases the bound function, establishes the termination of *LOCATE4*.

We have established that the desired post-condition is made true, but must also show that the data type invariant is maintained. As this operation has only read access to *size* and *dbarray*, their new values will be the same as the old ones, so if the invariant was initially true, it must remain so.

Exercise 13.3

Develop code to implement *FIND4*.

Solution 13.3

The post-condition contains *post-LOCATE4*(*k*, *db4*, *i*). To establish this we can just use the implementation of *LOCATE4*. The second part of the post-condition requires that:

$$dbarray(i).\ data = info$$

This can be seen as the post-condition of the assignment statement:

```
info := dbarray[i].data
```

The whole implementation is therefore:

```
i := 1;
while dbarray[i].key <> k do i := i + 1;
info := dbarray[i].data
```

Strictly, we should show that the condition *post-LOCATE4* established by the first part of the post-condition of *FIND4* is not invalidated by the second part;

this is clear because an assignment to `info` cannot affect an expression not involving `info`.

■

Implementing DELETE4

The post-condition requires us to establish, among other things, the condition expressed by *post-LOCATE4(k, db4, i)*. This locates the item to be deleted. It is then overwritten by moving the last item in the array into its position, and the size of the array is reduced by one.

The most straightforward way to make *post-LOCATE4* true is to execute the code for *LOCATE4*. The remaining clauses of the post-condition are trivially established, giving the following as the complete operation:

```
i := 1;
while dbarray[i].key <> k do
  i := i + 1;
dbarray[i] := dbarray[size];
size := size - 1;
```

Consideration of the definition of assignment to array components as defined above in *ASSIGN-X-TO-A-I* shows that the post-condition requirement on *dbarray* is met by this code.

Finally the invariant *inv-Dbase4* must be established. We can assume that it is true before this operation. As *size* is decreased, the new value certainly satisfies $size < 1000$, and so also $size \leq 1000$. Also, $0 \leq size$ requires that on entry $1 \leq size$. This follows from the pre-condition:

$$\exists i \in \mathrm{dom}(dbarray) \bullet dbarray(i).key = k \wedge i \leq size$$

Because $\mathrm{dom}(dbarray)$ is $1, \ldots, 1000$, it is true that $1 \leq i \leq 1000$ and $i \leq size$, from which $1 \leq size$.

The rest of the invariant *inv-Dbase4* is about uniqueness of keys. If the condition held beforehand for an array of *size* elements, it must hold for $size - 1$, whichever element is deleted. Therefore we have shown informally that this implementation of *DELETE4* both satisfies its specification and maintains the invariant.

Declarations

Our Pascal fragments operate on, and communicate, via global variables. Any program using these operations must include declarations of all variables used. The set of global variables will be those that occur in any ext declaration of an operation or as components of the external variables. They are collected here:

```
var
  dbarray: Array1000;
  size: 0..1000;
  r: integer;
  k: Keytype;
  info: Datatype;
  d: Datatype;
```

In addition, we must declare variables that were used 'locally', such as in loops. Because we are not implementing a procedure, global variables are used:

```
var r: integer;
```

13.4 Other aspects

We have provided Pascal equivalents for all the operations defined on objects of type *Dbase4* and shown that they meet their specifications. There are, however, a few areas which still deserve comment.

Access to data

We have assumed that the relevant declarations of global variables are obtained simply by collecting together from operations all the externally declared variables and their component, whatever their read/write status. If all variables are simply declared as global Pascal variables, all operations have access to all of them. Thus, in the Pascal we have lost the useful information about which operations needed access to which variables. This knowledge is useful not only for protection against unlawful access, but also in understanding the program code. It might be maintained that if the code for an operation is correct, it does not matter if it has access to more variables than necessary as it will never corrupt them, but given the realities of computing environments, enforcing a 'need to know' regime would seem more satisfactory.

Data type invariants and initialization

Consider the data type invariant *inv-Dbase4.* We have established that *INITIALIZE4* makes this true, and that all the other operations maintain it. Therefore during any sequence of operations beginning with *INITIALIZE* it will be true. Before the call to *INITIALIZE* it will probably not be true, as we have no reason to believe anything about the earlier values of variables. It is therefore essential that it is invoked before any other operation, but nowhere in the specification is this laid down. Even if it were, there is a period during the execution of a program when the invariant will not hold—namely all the time up to the completion of *INITIALIZE.* It is therefore curious to claim anything to be an invariant if during some period it is not true. There are ways within VDM of expressing a genuine initial state apart from by providing an initialization operator, and these have the advantage that there is then no period of time before the invariant is established.

Procedures

A more serious problem follows from the fact that for each operation we have given a piece of in-line code to implement it. Any particular database program will consist of hundreds of operations, mixed in some order. Our implementation technique will involve copying out numerous instances of the same code. Any Pascal programmer would, in fact, use procedures. We can package each operation as a parameterless procedure, operating on global variables. For example:

```
procedure delete4;
  (* deletes from the database the information associated with
     the key in global variable k *)
  var
     i: integer;
  begin
     i := 1;
     while dbarray[i].key <> k do i := i + 1;
     dbarray[i] := dbarray[size];
     size := size - 1;
  end; (* of delete4 *)
```

This has the advantage that variables used purely within one operation can be declared locally. An example is the loop variable in *LOCATE4*. However programs using these operations will still need to communicate all operands via global variables. A neater solution would be to use Pascal parameters. Proving such a refinement requires considerable complexity; the meaning of a procedure call has to be defined in terms of the meaning of its body acting on the parameters, together with an apparatus for systematically replacing all formal parameters by the actual parameters at the point of call. It can, however, be done for the case of parameters used solely as input by an operation. Operations will then have access both to global variables and to values of parameters.

Consider next the case of operations which return information to the caller, such as *LOCATE* or *FIND*. Currently, they return results in global variables, which is inelegant and can lead to problems of names clashing. A Pascal programmer would normally use functions, or **var** parameters. VDM has nothing corresponding to **var** parameters as all parameters are passed by value. It does have functions, which can return any type of result. However Pascal functions can return only scalars whereas a general VDM function can return values like maps and sets which cannot be represented by Pascal scalars. It is thus impossible in general to express naturally in VDM a specification for an operation which returns a result and which will eventually be coded in Pascal. VDM functions do not map easily into Pascal, and there is no VDM construct which maps into Pascal **var** parameters. With a less restrictive language than Pascal there would be fewer problems.

14 FORMAL METHODS TODAY

This book has briefly examined the role of formal methods such as VDM in various stages of the software life cycle. We have concentrated on specification, refinement, and code generation. While some software does make use of formal methods throughout, it is important to realize that this is not necessary—formal methods can have immense benefits even if used in only one or two stages.

Most formal methods have been restricted to specification. This is perhaps because of the widespread realization of the enormous costs of making mistakes here. Effort invested here can save one proceeding to the implementation of an inappropriate system, with the subsequent need to change specifications when code has already been written. Formal methods provide an unambiguous notation as a basis for communication between participants. With English language specifications, contradictory interpretations can persist among the different members of a software team. Mathematics does not have this problem.

So at one level, formal methods offer just a concise, shared language for modelling a system. Usually very little formal manipulation need be done as the consequences of particular choices or operations are considered obvious. The key to success is usually keeping unnecessary detail out of the specification. For example, if we are specifying an operating system kernel, and are concerned whether the system can deadlock, it is important not to clutter the specification with extraneous details such as where a process stores its registers when it is suspended. Partly this is because at present few formal methods provide satisfactory facilities for appropriately modularizing a specification.

If formal methods are pursued into refinement it is clear that more manipulation will have to be done, as the essence of refinement is a demonstration that two different levels of specification are in some sense 'the same'. However even here most of the proving can be done satisfactorily at a very informal level, rather than the semi-formal inductive style we used. The benefit often comes simply from everyone involved realizing that there *are* proof obligations to be discharged, such as the domain and result rules, rather than any requirement for formal proof.

Once a refined specification has been produced, in most cases the most cost-effective way to proceed is along a conventional path of designing modules and implementing code. Given sound programming practice, adequate implementations of operations can be produced without formal techniques. The errors in most software arise through failings of specification far more often than through weaknesses in coding. However, there are cases where provable code must be produced. Safety-critical software often requires that the code itself be demonstrably correct, and in such circumstances the techniques we illustrated can be used. This tends to require a far higher level of technical expertise than the informal use of mathematics during specification. Constructing formal proofs in any area of mathematics is always difficult, and will remain so. Fully proven software will always be expensive and rare.

In this book we have tended to give what might be called 'semi-formal' proofs. They illustrate the structure of a proof, but are not fully formal, in the sense that not every step of a deduction makes direct explicit appeal to a deduction rule. They are at the level that much mathematics is done, giving enough detail to show how something could be justified, and not so much that a mass of detail obscures the structure. Proofs themselves can contain mistakes, so in applying formal methods it is important to be clear what level of proof, if any, is required. In a well-understood area, judicious hand-waving over a succinctly expressed specification may produce more benefit than pages of detailed deductions. If greater formality is required, some form of machine assistance is almost essential.

There has been much activity in the last few years aimed at providing machine assistance to those working with formal methods. The simplest tools are little more than mathematical word-processors which can handle the notation. Most specifications are produced as mathematics interleaved with explanatory text in English. Text-based tools provide facilities such as syntax checking of the notation, sensible layout of mathematics, renaming variables throughout both the English and the mathematics, and cross-referencing of types, variables and refinements. As more understanding of the mathematics is incorporated, proof checking facilities can be included to check that one line of a proof really does follow on from earlier ones.

An often-expressed fear about formal methods is that they require a high level of mathematical sophistication and that they add to development costs. As we have seen in this book, the mathematical concepts used are actually extremely simple, and there is beginning to be enough evidence to suggest that they can be taught to anyone in a few days. Experience also suggests that costs are usually considerably reduced by all but the most rigorous of formal methods because the costs of not getting specifications correct is so high. There is, though, an added complication for management, because the use of formal methods means that there is less measurable output during the early stages of a project. Numerous versions of a specification are produced and scrapped, to be replaced by better ones. This may last for 30 per cent of the project life; to managers accustomed to other approaches where easily accessible documents are produced from the first day, there may well be difficulties in believing that any progress is being made.

This book has been concerned with VDM, but there are numerous other notations that have been used in formal software development. In the UK, one that is as well-known as VDM is Z, which originates in Oxford University. Z has much the same descriptive power as VDM for specifying systems. Specifications are presented as a number of ***schemas***, each of which consists of some part of the system state, together with the conditions that apply to it. Pre- and post-conditions are not separated, which can make it less comprehensible than VDM, but there is a well-defined schema-calculus which helps considerably in structuring large documents. The Z community has placed less emphasis on the production of code than the VDM one, which sometimes makes great play about being a complete development method. Z has had considerable industrial use, of which the most quoted example is by IBM who have used it to respecify one third of CICS, a teleprocessing monitor, representing 100 000 lines of code.

Concern with the mathematical aspects of software was originally a purely academic interest, concentrating on proving the correctness of existing code. Techniques tended to be difficult, and only trivially small programs could be handled. Over the last 20 years the emphasis in formal methods has shifted to specification, and greater understanding of the essentials has made them far more easily accessible so that they have finally earned their place in a commercial environment. Whatever the future of software technology, it is clear that formal methods will form an important part of it.

APPENDIX A: THREE-VALUED LOGIC OPERATORS

Three-valued Not operator $\neg$

p	$\neg p$
p = true	false
p = false	true
p = undefined	undefined

Three-valued And operator $\wedge$

$p \wedge q$	q = true	q = false	q = undefined
p = true	true	false	undefined
p = false	false	false	false
p = undefined	undefined	false	undefined

Three-valued Or operator $\vee$

$p \vee q$	q = true	q = false	q = undefined
p = true	true	true	true
p = false	true	false	undefined
p = undefined	true	undefined	undefined

Three-valued Implies operator $\Rightarrow$

$p \Rightarrow q$	q = true	q = false	q = undefined
p = true	true	false	undefined
p = false	true	true	true
p = undefined	true	undefined	undefined

Three-valued Equivalent operator $\Leftrightarrow$

$p \Leftrightarrow q$	q = true	q = false	q = undefined
p = true	true	false	undefined
p = false	false	true	undefined
p = undefined	undefined	undefined	undefined

SOLUTIONS TO REVIEW QUESTIONS

Solutions for Chapter 3: Modelling data with sets

Solution to Review Question 3.1

We give only one possible answer below. Your answer to (i) should be a finite set of natural numbers. Your answer to (ii) should be a finite set of finite sets of natural numbers.

(i) $\{2, 3, 4\}$. (ii) $\{\{2, 3, 4\}, \{2\}, \{0, 1\}\}$.

Solution to Review Question 3.2

It would not usually make sense to model a program as a set since repetition is possible and order is important. A sequence type (see Chapter 4) would be the natural choice.

Solution to Review Question 3.3

{CHRISTA, EMMA, LISA, HELEN, PAULINE, ELIZABETH}

Solution to Review Question 3.4

Any infinite set of real numbers, for instance the integers, will not be an element of the data type.

Solution to Review Question 3.5

post $trip = \overleftarrow{trip} \cup new\text{-}on\text{-}trip$

or using distributed union:

post $trip = \bigcup\{\overleftarrow{trip}, new\text{-}on\text{-}trip\}$

Solutions for Chapter 4: Sequence types

Solution to Review Question 4.1

The order of an element in a sequence is significant; order is not relevant to sets. A value may appear more than once in a sequence, whereas values may only appear once in sets.

Solution to Review Question 4.2

The following is too cumbersome:

[['B', 'u', 'f', 'f', 'e', 'r', ' '], ['o', 'v', 'e', 'r', 'f', 'l', 'o', 'w', ':', ' '],
['f', 'i', 'l', 'e', ' '], ['t', 'r', 'a', 'n', 's', 'f', 'e', 'r', ' '],
['a', 'b', 'o', 'r', 't', 'e', 'd', '.']]

This second version is preferred:

["Buffer" , "overflow:" , "file" , "transfer" , "aborted."]

When we modelled a string as a sequence of characters, all the inherent properties of a VDM sequence were implied, including empty sequences, and so an empty string was allowed.

Solution to Review Question 4.3

(i) [COMPAK, FUJEE]
(ii) [ ]
(iii) [COMPAK, FUJEE]
(iv) [APPEL]

Solution to Review Question 4.4

[ ] ⌢ [ ] evaluates to [ ]

Solution to Review Question 4.5

(i) ['a', 'b', 'a', 'a', 'c'] or "abaac"
(ii) 5
(iii) "DSK"

Solution to Review Question 4.6

(i) false because inds [1, 3, 2, 1] results in {1, 2, 3, 4}
(ii) true
(iii) true
(iv) invalid expression since (hd *sq*) is the value 1 and not a sequence.
(v) false because tl *t* is [ ] and tl [ ] is undefined.
(vi) true
(vii) true
(viii) true
(ix) true
(x) invalid expression since (hd *sq*) is the value 1 and not a sequence.

Solution to Review Question 4.7

Recall the structure of operations (from Chapter 3): the first line of the operation simply specifies its name and the names and types of its parameters. The second line gives access to a variable *file* of type *Text-file* which represents the state of the system; the wr symbol means that the operation changes the value of the file. The pre-condition in the third line demands that the position given must be within the text file for the operation to work. Finally, the post-condition in the fourth line says how the new value of the state *file* is related to the old value $\overleftarrow{file}$: the new file is the same as the old one except that the value of new-word is at position *pos*.

Solution to Review Question 4.8

post $file = \overleftarrow{file}(1, \ldots, pos-1) \frown [new\text{-}word] \frown \overleftarrow{file}(pos + 1, \ldots, \text{len}(\overleftarrow{file}))$

Solutions for Chapter 5: Specifying functions

Solution to Review Question 5.1

The possibility of strings being empty comes from the definition *String* = char* which from the nature of sequences permits the empty sequence.

Solution to Review Question 5.2

(i) 0 (ii) 2

(iii) The result is not defined because the pattern is the empty sequence.

Solution to Review Question 5.3

For ['u', 'p'] to be a substring of itself there must be a prefix sequence, *p*, and a suffix sequence, *s*, such that $p \frown$ ['u', 'p'] $\frown s$ = ['u', 'p']. An empty sequence for both the prefix and suffix satisfies this, so ['u', 'p'] is a substring of ['u', 'p'].

Solution to Review Question 5.4

The sequences ['b', 'a'] and ['b', 'a', 'n', 'a'] are both possible values for *p* for which *is-prefix*(*p*, ['n', 'a'], ['b', 'a', 'n', 'a', 'n', 'a']) would be true.

Solution to Review Question 5.5

The value is false because ['a'] is a shorter prefix of ['c', 'a'] than ['a', 'c', 'a', 'b'] in the sequence ['a', 'c', 'a', 'b', 'c', 'a'].

Solution to Review Question 5.6

To explain why the two statements below, which are equivalent for given strings *s* and *t* are true in the same situation:

$\exists p : String \bullet is\text{-}prefix(p, s, t)$
$\exists q : String \bullet is\text{-}shortest(q, s, t)$

suppose that the first statement is true. Then there is a string *p* which is a prefix of *s* in *t*. By comparing lengths of all such prefixes we can find a shortest one. That shortest prefix is the *q* required to make the second statement true. Now suppose the second statement is true. Then there is a string *q* which is a shortest prefix of *s* in *t*. That string *q* is a prefix of *s* in *t*. So it can be substituted for *p* in the first statement to make that statement true.

Note that we have not said that the *concept* of shortest prefix is the same as the concept of prefix. We have said that the *existence* of a shortest prefix is equivalent to the existence of a prefix.

Solutions for Chapter 6: Composite object types

Solution to Review Question 6.1

The three fields of *s* are denoted as follows:

$s.name$
$s.tonnage$
$s.takes\text{-}passengers$

Solution to Review Question 6.2

(i) $mk\text{-}Date(26, 4, 1943)$ (ii) $mk\text{-}Date(d, m, y)$

Solution to Review Question 6.3

$da.month = 2$, $da.year = 1940$ and $is\text{-}leap\text{-}year(1940)$ is true. Furthermore, $da.day = 29 \in \{1, \ldots, 29\}$ is true, so the value of $inv\text{-}Date(29, 2, 1940)$ is true.

Solution to Review Question 6.4

$inv\text{-}Date(da) \triangleq$
  let $d = da.day$ in
  let $m = da.month$ in
  let $y = da.year$ in
  $(m \in \{1, 3, 5, 7, 8, 10, 12\} \wedge d \in \{1, ..., 31\}) \vee$
  $(m \in \{4, 6, 9, 11\} \wedge d \in \{1, ..., 30\}) \vee$
  $((m = 2) \wedge (\neg\ is\text{-}leap\text{-}year(y)) \wedge (d \in \{1, ..., 28\})) \vee$
  $((m = 2) \wedge (is\text{-}leap\text{-}year(y)) \wedge (d \in \{1, ..., 29\}))$

The three let constructs could be replaced by:

  let $d = da.day$, $m = da.month$, $y = da.year$ in

Solution to Review Question 6.5

$inv\text{-}Date(da) \triangleq$
  let $d = da.day$ in
  let $m = da.month$ in
  let $y = da.year$ in
  cases m :
    $1, 3, 5, 7, 8, 10, 12 \rightarrow d \in \{1, ..., 31\}$,
    $4, 6, 9, 11 \rightarrow d \in \{1, ..., 30\}$,
    $2 \rightarrow$
      if $is\text{-}leap\text{-}year(y)$
      then $d \in \{1, ..., 29\}$
      else $d \in \{1, ..., 28\}$
  end

The three let constructs could be replaced by:

  let $d = da.day$, $m = da.month$, $y = da.year$ in

Solution to Review Question 6.6

$\mu(da, year \mapsto 1977)$

Solution to Review Question 6.7

CHANGE-PRICE(p: $\mathbb{R}$)
ext wr s: *StockItem*
pre $p \geq 0.0$
post $s = \mu(\overleftarrow{s}, price \mapsto p)$

Solutions for Chapter 7: Specification with operations

Solution to Review Question 7.1

$stock = \overleftarrow{stock} - k$

Solution to Review Question 7.2

(i) card $\overleftarrow{fl} < 150$. (ii) card $fl \leq 150$.

Solution to Review Question 7.3

We cannot prove this because when card $\overleftarrow{fl} = 150$ there does not exist a value of fl for which ($fl = \overleftarrow{fl} \cup \{p\}$) $\wedge$ (card $fl \leq 150$) is true; i.e. *ADD-PASS1* allows full flights and new passengers for which adding the new passenger would result in an overbooked flight. Thus, *ADD-PASS1* is not implementable.

Solution to Review Question 7.4

The model is very simple. It includes three sequences of natural numbers. The data invariant has two conjuncts. The first states that if you take any two different elements of the sequence the natural numbers in those elements will not be equal. The second conjunct states that if you take any elements of the sequence which are not the same element and in order, their contents will be in order.

$Seqnat = \mathbb{N}^*$

$inv\text{-}Seqnat\ (sn) \triangleq$
$\forall\, i, j \in$ inds $sn \bullet i \neq j \Rightarrow sn\,(i) \neq sn\,(j) \wedge$
$\forall\, i, j \in$ inds $sn \bullet i < j \Rightarrow sn\,(i) < sn\,(j)$

Seqstate::
seq1: *Seqnat*
seq2: *Seqnat*
sfinal: *Seqnat*

The operation *MERGE* processes the two sequences and produces the final sequence. Since the data invariant for the sequences specifies that they are unique and ordered, the post-condition is simple. All that it needs to specify is that the union of the elements of the sequences to be merged is equal to the set of elements in the final merged sequence:

MERGE ( )
ext wr: *Seqstate*
post let *mk-Seqstate* ($s1$, $s2$, sf) = s in
elems $\overleftarrow{s1}$ $\cup$ elems $\overleftarrow{s2}$ = elems sf

Solutions for Chapter 8: Map types

Solution to Review Question 8.1

(i) This is a finite subset of $\mathbb{Z} \times \mathbb{N}$ with no two distinct maplets having the same first element. Therefore it is a map from $\mathbb{Z}$ to $\mathbb{N}$.

(ii) This is a finite subset of $\mathbb{Z} \times \mathbb{N}$, but there are two different maplets with first element 0. Therefore it is not a map.

(iii) This is a map for the same reason as (i).

Solution to Review Question 8.2

$\{2, 3, 4\}$

Solution to Review Question 8.3

(i) $\mathsf{dom}\ m = \{1, 12, 13\}$, $\mathsf{rng}\ m = \{0\}$, $m(12) = 0$.

(ii) $\mathsf{dom}\ m = \{\ \}$, $\mathsf{rng}\ m = \{\ \}$.

Solution to Review Question 8.4

(i) $sp \triangleleft hs$. (ii) $sp \ntriangleleft hs$.

Solution to Review Question 8.5

(i) 210, 123; (ii) 6220; (iii) 2213, 3040, 6220.

Solution to Review Question 8.6

(i) The value nil will never be used to identify an actual team. Only actual team identifiers may appear in the domain of the map.

(ii) No, because the empty set indicates that there are no players in the team.

Solution to Review Question 8.7

le.teams(210) is the set of players.

Solution to Review Question 8.8

REM-PL(pid: Player-id, tid: Team-id) -- *Removes a player from a team.*
ext wr *le*: *League*
pre $(pid \in \mathsf{dom}\ le.players) \wedge (tid \in \mathsf{dom}\ le.teams) \wedge (pid \in le.teams(tid))$
post $(le.teams = \overleftarrow{le}.teams \dagger \{tid \mapsto (\overleftarrow{le}.teams(tid) - \{pid\})\}) \wedge$
$(le.players = \overleftarrow{le}.players \dagger \{pid \mapsto \mathsf{nil}\})$

Solutions for Chapter 9: Reifying abstract data types

Solution to Review Question 9.1

Proof obligations are generated because we need to be convinced that the reified data types and the original abstract data types share the specified properties. Similarly we need to be convinced that the decomposed operations on the elements of the concrete data structures have the effect which corresponds to the operations on the elements of the abstract type.

Solution to Review Question 9.2

Yes, it represents a database with no values in it.

Solution to Review Question 9.3

(i) $inv\text{-}Nbase2\ (s) \triangleq \forall\, i, j \in \{1,..,\text{len}\ s\} \cdot s(i) = s(j) \Rightarrow i = j$

(ii) $inv\text{-}Nbase2\ (s) \triangleq \forall\, i, j \in \{1,..,\text{len}\ s\} \cdot i < j \Rightarrow s(i) < s(j)$

(iii) $inv\text{-}Nbase2\ (s) \triangleq \forall\, i, j \in \{1,..,\text{len}\ s\} \cdot i \leq j \Rightarrow s(i) < s(j)$

Solutions for Chapter 10: Proof obligations of stacks and queues

Solution to Review Question 10.1

The component *ctr* is of type $\mathbb{N}$ in order that it can take on the value 0, to indicate that the stack is empty. The component *els* will never be indexed by zero, but the subsequence *els*(1, …, *ctr*) will return [ ] if *ctr* is 0.

Solution to Review Question 10.2

The function *reverse* returns a sequence which contains the same elements as the sequence supplied as an argument, but in reverse order. We have recursively defined the reverse of a list to be the reverse of the tail of the list, with the head of the list appended at the end.

The function *retr-Stack* builds a sequence out of the first *ctr* elements in *els*, in reverse order. The reversal is necessary as in the original specification the stack has new elements added to the left-hand end of the sequence which modelled it, while the reified stack has elements added to the right-hand end.

Solution to Review Question 10.3

```
retr-Queue: Queue1 → Queue
retr-Queue (mk-Queue1(buf, next, free)) ≜
   if next < free
   then buf(next, …, free−1)
   else let lhpart = buf(next, …, m) in
        let rhpart =  buf(1, …, free−1) in
        lhpart ⁀ rhpart
```

alternatively, the let construct may be abbreviated:

```
   else let lhpart = buf(next, …, m), rhpart =  buf(1, …, free−1) in
        lhpart ⁀ rhpart
```

Solution to Review Question 10.4

The only operation that alters *writes* is *ENQUEUER*, which increments it. The pre-condition is ($q.writes - q.reads < m$), so after incrementing we know that ($q.writes - q.reads \leq m$).

From the initialization we know that ($0 \leq q.writes - q.reads$) and after incrementing *writes* this will still be true. The operation *ENQUEUER* has therefore not disturbed the alleged invariant.

Similarly, *DEQUEUER* is the only operation that alters *reads*, and it increases it. Its pre-condition is ($q.writes > q.reads$). After incrementing, we will still have ($0 \leq q.writes - q.reads$), which is what is required in the alleged invariant. Also, if ($q.writes - q.reads$) $\leq m$ before the operation, increasing *reads* will leave it true, so the whole of the alleged invariant will still hold after *DEQUEUER*. Thus the alleged invariant really is an invariant of all the operations on *QueueR*. It is therefore not strictly necessary to have this clause in the invariant of *QueueR* because we can deduce it. However, if in the future some further operation were to be defined on *QueueR* it would be easy to overlook the fact that it ought to maintain this invariant if it is not expressed explicitly.

Solution to Review Question 10.5

IS-EMPTYR() r: $\mathbb{B}$	*IS-FULLR*() r: $\mathbb{B}$
ext rd s : *StackR*	ext rd s : *StackR*
pre true	pre true
post $r \Leftrightarrow (s.writes = s.reads)$	post $r \Leftrightarrow (s.writes - s.reads = m)$

Solutions for Chapter 11: Correctness statements and proof rules

Solution to Review Question 11.1

(i) Valid. (ii) Invalid: squares are always non-negative.

Solution to Review Question 11.2

The pre-condition is $P(\sigma) \triangleq \sigma.x < \sigma.y$
The post-condition is $R(\sigma_0, \sigma_1) \triangleq \sigma_1.x < 2 \times \sigma_0.x$

Solution to Review Question 11.3

(i) Valid.

(ii) Invalid. In the post-condition the hooks are the wrong way round, and should read $\{\overleftarrow{x} > 2 \wedge x < 0\}$

(iii) Invalid. One hook is missing in the post-condition, making a contradiction. We could validly deduce

$$\{x > 2\}\ S\ \{x < 0 \wedge \overleftarrow{x} > 2\}$$

Solution to Review Question 11.4

A correctness statement is used 'forwards' to deduce which post-condition will hold whenever the given statement is executed on a state where the pre-condition applies.

A correctness statement is used 'backwards' when you wish to discover under which circumstances (i.e. pre-condition) a particular statement can bring about a given post-condition.

Solution to Review Question 11.5

(i) The post-condition of the assignment statement is

$$\{lodging = 43\}.$$

Our aim is therefore to achieve the conjunction

$\{lodging = 43 \wedge board + lodging < 100\}$

This can be achieved by the assignment *lodging* := 43, under the pre-condition found by pushing back $\{board + lodging < 100\}$ through the assignment, substituting the assigned value, 43, for *board*. That is, the pre-condition is $\{board + 43 < 100\}$ or $\{board < 57\}$.

(ii) The rise in the cost of *board* can be captured by:

```
board := 2 * board + 10.
```

By the definition of assignment, this produces a post-condition of

$\{board = 2 \times \overleftarrow{board} + 10\}$.

If we also want to achieve:

$\{board + lodging < 100\}$

our total post-condition is:

$\{board = 2 \times \overleftarrow{board} + 10 \wedge board + lodging < 100\}$.

Pushing the second part of this back through the assignment gives:

$\{(2 \times board + 10) + lodging < 100\}$.

This simplifies to the following pre-condition:

$\{2 \times board + lodging < 90\}$

(iii) Pushing the post-condition back through the assignment gives:

$\{3(x + y) + 4y > 110 \wedge (x + y) > 30\}$

This simplifies to $\{3x + 7y > 110 \wedge x + y > 30\}$

Solution to Review Question 11.6

(i) $R1 \mid R2$ is defined by:

$$(R1 \mid R2)(\sigma_A, \sigma_B) \triangleq \exists \sigma_t \bullet R1(\sigma_A . x, \sigma_t . x) \wedge R2(\sigma_t . x, \sigma_B . x)$$
$$= \exists \sigma_t \bullet \sigma_A . x^2 = \sigma_t . x \wedge 2 \times \sigma_t . x = \sigma_B . x$$
$$= \exists \sigma_t \bullet 2 \times \sigma_A . x^2 = \sigma_B . x$$

Because none of the variables in σ_t occurs in the expression, σ_t can be dropped, giving:

$$(R1 \mid R2)(\sigma_A, \sigma_B) \triangleq 2 \times \sigma_A . x^2 = \sigma_B . x$$

(ii) $(R1 \mid R2)(\sigma_A, \sigma_B) \triangleq \exists \sigma_t \bullet R1(\sigma_A . x, \sigma_t . x) \wedge R2(\sigma_t . x, \sigma_B . x)$

$$= \exists \sigma_t \bullet \sigma_A < \sigma_t . x \wedge \sigma_t . x < \sigma_B . x$$

From the properties of real numbers, and of the relation <, this can be re-expressed as:

$$(R1 \mid R2)(\sigma_A, \sigma_B) = \exists \sigma_t \bullet \sigma_A . x < \sigma_B . x$$
$$= \sigma_A . x < \sigma_B . x$$

Here $R1$ and $R2$ are the same, and happen to be transitive. For a transitive relation, we have thus shown that $R \mid R$ is the same as R. So for example, an operation whose sole function is to make a variable larger than it was before can be applied once or repeatedly and the post-condition will still be true.

(iii) $(R1 \mid R2)(\sigma_A, \sigma_B) \triangleq \exists \sigma_t \bullet R1(\sigma_A . x, \sigma_t . x) \wedge R2(\sigma_t . x, \sigma_B . x)$

$$= \exists \sigma_t \bullet \sigma_t . x = - \sigma_A . x \wedge \sigma_B . x = \sqrt{\sigma_A . x}$$
$$= \exists \sigma_t \bullet \sigma_B . x = \sqrt{-\sigma_A . x}$$
$$= \sigma_B . x = \sqrt{-\sigma_A . x}$$

Clearly this relation is not defined for all values of $\sigma_A . x$ and $\sigma_B . x$.

Solution to Review Question 11.7

We can write the post-conditions of the two separate statements in the general form:

$$R1(\sigma_A, \sigma_B) \triangleq \sigma_B . y = \sigma_A . x + 1$$
$$R2(\sigma_A, \sigma_B) \triangleq \sigma_B . z = \sigma_A . y^2$$

By the proof rule for sequences, we can deduce:

{true} `y := x + 1; z := y * y` $\{R1 \mid R2\}$

where:

$$(R1 \mid R2)(\sigma_A, \sigma_B) \triangleq \exists \sigma_t \bullet R1(\sigma_A, \sigma_t) \wedge R2(\sigma_t, \sigma_B)$$
$$= \exists \sigma_t \bullet y = \sigma_A . x + 1 \wedge \sigma_B . z = y^2$$
$$= \exists \sigma_t \bullet \sigma_B . z = (\sigma_A . x + 1)^2$$
$$= \sigma_B . z = (\sigma_A . x + 1)^2$$

As the post-condition for the combined sequence now involves references to only two states, the input and output for the sequence, we could translate this back into the hook notation as:

{true} `y := x + 1; z := y * y` $\{z = (\overleftarrow{x} + 1)^2\}$

Solution to Review Question 11.8

Looking for conditions of the form $\{P \wedge B\}$, $\{P \wedge \neg B\}$ suggests:

$\{1 \le today \le 365 \wedge today = 365\}$ *END-OF-YEAR* $\{(tomorrow = \overleftarrow{today} \bmod 365) + 1\}$
$\{1 \le today \le 365 \wedge today \ne 365\}$ *NORMAL-CASE* $\{(tomorrow = \overleftarrow{today} \bmod 365) + 1\}$

If we could implement these, the solution would be:

if *today* = 365 **then** *END-OF-YEAR* **else** *NORMAL-CASE*

Simplifying the specification of *END-OF-YEAR* gives:

$\{today = 365\}$ *END-OF-YEAR* $\{(tomorrow = \overleftarrow{today} \bmod 365) + 1\}$

By inheriting the pre-condition, it becomes:

$\{today = 365\}$ *END-OF-YEAR* $\{tomorrow = 1\}$

which can be implemented by:

```
tomorrow := 1
```

Simplifying the pre-condition of *NORMAL-CASE* gives:

$$\{1 \le today < 365\}\ NORMAL\text{-}CASE\ \{tomorrow = (\overleftarrow{today} \bmod 365) + 1\}$$

Inheriting the pre-condition into the post-condition, and simplifying by use of the properties of mod gives:

$$\{1 \le today < 365\}\ NORMAL\text{-}CASE\ \{tomorrow = \overleftarrow{today} + 1\}$$

Knowing the properties of assignment, we could easily prove that this is satisfied by the program:

```
tomorrow := today +1
```

We thus have as a program satisfying the whole specification:

```
{1≤today≤365}
  if today = 365
  then tomorrow := 1
  else tomorrow := today + 1
{tomorrow=(today mod 365)+1}
```

Solutions for Chapter 12: Programs with loops

Solution to Review Question 12.1

(i) Yes, because the post-condition $\{x > 10\}$ implies the pre-condition $\{x > 1\}$. Executing S therefore guarantees that conditions are suitable for it to be executed again.

(ii) No. The post-condition does not imply the pre-condition. For some executions it may well happen that a state satisfying the post-condition also happens to satisfy the pre-condition but it cannot be guaranteed in all cases.

(iii) Yes. The post-condition is the same as the pre-condition, and therefore implies it. Here the pre-condition is unaffected by the execution of S. It can be described as an invariant of S.

(iv) Yes and no! The post-condition does imply the pre-condition, so if it were ever meaningful to execute S, it would be meaningful to execute it again. We can therefore put S in a loop. However, as the pre-condition of S is false in all possible program states, it is never meaningful to execute S the first time.

Solution to Review Question 12.2

(i) No. Evenness will not be preserved.

(ii) Yes. Pushing the post-condition back through the second assignment gives:

$sn+n^2 = \sum_{i=1}^{n} i^2.$

Pushed through the first assignment then gives:

$sn+(n+1)^2 = \sum_{i=1}^{n+1} i^2$ which simplifies to the original condition. Therefore, if the original condition holds after the double assignment, it must hold before, and is therefore an invariant for the assignments.

This invariant is at the heart of any loop to compute sums of squares.

Solution to Review Question 12.3

(i) No. The square of the wrong number is added to *sn*.
(ii) Yes. From a longer sum of squares it builds a shorter sum of squares.
(iii) Yes. This is equivalent to the original version.

Solution to Review Question 12.4

Some other possibilities are:

- `n := 0; sn := 0`
- `n := 2; sn := 5`
- `n := 3; sn := 14`

Solution to Review Question 12.5

```
n := 9; sn := 181
```

This is only useful if one happens to realize already that:

$$181 = \sum_{i=9}^{10} i^2$$

Another initialization that also makes P true and makes the whole of the loop redundant would be:

```
n := 1;    sn := 385
```

Of course, if we knew this did establish P, we would not have needed to establish a program to compute *sn*. Thus, in choosing an implementation of `INIT` we want to depend on as little prior knowledge as possible.

Solution to Review Question 12.6

Use the assignment rule, passing the post-condition back through the assignment. This gives $\{1 \le k+1 \le 10\}$ or $\{0 \le k \le 9\}$. This is the weakest pre-condition that would guarantee the post-condition. The actual pre-condition, $\{1 \le k \le 9\}$, can be shown to imply the weakest pre-condition, so the correctness statement is valid.

Solutions for Chapter 13: Data types: from VDM to Pascal

Solution to Review Question 13.1

It is undefined, as the pre-condition is not satisfied. A correct implementation could do anything in this case, such as clearing the whole array!

Solution to Review Question 13.2

```
type
   Array1000 = ...;
   Dbase = record
               dbarray: Array1000;
               size: integer;
           end;
var
   db1, db2: Dbase;
```

Solution to Review Question 13.3

$$post\text{-}LOCATE4 : Keytype \times Dbase4 \times \mathbb{N} \rightarrow \mathbb{B}$$

Solution to Review Question 13.4

The condition *post-DELETE4* says that after executing *DELETE4* it must be the case that there is a subscript i which satisfies *post-LOCATE4* (i.e. the ith member of the database has key k), the ith member of the database is overwritten with the nth, and the field *db.size* is decreased by one. The old ith member has disappeared, and the old copy of the nth member is inaccessible (because now at position $size + 1$) but an equivalent item is in the database at position i. Nowhere is it said that all the other elements must remain unchanged. It would be possible for *DELETE4* to set them all to arbitrary values! The invariance of the other members could be captured by adding a clause like:

$$\forall j \in \{1, ..., db.size\} \cdot j \neq i \Rightarrow db.dbarray(j) = \overleftarrow{db}.dbarray(j)$$

Forgetting to capture what an operation does *not* do—i.e. what it leaves unaltered—is a common weakness in specification.

Solution to Review Question 13.5

It asserts that if two identical keys are found, they must be in the same place. The same constraint could be expressed by saying directly that for each element i there is not an element j with the same key where j is different from i.

$$uniquekeys(a, k) \triangleq$$
$$\forall i : \mathbb{N} \cdot$$
$$i \leq n \wedge \neg \exists j : \mathbb{N} \cdot j \leq n \wedge (i \neq j \wedge a(i).key \neq a(j).key)$$

Solution to Review Question 13.6

The pre-condition of *INSERT4* is that $size < 1000$. After initialization, *size* has value 0, and every insertion increases it by one. Insertions are therefore valid only while $0 \leq size < 1000$, which limits the number of items to 1000 at most.

Solution to Review Question 13.7

From the pre-condition that $size < 1000$, we know that after the operation $size \leq 1000$, so that part of the invariant is maintained. If the invariant were initially true, the keys in items $1, \ldots, size$ were unique. From the pre-condition of *INSERT* we know that the new key is not present, so inserting it will also maintain the uniqueness condition. Thus, the whole of the invariant is maintained.

Solution to Review Question 13.8

If P holds beforehand, k is not in the index range $1,\ldots,r-1$. If B holds, k is not at item r in the array. Therefore, when $P \wedge B$ holds, k does not occur in the array components $1,\ldots,r$. If r is increased by one, the components which do not contain the key, previously at the indexes $1,\ldots,r$, are now at the indexes $1,\ldots,r-1$. Therefore, the condition P still holds.

Note that we do not, in general, have $\{P\}\ S\ \{P\}$, but only $\{P \wedge \neg B\}\ S\ \{P\}$. In most searching programs, the loop invariant P eventually becomes false when B is false.

ADDITIONAL EXERCISES

Question X1

A Boolean function *occursonce* determines whether one given sequence of characters appears exactly once as a subsequence in another given sequence of characters, as, for example, does the sequence "cat" in the sequence "scatter". Using the VDM specification language, write an implicit definition of the function *occursonce*. (Do not use the quantifier $\exists!$ in your description.)

Question X2

Consider the following VDM data type which models a directory of information on computer programs: the language and length of the program.

$Directory = Name \xrightarrow{m} ProgramInfo$

ProgramInfo::
  length: $\mathbb{N}$
  language: {ADA, PASCAL, C, MODULA2}

Write a function *short-pascal* which, given an argument of type *Directory* and a natural number (of type $\mathbb{N}$), returns the set of names of all Pascal programs in the directory which have length less than the given number. Use the following signature and the explicit style of function definition:

$short\text{-}pascal : Directory \times \mathbb{N} \rightarrow Name\text{-set}$

(The data type *Name* should be left undefined.)

Question X3

Consider the following statement of requirements:

```
A stock control system is required for a factory store
which acts as a central repository for machine parts
needed by several workshops. The system must keep
information on each part and on how many are in stock.
Each part has a unique 6-character code by which it
can be identified. Each code begins with one of a pair
of letters "DC", "DX" or "FP". Larger parts may also
have a common name associated with them. If a part is
built from other components these must also be stored
```

```
by the system, even though there may not be sufficient
in stock. Components are never given names.
```

(i) Define a data type *Part-code* to model the 6-character code described in the statement of requirements.

(ii) Define the type *Stock-system* to model the attributes described above, defining any other data types needed.

(iii) Specify a function *stock-level*, which returns the stock level of a part in a stock system. The part is identified by its code.

(iv) Define an operation *ENOUGH* which, when given a part code and the number of parts required, returns true if sufficient parts and sub-components are in stock.

Question X4

Consider the following statement of requirements:

```
A purchasing system keeps a queue of orders which are
waiting to be shipped to customers. Each queue element
contains a unique order number and the value of the
order rounded up to pounds.
```

(i) Model the problem using suitable VDM data types and including any necessary data type invariant.

(ii) Write down a recursive function which calculates the total value of orders on the queue.

Question X5

When a software system requires more than one queue it can be very wasteful to maintain them as separate data structures, for example, many of the queues might only be half full, or contain only a few items. One solution to this problem of wasted space is to keep the queues in a single data structure.

Assume that you have a system which contains two queues. These queues are to be modelled as one sequence containing one queue at the beginning of the sequence and the other at the end. Items to be added to the first queue are added in order from the front of the sequence, while items to be added to the second queue are added to the end of the sequence in reverse index order.

(i) Model the double queue data structure described using VDM. Include an invariant which limits the total number of items in the double queue to n. You should not specify the type of the item held.

(ii) Specify three operations: *FULL*, which returns the value true when no more items can be added to either of the queues, *ENTERFIRST*, which adds an item to the first queue, and *ENTERSECOND*, which adds one to the second.

In order to help you envisage what is needed, the diagrams below show the addition of the integer 3 to the first queue, followed by the addition of 5 to the second queue, then 4 to the first queue, and finally the addition of the 6 to the second:

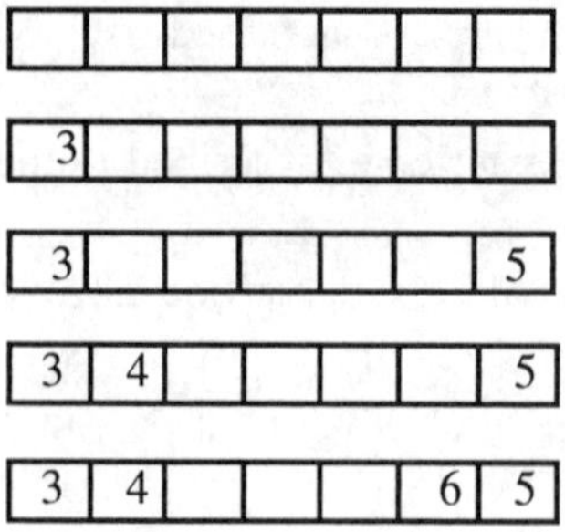

							Empty queue
3							Addition of 3 to first queue
3						5	Addition of 5 to second queue
3	4					5	Addition of 4 to first queue
3	4				6	5	Addition of 6 to second queue

Question X6

Consider the following statement of requirements.

```
The bank is small and administers only current
accounts. Each customer is allowed to have one current
account. The account is distinguished by a unique
account number (a six-digit natural number) and the
balance as a whole number of pence. No customer is
allowed to have an overdraft of more than £10,000.
```

(i) Write a VDM model of the bank including any data invariant.

(ii) Write down three operations. *ADDAMOUNT* adds an amount of n pounds to the account a. *OVERDRAWN* returns true if the account a has a balance which is negative. *REMOVE* removes the account a from the bank system. For the account to be removed, the balance of the account must be zero.

Question X7

Consider the following statement of requirements:

```
The company needs a stock control system to maintain
an inventory of products that are available at its
chain of shops. All the products held at different
shops must appear in the company's catalogue. However,
there are occasions when some products in the
catalogue may not be stocked at any shop. (This can
happen when a new product is being introduced or when
an old one is being withdrawn.)

Shops have limited storage capacity and some sell more
of one product than another. Therefore different
maximum stock levels for products are set for
different shops and when a shop requires a delivery of
stock from the central warehouse, the number required
to re-stock to the maximum level from the warehouse
can be calculated from the stock level at the shop.
Furthermore, not all shops sell all products and they
```

```
will not keep details of products which they do not
sell.

The inventory system should also record the current
price of all products currently sold. The price of a
product is the same at all shops.
```

The following is part of a VDM specification for the stock control system described. We shall assume that the data types *Product*, *Shop*, and *Price* are given:

Prod-holding::
  level: $\mathbb{N}$
  max: $\mathbb{N}_1$

Stock-details = *Product* $\xrightarrow{m}$ *Prod-holding*

Inventory::
  catalogue: *Product* $\xrightarrow{m}$ *Price*
  stocks: *Shop* $\xrightarrow{m}$ *Stock-details*

inv-Inventory(*i*) $\triangleq$
  let *stks* = *i.stocks* in
  let *cat* = *i.catalogue* in
  $\forall$ *details* $\in$ rng *stks* • dom *details* $\subseteq$ dom *cat*

required (*p*: *Product*, *sh*: *Shop*, *invent*: *Inventory*) *num-reqd*: $\mathbb{N}$
pre *p* $\in$ dom *invent.stocks*(*sh*)
post let *shop-details* = *invent.stocks*(*sh*) in
  let *this-holding* = *shop-details*(*p*) in
  let *local-max* = *this-holding.max* in
  let *current-level* = *this-holding.level* in
  num-reqd = *local-max* – *current-level*

(i) Without reference to the invariant on *Inventory*, explain the data model by describing the data types *Inventory*, *Prod-holding* and *Stock-details* in relation to the statement of requirements. In your explanation, describe how the difference between a shop not selling a product (and thus not stocking it) and a shop having run out of stock is modelled.

Suggest how the data model could be improved to better reflect the statement of requirements. (Again, do not consider *inv-Inventory* at this stage.)

(ii) Explain the purpose of each line in the data type invariant *inv-Inventory*.

(iii) Consider the following change to the statement of requirements:

```
Following a change of company policy, all products in
the catalogue will now be available at all shops. As
before, all products in any shop must be in the
catalogue.
```

Rewrite the invariant so that it guarantees that all shops stock all products in the catalogue.

(iv) Consider the following addition to the statement of requirements:

```
When the number of items of a product at a shop falls
below a set level new items must be requested from the
warehouse.
```

Change the data model so that it includes the minimum stock level for a product at each shop.

(v) What is the value of the function *required*? Explain each line of its pre-condition and each line of its post-condition.

(vi) Specify an operation:

RECEIVE(*p*: *Product*, *sh*: *Shop*, *n*: $\mathbb{N}_1$)

that updates the external variable *invent* when *n* items of a product *p* are delivered from the warehouse to a shop *sh* which sells the product *p*.

Question X8

A playing card within a suit might be represented by an integer in the range 1, …, 13. *Hand*, the set of cards held by a particular player, could be represented in various ways. *Hand1* might be represented as a set of cards, and *Hand2* as a map from the cards to a flag which would be either PRESENT or ABSENT.

(i) Define a type *Card*, and then two different representations for *Hand.*

(ii) Define a retrieve function, *retr-Hand1*, which constructs a set given a value in *Hand2*, a mapping.

(iii) It would also be possible to construct a retrieve function, *retr-Hand2*, which constructed a map given a set. What are the conditions on two types for it to be possible to construct retrieve functions in both directions?

(iv) Write a function *retr-Hand2* which computes a map given a set.

Question X9

A club specifies a membership system as follows:

Club::
  fullmems: *Memnums*-set
  associatemems: *Memnums*-set

Memnums = $\mathbb{N}_1$

A software designer decides to refine this as:

Club2 = *Memdetail**

Memdetail::
  memno: *Memnums*
  memtype: {FULL, ASSOC}

(i) In general, this refinement cannot represent all the possibilities for club membership as allowed in the original specification. It will probably work in practice because of an undocumented assumption about the membership. Document this assumption by adding an invariant to *Club*.

(ii) Write the retrieve function from *Club2* to *Club*.

Question X10

The following is an extract from a statement of requirements for a system to mechanize the handling of a building society savings account scheme:

```
Customers are identified solely by name, which is
assumed unique, and accounts are identified by a
unique six-digit account number.  There are three
types of account - gold, silver and bronze - each of
which has different attributes such as the interest
rate and the minimum balance. New customers are
registered with just a bronze account, but may in
addition have one of each of the other types.  The
current rules governing the accounts are as follows:
```

	gold	silver	bronze
interest	15%	14%	13%
minimum starting balance	£10,000	£5,000	£1

A model for such a system is sketched below:

Acc-type = {GOLD, SILVER, BRONZE}
Acc-attribute::
  interest: $\mathbb{R}$
  minbalance: $\mathbb{R}$

Account::
  type: *Acc-type*
  balance: $\{r \mid r : \mathbb{R} \bullet r \geq 0.0\}$
Name = is not yet defined
Acc-no = $\{n \mid n : \mathbb{N} \bullet 100000 \leq n \wedge n \leq 999999\}$

Building-society::
  rules: *Acc-type* $\xrightarrow{m}$ *Acc-attribute*
  customeraccnos: *Name* $\xrightarrow{m}$ *Acc-no*-set
  accounts: *Acc-no* $\xrightarrow{m}$ *Account*

inv-Building-society(bs) $\triangleq$
  ??? -- *rules are stored for every account type*
  $\wedge$??? -- *all customer account numbers in use are associated with accounts*

(i) Complete the invariant for *Building-society* by replacing the ??? with two clauses of VDM notation to reflect the comments.

(ii) The component *rules* of *Building-society* is a mapping of *Acc-type* to *Acc-attribute*. Define a parameterless operation *SETRULES* which makes the component *rules* correspond to the rules in the table above.

[Hint: The function *mk-Acc-attribute* can be used to construct a value of type *Acc-attribute* for any type of account.]

(iii) The following is an outline of an operation to register a previously unregistered customer and to open for them a bronze account with a given account number, starting with an initial deposit.

NEWBRONZECUSTOMER(*nm*: *Name*, *accno*: *Acc-no*, *deposit*: $\mathbb{R}$)
ext wr *bs*: *Building-society*
pre *nm* $\notin$ dom *bs.customeraccnos* $\wedge$
accno $\notin$ dom *bs.accounts* $\wedge$
deposit ≥ 1.00
post let *rules* = $\overleftarrow{bs}$*.rules* in
let *customers* = ??? in
let *accs* = ??? in
let *newbronzeacc* = ??? in
let *updatedcustomers* = ??? in
let *updatedaccs* = ??? in
bs = ???

Write out a complete specification by completing the gaps marked '???'.

(iv) In order to calculate customer assets, a function *sumbalances* is required which, given a set of accounts, returns the total of all the balance fields. Write the signature of this function and give an explicit definition.

(v) By replacing the gaps marked ???, complete the following specification of the function *ASSETSFORCUST*, which computes the total assets of a named customer, in all accounts held:

ASSETSFORCUST(*nm*: *Name*)*r* : $\mathbb{R}$
ext wr *bs*: *Building-society*
pre ???
post let *bscustomers* = *bs.customeraccnos* in
let *bsaccounts* = *bs.accounts* in
let *thiscustomersaccountnumbers* = ??? in
let *thiscustomersaccounts* = ??? in
r = *sumbalances*(???)

SOLUTIONS TO ADDITIONAL EXERCISES

Solution to Question X1

$$occursonce: \text{char}^* \times \text{char}^* \rightarrow \mathbb{B}$$
$$occursonce\ (s1, s2) \triangleq$$
$$\exists\ r, t : \text{char}^* \cdot (s2 = r \frown s1 \frown t \land \forall\ u, v : \text{char}^* \cdot s2 = u \frown s1 \frown v \Rightarrow u = r \land v = t)$$

Solution to Question X2

$$short\text{-}pascal: Directory \times \mathbb{N} \rightarrow Name\text{-set}$$
$$short\text{-}pascal\ (d, n) \triangleq$$

if $d = \{\ \}$
then $\{\ \}$
else let $d = \{name \mapsto mk\text{-}ProgramInfo\ (leng, lang)\} \cup e$ in
    if $leng < n \land lang = \text{PASCAL}$
    then $\{name\} \cup short\text{-}pascal\ (e, n)$
    else $short\text{-}pascal\ (e, n)$

Solution to Question X3

(i) $Part\text{-}code = \text{char}^*$

$inv\text{-}Part\text{-}code\ (c) \triangleq$
    len $c = 6 \land c\ (1, \ldots, 2) \in \{\text{“DC”}, \text{“DX”}, \text{“FP”}\}$

(ii) $Stock\text{-}system = Part\text{-}code \xrightarrow{m} Part$

Part::
  $name = [\text{char}^*]$
  $stock\text{-}level: \mathbb{N}$
  $sub\text{-}parts: Component\text{-set}$

Component::
  $code: Part\text{-}code$
  $number: \mathbb{N}_1$ -- *number of components required to make a part*

(iii) $stock\text{-}level\ (sys: Stock\text{-}system,\ c: Part\text{-}code)\ l: \mathbb{N}$

pre $c \in \text{dom } sys$

post $l = sys(c).stock\text{-}level$

(iv) $ENOUGH\ (c: Part\text{-}code,\ n: \mathbb{N}_1)\ r: \mathbb{B}$

ext rd $sys: Stock\text{-}system$

pre $c \in \text{dom } sys$

post let $mk\text{-}Part(name, level, sub) = sys(c)$ in

$r = (level \geq n \wedge$

$\forall s \in sub \bullet n \times s.number \leq sys(s.code).stock\text{-}level)$

Solution to Question X4

(i) The queue can be modelled by means of a sequence of composite objects. Each composite object contains the order number and a natural number which represents the value of the order in pounds. This is shown below. The data invariant states that each order number will be unique, i.e. the cardinality of the set of order numbers in the queue will equal the number of items in the queue:

Order-number = is not yet defined

Order::

order-n: *Order-number*

value: $\mathbb{N}$

$Orderqueue = Order^*$

$inv\text{-}Orderqueue\ (q) \triangleq$

$\text{card } \{on \mid on : Order\text{-}number \bullet \exists i \in \text{elems } q \bullet on = q(i).order\text{-}n\} = \text{len } q$

(ii) The recursive function which calculates the total value of orders on a queue is shown below. It extracts the first order amount and then adds it to the total of the remaining orders:

$find\text{-}total: Orderqueue \rightarrow \mathbb{N}$

$find\text{-}total\ (q) \triangleq$

if $q = [\,]$

then 0

else $value\ (\text{hd } q) + find\text{-}total\ (\text{tl } q)$

Solution to Question X5

The double queue is represented by a composite object type which contains a sequence of natural numbers and two pointers: *first* and *last*. The former points at the next locations for the first queue to which the next natural number is added, while the latter represents the next location for items in the second queue.

The data type invariant has two components: the first limits the number of items in the queue to be n while the second describes the fact that the two pointers can only overlap by one location:

Item = is not yet defined
Double-queue::
  first: $\{1, ..., n\}$
  last: $\{1, ..., n\}$
  dqueue: $Item^*$

inv-Double-queue $(dq) \triangleq$
  let $f = dq.first$ in
  let $l = dq.last$ in
  let $d = dq.dqueue$ in
  len $dq = n \wedge l - f + 1 \geq 0$

Alternatively, either of the following:

inv-Double-queue $(dq) \triangleq$
  let $f = dq.first, l = dq.last, d = dq.dqueue$ in
  len $dq = n \wedge l - f + 1 \geq 0$

inv-Double-queue $(dq) \triangleq$
  let $mk\text{-}Double\text{-}queue(f, l, d) = dq$ in
  len $dq = n \wedge l - f + 1 \geq 0$

The operations are shown below. The first operation *FULL* returns true if the pointers have just overlapped.

FULL ( ) b: $\mathbb{B}$
ext rd d: *Double-queue*
post $b \Leftrightarrow d.last - d.first + 1 = 0$

The remaining two operations have as their pre-conditions a check that the queue is not full:

ENTERFIRST (n: $\mathbb{N}$)
ext wr dq: *Double-queue*
pre $dq.last - dq.first + 1 \geq 0$
post let $mk\text{-}Double\text{-}queue\ (f, l, d) = dq$ in
  $d(f) = n \wedge f = \overleftarrow{f} + 1$

ENTERSECOND (n: $\mathbb{N}$)
ext wr dq: *Double-queue*
pre $dq.last - dq.first + 1 \geq 0$
post let $mk\text{-}Double\text{-}queue\ (f, l, d) = dq$ in
  $d(s) = n \wedge l = \overleftarrow{l} - 1$

Solution to Question X6

(i) The system can be modelled by means of a map which maps customers to a set of records, each of which contains an account number and a balance. This is specified below. The data invariant specifies the limit on an account overdraft:

$Accid = \{100000, \ldots, 999999\}$
$Bank = Accid \xrightarrow{m} \mathbb{N}$

inv-Bank $(b) \triangleq \forall c \in \text{dom}\ b \cdot b\ (c) \geq -10000$

(ii) The three operations are shown below:

ADDAMOUNT (n: $\mathbb{N}$, a: *Accid*)
ext rd b: *Bank*
pre $a \in \text{dom}\ b$
post $b = \overleftarrow{b} \dagger \{a \mapsto \overleftarrow{b}\ (a) + n\}$

REMOVE (a: *Accid*)
ext wr b: *Bank*
pre $a \in \text{dom}\ b \wedge b\ (a) = 0$
post $b = \{a\} ⩤ \overleftarrow{b}$

OVERDRAWN (a: *Accid*) ov: $\mathbb{B}$
ext rd b: *Bank*
pre $a \in \mathrm{dom}\ b$
post $ov \Leftrightarrow b\,(a) < 0$

Solution to Question X7

(i) The data type *Inventory* is a record (composite object) type which contains two fields: *catalogue* and *stocks*:

The field *catalogue* contains all the valid products in the system (i.e. values of the type *Product* which are in use) and the price of each product.

The field *stocks* contains current shops and details of how many products are stored at each shop. These shop-specific details are held in a map from *Product* to record details about the product at a given shop.

The *Prod-holding* composite object type records the current stock-level and permitted maximum for a product at a shop.

The *Stock-details* mapping is used for holding shop-specific information about products.

If a product is not sold/stocked by a shop then the value representing that product will not be in the domain of the *Stock-details* map for that shop. If the shop does sell it but has run out of it, the value representing the product will be in the domain of the map and mapped to 0.

The most obvious improvement is to include an invariant to the type *Prod-holding* as follows:

Prod-holding::
 level: $\mathbb{N}$
 max: $\mathbb{N}_1$

$inv\text{-}Prod\text{-}holding(pr) \triangleq pr.level \leq pr.max$

(ii) The first line defines the invariant as a boolean-valued function which takes any value of type *Inventory* as its argument. The second line of the data type invariant associates the name *stks* with the *stocks* field of any value of the type *Inventory*. The third line of the data type invariant associates the name *cat* with any value of the *catalogue* field of *Inventory*:

$\forall\ details \in \mathrm{rng}\ stks$	means for all stock details at all shops
$\mathrm{dom}\ details \subseteq \mathrm{dom}\ cat$	means that for any product to be available at any of the shops it must be in the catalogue

(iii) $inv\text{-}Inventory(i) \triangleq$
 $\forall\ details \in \mathrm{rng}\ stks \cdot \mathrm{dom}\ details = \mathrm{dom}\ cat$

(iv) Only *Prod-holding* needs changing by adding *min*:

Prod-holding::
 level: $\mathbb{N}$
 max: $\mathbb{N}_1$
 min: $\mathbb{N}$

(v) The function *required* returns the difference between the maximum level and the current level of stock for the product p at shop sh; this value is the number of items of product p which are needed to restore the maximum stock level for p at the shop sh. The pre-condition:

pre $p \in$ dom $invent.\ stocks(sh)$

guarantees that the product p is stocked at the shop sh.

In the post-condition:

let $shop\text{-}details = invent.\ stocks(sh)$ in

associates *shop-details* with details for the shop *sh*.

let $this\text{-}holding = shop\text{-}details(p)$ in

associates *this-holding* with data for the product p at shop *sh*.

let $local\text{-}max = this\text{-}holding.max$ in

associates *local-max* with maximum level for p at shop *sh*.

let $current\text{-}level = this\text{-}holding.level$ in

associates *current-level* with number of p products at shop *sh*.

(vi) $RECEIVE$ (p: $Product$, sh: $Shop$, n: $\mathbb{N}_1$)
ext wr $invent$: $Inventory$
pre $p \in$ dom $invent.catalogue \wedge sh \in$ dom $invent.stocks \wedge$
$p \in$ dom $invent.stocks(sh) \wedge$
$n \leq required(p, sh, invent)$

post let $old\text{-}stocks = \overleftarrow{inventstocks}$ in
let $shop\text{-}details = old\text{-}stocks(sh)$ in
let $this\text{-}holding = shop\text{-}details(p)$ in
let $local\text{-}max = this\text{-}holding.max$ in
let $current\text{-}level = this\text{-}holding.level$ in
let $new\text{-}level = current\text{-}level + n$ in
let $new\text{-}Prod\text{-}holding = \mu(this\text{-}holding, level \mapsto new\text{-}level)$ in
let $new\text{-}details = shop\text{-}details \dagger \{p \mapsto new\text{-}Prod\text{-}holding\}$ in
$invent = \mu(\overleftarrow{invent}, stocks \mapsto old\text{-}stocks \dagger \{sh \mapsto new\text{-}details\})$

Solution to Question X8

(i) $Card$::
$Suit$: {CLUBS, DIAMONDS, SPADES, HEARTS}
$Value$: $\{1, \ldots, 13\}$
$Hand1 = Card$-set
$Hand2 = Card \xrightarrow{m} \{\text{PRESENT, ABSENT}\}$

(ii) $retr\text{-}Hand1 : Hand2 \rightarrow Hand1$
$retr\text{-}Hand1\ (h2) \triangleq \{c \mid c \in Card \bullet h2\ (c) = \text{PRESENT}\}$

(iii) There must be a unique member of each type corresponding to each member of the other type.

(iv) $retr\text{-}Hand2: Hand1 \rightarrow Hand2$
$retr\text{-}Hand2(h1) \triangleq$
$\{i \mapsto \text{PRESENT} \mid i : Card \cdot i \in h1\} \cup$
$\{i \mapsto \text{ABSENT} \mid i : Card \cdot i \notin h1\}$

alternatively:

$retr\text{-}Hand2(h1) \triangleq$
$\{i \mapsto j \mid i : Card \cdot j \Leftrightarrow \textsf{if } i \in h1 \textsf{ then } \text{PRESENT} \textsf{ else } \text{ABSENT}\}$

Solution to Question X9

(i) The assumption is that the full and associate memberships do not overlap. If they do, the second representation cannot represent a member who falls into both categories. A suitable invariant is:

$inv\text{-}Club\,(c) \triangleq c.fullmems \cap c.associatemems = \{\,\}$

(ii) $retr\text{-}Club: Club2 \rightarrow Club$
$retr\text{-}Club\,(c2) \triangleq$
let $fullmems = \{md.memno \mid md \in \textsf{elems } c2 \wedge md.memtype = \text{FULL}\}$ in
let $assmems = \{md.memno \mid md \in \textsf{elems } c2 \wedge md.memtype = \text{ASSOC}\}$ in
$mk\text{-}Club\,(fullmems, assmems)$

Alternatively:
$retr\text{-}Club: Club2 \rightarrow Club$
$retr\text{-}Club\,(c) \triangleq$
let $fullmems = \{mn \mid \exists\, m \in \textsf{elems } c \cdot m.memtype = \text{FULL} \wedge m.memno = mn\}$ in
let $assmems = \{mn \mid \exists\, m \in \textsf{elems } c \cdot m.memtype = \text{ASSOC} \wedge m.memno = mn\}$ in
$mk\text{-}Club\,(fullmems, assmems)$

Solution to Question X10

(i) $\forall\, ac : Acc\text{-}type \cdot ac \in \textsf{dom } bs.rules$
$\forall\, cans \in \textsf{rng } bs.customeraccnos \cdot cans \subseteq \textsf{dom } bs.accounts$

(ii) *SETRULES*
ext wr bs: *Building-society*
pre true
post let $goldrule = \text{GOLD} \mapsto mk\text{-}Acc\text{-}attributes\,(15, 10000.00)$ in
let $silverrule = \text{SILVER} \mapsto mk\text{-}Acc\text{-}attributes\,(14, 50000.00)$ in
let $bronzerule = \text{BRONZE} \mapsto mk\text{-}Acc\text{-}attributes\,(13, 1.00)$ in
let $newrules = \{goldrule, silverrule, bronzerule\}$ in
$bs = \mu(\overleftarrow{bs}, rules \mapsto newsrules)$

Alternatively (replacing the last line above):

let *custaccnos* = *bs.customeraccnos* in
let *accs* = *bs.accounts* in
bs = *mk-Building-society* (*newrules*, *custaccnos*, *accs*)

(iii) let *rules* = $\overleftarrow{bs}$*.rules* in
let *customers* = $\overleftarrow{bs}$*.customeraccnos* in
let *accs* = $\overleftarrow{bs}$*.accounts* in
let *newbronzeacc* = *mk-Account* (BRONZE, *deposit*) in
let *updatedcustomers* = *customeraccnos* † {*nm* ↦ {*accno*}} in
let *updatedaccs* = *accs* † {*accno* ↦ *newbronzeacc*} in
bs = *mk-Building-society* (*rules*, *updatedcustomers*, *updatedaccs*)

Alternatively (replacing the last line above):

bs = μ($\overleftarrow{bs}$, *customeraccnos* ↦ *updatedcustomers*, *accounts* ↦ *updatedaccs*)

(iv) *sumbalances*: *Account*-set → $\mathbb{R}$
sumbalances (*accs*) $\triangleq$
  if *accs* = { }
  then 0.0
  else let *ac* ∈ *accs* in
    ac.balance + *sumbalances* (*accs* – {*ac*})

(v) pre *nm* ∈ dom *bs.customeraccnos*

post
  let *bscustomers* = *bs.customeraccnos* in
  let *bsaccounts* = *bs.accounts* in
  let *thiscustomersaccountnumbers* = *bscustomers* (*nm*) in
  let *thiscustomersaccounts* = rng (*thiscustomersaccountnumbers* ◁ *bsaccounts*) in
  r = *sumbalances* (*thiscustomersaccounts*)

INDEX